Mechanics for Engineers

STATICS

Mechanics for Engineers

STATICS

Ferdinand P. Beer

PROFESSOR AND HEAD OF THE DEPARTMENT OF MECHANICS
LEHIGH UNIVERSITY

E. Russell Johnston, Jr.

PROFESSOR OF CIVIL ENGINEERING
WORCESTER POLYTECHNIC INSTITUTE

1956

McGRAW-HILL BOOK COMPANY, INC.
New York, Toronto, London

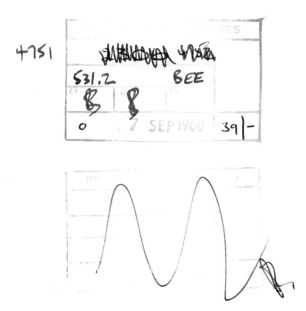

MECHANICS FOR ENGINEERS: Statics

Preface

The main objective of a first course in mechanics should be to develop in the engineering student the ability to analyze a practical situation in a simple and logical manner and to apply to its solution a few well-understood basic principles. It is hoped that this text, designed for the first course in statics offered in the sophomore year, and the volume that follows, "Mechanics for Engineers: Dynamics," will help the instructor achieve this goal.†

One of the characteristics of the approach used in these volumes is that the mechanics of *particles* has been clearly separated from the mechanics of *rigid bodies*. This approach makes it possible to consider simple practical applications at an early stage and to postpone the introduction of more difficult concepts. In this volume, for example, the statics of particles is treated first (Chap. 2), and the principle of equilibrium is immediately applied to practical situations involving only concurrent forces. The statics of rigid bodies is considered in Chaps. 3 and 4, where the principle of transmissibility and the associated concept of moment of a force are introduced. In the volume on dynamics, the same division is observed. The basic concepts of force, mass, and acceleration, of work and energy, and of impulse and momentum are introduced and first applied to problems involving only particles. Thus the student may familiarize himself with the three basic methods used in dynamics and learn their respective advantages before facing the difficulties associated with the motion of rigid bodies.

Since this text is designed for a first course in statics, new concepts have been presented in simple terms and every step explained in detail. On the other hand, by discussing the broader aspects of the problems considered and by pointing out the limitations as well as the possible extensions of the results obtained, a definite maturity of approach has been achieved. For example, the concepts of instability and statical indeterminacy are introduced early in the text and used throughout.

A large number of optional sections have been included. These sections are indicated by asterisks and may thus easily be distinguished from those which form the core of the basic statics course. They may be omitted without prejudice to the understanding of the rest of the text.

† Both texts are also available in a single volume, "Mechanics for Engineers: Statics and Dynamics."

Among the topics covered in these additional sections are the graphical methods for the analysis of coplanar forces, applications to hydrostatics, shear and bending-moment diagrams for beams, equilibrium of cables, products of inertia and Mohr's circle, and the method of virtual work. The sections on beams are especially useful when the course in statics is immediately followed by a course in mechanics of materials.

The fact that mechanics is essentially a *deductive* science based on a few fundamental principles has been stressed. Derivations have been presented in their logical sequence and with all the rigor warranted at this level. However, the learning process being largely *inductive*, simple applications have been considered first. Thus the statics of particles precedes the statics of rigid bodies; coplanar forces are introduced before forces in space; and problems involving internal forces are postponed until Chap. 6.

Free-body diagrams are introduced early and their importance is emphasized throughout the text. They are used not only to solve equilibrium problems but also to express the equivalence of two systems of forces or, more generally, of two systems of vectors. This approach is particularly useful as a preparation for the study of the dynamics of rigid bodies. As will be shown in the volume on dynamics, by placing the emphasis on "free-body-diagram equations" rather than on the standard algebraic equations of motion, a more intuitive and more complete understanding of D'Alembert's principle and of the principle of impulse and momentum may be achieved.

The material presented in the text and most of the problems require no mathematical knowledge beyond algebra, trigonometry, and elementary calculus. A greater emphasis has been placed on the correct understanding and application of the concepts of differentiation and integration than on the nimble manipulation of mathematical formulas. In this connection, it should be mentioned that the determination of the centroids of composite areas precedes the calculation of centroids by integration, thus making it possible to establish the concept of moment of area firmly before introducing the use of integration.

Since students are often given no formal training in the use of the slide rule, special notes have been included in Chap. 2, stressing the proper use of the slide rule in the solution of problems involving proportions or trigonometric relations.

The text has been divided into units, each consisting of one or several theory sections, one or several Sample Problems, and a large number of problems to be assigned. Each unit corresponds to a well-defined topic and generally may be covered in one lesson. In a number of cases, however, the instructor will find it desirable to devote more than one lesson to a given topic. The Sample Problems have been set up in much the same form that a student will use in solving the assigned problems.

They thus serve the double purpose of amplifying the text and demon-
strating the type of neat and orderly work that the student should
cultivate in his own solutions.   Most of the problems to be assigned are
of a practical nature and should appeal to the engineering student.
They are primarily designed, however, to illustrate the material presented in the text and to help the student understand the basic principles
of mechanics.   The problems have been grouped according to the portions of material they illustrate and have been arranged in order of
increasing difficulty.   Problems requiring special attention have been
indicated by asterisks.   Answers to all even-numbered problems are
given at the end of the book.

Although the terminology used in this text generally conforms to the
standard practice, attention is called to the use of a few specific terms.
For example, a *couple* represents a *system* of two parallel forces, of the
same magnitude and opposite sense, and will be indicated in the free-body
diagram by the symbols $\rangle$ or $\rangle$.   On the other hand, the *moment* of a
force about an axis is the *product* of the magnitude of a force and a distance and will never be shown in a free-body diagram.

For several years this text was used in preliminary form at Lehigh
University.   The authors gratefully acknowledge the many helpful sug-
gestions offered by their colleagues during that period.

FERDINAND P. BEER
E. RUSSELL JOHNSTON, JR.

Contents

List of Symbols

a Radius; distance

A Area

$A, B, C, \ldots$ Points; reactions at supports and connections

b Width; distance

c Constant

C Centroid

d Distance

e Base of natural logarithms

F Force; friction force

g Acceleration of gravity

G Center of gravity

h Height; vertical distance; sag of cable

$I, I_x, \ldots$ Moment of inertia

$\bar{I}$ Centroidal moment of inertia

J Polar moment of inertia

k Spring constant

k_x, k_y, k_O Radius of gyration

$\bar{k}$ Centroidal radius of gyration

l Length

L Length; span

m Mass

M Moment

N Normal component of reaction

O Origin of coordinates

p Pressure

P Point; force

$P_{xy}, \ldots$ Product of inertia

Q Force

r Radius; distance; polar coordinate

R Resultant force; reaction; radius

s Displacement; length of cable

S Force

t Time; thickness

T Tension

u Rectangular coordinate

U Work

v Rectangular coordinate

V Volume; potential energy; shear

w Load per unit length

W Weight; load

x, y, z Rectangular coordinates; displacements

$\bar{x}, \bar{y}, \bar{z}$ Rectangular coordinates of centroid, center of gravity, or mass center

α Angle

β Angle of contact; angle

γ Specific weight; angle

$\delta s,\ \delta\theta$ Virtual displacement

δU Virtual work

η Efficiency

θ Angle; polar coordinate

μ Coefficient of friction

ρ Density

ϕ Angle of friction; angle

Mechanics for Engineers

PART 1

Statics

1. Introduction

1.1. What Is Mechanics? Mechanics may be defined as that science which describes and predicts the conditions of rest or motion of bodies under the action of forces. It is divided into three parts: mechanics of *rigid bodies*, mechanics of *deformable bodies*, and mechanics of *fluids*.

The mechanics of rigid bodies is subdivided into *statics* and *dynamics*, the former dealing with bodies at rest, the latter with bodies in motion. In this part of the study of mechanics, bodies are assumed to be perfectly rigid. Actual structures and machines, however, are never absolutely rigid and deform under the loads to which they are subjected. But these deformations are usually small and do not appreciably affect the conditions of equilibrium or motion of the structure under consideration. They are important, though, as far as the resistance of the structure to failure is concerned and are studied in mechanics of materials, which is a part of the mechanics of deformable bodies. The third division of mechanics, the mechanics of fluids, is subdivided into the study of *incompressible fluids* and of *compressible fluids*. An important subdivision of the study of incompressible fluids is *hydraulics*, which deals with problems involving liquids.

Mechanics is a physical science, since it deals with the study of physical phenomena. However, some associate mechanics with mathematics, while many consider it as an engineering subject. Both these views are justified in part. Mechanics is the foundation of most engineering sciences and is an indispensable prerequisite to their study. However, it does not have the *empiricism* found in many engineering sciences; by its rigor and the emphasis it places on deductive reasoning it resembles mathematics. But, again, it is not an *abstract* or even a *pure* science; mechanics is an *applied* science. The purpose of mechanics is to explain and predict physical phenomena and thus to lay the foundations for engineering applications.

1.2. Fundamental Concepts and Principles. Although the study of mechanics goes back to the time of Aristotle (384–322 B.C.) and Archimedes (287–212 B.C.), one has to wait until Newton (1642–1727) to find a satisfactory formulation of its fundamental principles. These principles were later expressed in a modified form by D'Alembert, Lagrange,

3

and Hamilton. Their validity remained unchallenged, however, until Einstein formulated his *theory of relativity* (1905). While its limitations have now been recognized, *newtonian mechanics* still remains the basis of today's engineering sciences.

The basic concepts used in mechanics are *space*, *time*, *mass*, and *force*. These concepts cannot be truly defined; they should be accepted on the basis of our intuition and experience and used as a mental frame of reference for our study of mechanics.

The concept of *space* is associated with the notion of the position of a point P. The position of P may be defined by three lengths measured from a certain reference point, or *origin*, in three given directions. These lengths are known as the *coordinates* of P.

In order to define an event, it is not sufficient to indicate its position in space. The *time* of the event should also be given.

The concept of *mass* is used to characterize and compare bodies on the basis of certain fundamental mechanical experiments. Two bodies of the same mass, for example, will be attracted by the earth in the same manner; they will also offer the same resistance to a change in translational motion.

A *force* represents the action of one body on another. It may be exerted by actual contact or at a distance, as in the case of gravitational forces and magnetic forces. A force is characterized by its *point of application*, its *magnitude*, and its *direction*.

In newtonian mechanics, space, time, and mass are absolute concepts, independent of each other. (This is not true in *relativistic mechanics*, where the time of an event depends upon its position, and where the mass of a body varies with its velocity.) On the other hand, the concept of force is not independent of the other three. Indeed, one of the fundamental principles of newtonian mechanics listed below indicates that the resultant force acting on a body is related to the mass of the body and to the manner in which its velocity varies with time.

We shall study the conditions of rest or motion of particles and rigid bodies in terms of the four basic concepts we have introduced. By *particle* we mean a very small amount of matter which may be assumed to occupy a single point in space. A *rigid body* is a combination of a large number of particles occupying fixed positions with respect to each other. The study of the mechanics of particles is obviously a prerequisite to that of rigid bodies. Besides, the results obtained for a particle may be used directly in a large number of problems dealing with the conditions of rest or motion of actual bodies.

The study of elementary mechanics rests on six fundamental principles based on experimental evidence:

The Parallelogram Law for the Addition of Forces. This states that two forces acting on a particle may be replaced by a single force, called their *resultant*, obtained by drawing the diagonal of the parallelogram which has sides equal to the given forces (Sec. 2.1).

The Principle of Transmissibility. This states that the conditions of equilibrium or of motion of a rigid body will remain unchanged if a force acting at a given point of the rigid body is replaced by a force of same magnitude and same direction, but acting at a different point, provided that the two forces have the same line of action (Sec. 3.2).

Newton's Three Fundamental Laws. Formulated by Sir Isaac Newton in the latter part of the seventeenth century, these laws may be stated as follows:

FIRST LAW. If the resultant force acting on a particle is zero, the particle will remain at rest (if originally at rest) or will move with constant speed in a straight line (if originally in motion) (Sec. 2.7).

SECOND LAW. If the resultant force acting on a particle is not zero, the particle will have an acceleration proportional to the magnitude of the resultant and in the direction of this resultant force.

As we shall see in Sec. 12.1, this law may be stated as

$$F = ma \qquad (1.1)$$

where F, m, and a represent, respectively, the resultant force acting on the particle, the mass of the particle, and the acceleration of the particle, expressed in a consistent system of units.

THIRD LAW. The forces of action and reaction between bodies in contact have same magnitude, same line of action, and opposite sense (Sec. 6.1).

Newton's Law of Gravitation. This states that two particles of mass m_1 and m_2 are mutually attracted with a force F given by the formula

$$F = G \frac{m_1 m_2}{r^2} \qquad (1.2)$$

where r = distance between the two particles

G = a universal constant called the *constant of gravitation*

A particular case of great importance is that of the attraction exerted by the earth on a particle located on its surface. The force F is then defined as the *weight* W of the particle. Taking m_1 equal to the mass of the earth, m_2 equal to the mass m of the particle, and r equal to the radius of the earth, and introducing the constant

$$g = \frac{Gm_1}{r^2} \qquad (1.3)$$

the weight of a particle of mass m may be expressed as†

$$W = mg \qquad (1.4)$$

† A more accurate definition of the weight W should take into account the rotation of the earth.

The value of r in formula (1.3) depends upon the elevation of the point considered; it also depends upon its latitude, since the earth is not truly spherical. The value of g therefore varies with the position of the point considered. As long as the point actually remains on the surface of the earth, it is sufficiently accurate in most engineering computations to assume that g equals 32.2 ft/sec².

As noted earlier, the six fundamental principles listed above are based on experimental evidence; they cannot be derived mathematically. On these principles rests most of the intricate structure of newtonian mechanics. For more than two centuries a tremendous number of problems dealing with the conditions of rest and motion of rigid bodies, deformable bodies, and fluids have been solved by applying these fundamental principles. Many of the solutions obtained could be checked experimentally, thus providing a further verification of the principles from which they were derived. It is only recently that Newton's mechanics was found at fault, in the study of the motion of atoms and in the study of the motion of certain planets, where it must be supplemented by the theory of relativity. But on the human or engineering scale, where velocities are small compared with the velocity of light, Newton's mechanics has yet to be disproved.

1.3. Units. With the four basic concepts introduced in the preceding section are associated the units of *length, time, mass,* and *force*. These four units are not independent. As we shall see in greater detail in Sec. 12.2, three of these units may be defined arbitrarily, but the fourth one must be chosen in accordance with formula (1.1).

The fundamental units chosen by engineers everywhere are the units of length, time, and force. The standard unit of length used by American engineers is the *foot* (ft), subdivided into 12 *inches* (in.); a multiple of the foot is the *mile*, equal to 5,280 ft. The standard unit of time is the *second* (sec); a multiple of the second is the *hour* (hr), equal to 3,600 sec. The standard unit of force is the *pound* (lb), defined as the force (weight) with which a certain mass of platinum is attracted by the earth at the latitude of 45° and at sea level. Multiples of the pound frequently used are the *kilopound* (kip, or k), equal to 1,000 lb, and the *ton*, equal to 2,000 lb.

All quantities other than length, time, and force should be expressed in units obtained from the fundamental units ft, sec, and lb. For example, an area, obtained by multiplying a length (ft) by a length (ft), should be expressed in ft². A pressure, obtained by dividing a force (lb) by an area (ft²), should be expressed in lb/ft². A velocity, obtained by dividing a length (ft) by a time (sec), should be expressed in ft/sec. An acceleration, obtained by dividing a velocity (ft/sec) by a time (sec), should be expressed in ft/sec². Since, according to formula (1.1), a mass may be obtained by dividing a force (lb) by an acceleration (ft/sec²), a mass should be expressed in lb-sec²/ft.

A useful check of our computations may be obtained if we carry out the computations with the units as well as the numerical values. For example, the moment of a 10-lb force about an axis 2 ft from its line of action will be determined as follows (Sec. 3.4):

$$M = Fd = (10 \text{ lb})(2 \text{ ft}) = 20 \text{ lb-ft}$$

The unit lb-ft obtained by multiplying lb by ft is the correct unit for the moment of a force; if another unit had been obtained, we would have known that some mistake had been made.

Sometimes a quantity is expressed in units other than the standard units. For example, a velocity may be given as $v = 30$ mph (miles per hour). To express this velocity in ft/sec, we shall proceed as follows:

First we write

$$v = 30 \frac{\text{miles}}{\text{hr}}$$

Since we want to get rid of the unit miles and introduce instead the unit feet, we should multiply the right-hand member of the equation by an expression containing miles in the denominator and feet in the numerator. But, since we do not want to change the value of the right-hand member, the expression used should have a value equal to unity. The quotient 5,280 ft/1 mile is such an expression. Operating in a similar way to transform the unit hour into seconds, we write

$$v = \left(30 \frac{\text{miles}}{\text{hr}}\right)\left(\frac{5{,}280 \text{ ft}}{1 \text{ mile}}\right)\left(\frac{1 \text{ hr}}{3{,}600 \text{ sec}}\right)$$

Carrying out the numerical computations and canceling out units which appear both in the numerator and the denominator, we obtain

$$v = 44 \frac{\text{ft}}{\text{sec}} = 44 \text{ ft/sec}$$

1.4. Method of Problem Solution. The student should approach a problem in mechanics as he would approach an actual engineering situation. By drawing on his own experience and on his intuition, he will find it easier to understand and formulate the problem. Once the problem has been clearly stated, however, there is no place in its solution for the student's particular fancy. *The solution must be based on the six fundamental principles stated above or on theorems derived from them.* Every step taken must be justified on that basis. Strict rules must be followed, which lead to the solution in an almost automatic fashion, leaving no room for the student's intuition or "feeling." After an answer has been obtained, it should be checked. Here again, the student may call upon his common sense and personal experience. If not completely satisfied with the result obtained, he should carefully check his formulation of the problem, the validity of the methods used for its solution, and the accuracy of his computations.

The *statement* of a problem should be clear and precise. It should contain the given data and indicate what information is required. A neat drawing showing all quantities involved should be included. Separate diagrams should be drawn for all bodies involved, indicating clearly the forces acting on each body. These diagrams are known as *free-body diagrams* and are described in detail in Secs. 2.8 and 3.13.

The *fundamental principles* of mechanics listed in Sec. 1.2 *will be used to write equations* expressing the conditions of rest or motion of the bodies considered. Each equation should be clearly related to one of the free-body diagrams. The student will then proceed to solve the problem, observing strictly the usual rules of algebra and recording neatly the various steps taken.

After the answer has been obtained, it should be *carefully checked*. Mistakes in reasoning may often be detected by checking the units, as indicated in Sec. 1.3. Errors in computation will usually be found by substituting the numerical values obtained into an equation which has not yet been used and verifying that the equation is satisfied. The importance of correct computations in engineering cannot be overemphasized.

1.5. Numerical Accuracy. The accuracy of the solution of a problem depends upon two items: (1) the accuracy of the given data; (2) the accuracy of the computations performed.

The solution cannot be more accurate than the less accurate of these two items. For example, if the loading of a bridge is known to be 75,000 lb with a possible error of 100 lb either way, the relative error which measures the degree of accuracy of the data is

$$\frac{100 \text{ lb}}{75,000 \text{ lb}} = 0.0013 = 0.13 \text{ per cent}$$

It would then be meaningless, in computing the reaction at one of the bridge supports, to record it as 14,322 lb. The accuracy of the solution cannot be greater than 0.13 per cent, no matter how accurate the computations are, and the possible error in the answer may be as large as $(0.13/100)(14,322 \text{ lb}) \sim 20 \text{ lb}$. The solution should be properly recorded as $14,320 \pm 20$ lb.

In engineering problems, the data are seldom known with an accuracy greater than 0.2 per cent. It is therefore unnecessary to carry out computations with a greater accuracy. In almost all cases, the slide rule will provide the desired accuracy. On looking at the main scales of a 10-in. slide rule, it will be observed that the number 502 may be easily interpolated between the graduations corresponding, respectively, to 500 and 505. It might possibly be mistaken for 501 or 503, but no larger error in reading or in adjusting the rule will be made if a minimum of care is observed. The error involved is thus at most 1 unit out of 500; the relative error is 0.2 per cent. For other positions on the rule, the absolute error will be different (for example, 2 units out of 1,000); owing to the logarithmic nature of the scales, however, the relative error will remain 0.2 per cent.

It is sometimes said that the accuracy obtained on the slide rule is *three significant figures*. This is correct as far as the central portion of the scale is concerned, where numbers such as 298, 299, 300, 301 may be easily read. The third significant figure, however, becomes doubtful toward the right end of the scale, where it is difficult to tell 997 from 998. On the other hand, one should be able, toward the left end of the scale, to estimate the fourth significant figure within a couple of units. The relative error between 996 and 998 is the same as between 1,002 and 1,004 (0.2 per cent in both cases). We should therefore define the accuracy of a computation by the possible relative error involved, rather than by the number of significant figures obtained, and we shall attempt to obtain all answers with an accuracy of about 0.2 per cent. A practical rule consists in using four figures to record readings taken on a 10-in. slide rule between 1 and 2 and three figures to record readings between 2 and 10. Unless otherwise indicated, the data given in a problem should be assumed known with a comparable degree of accuracy. A force of 40 lb, for example, should actually be read 40.0 lb, and a force of 15 lb should be read 15.00 lb.

2. Statics of Particles

2.1. Force on a Particle. Resultant of Two Forces. A force represents the action of one body on another. It is characterized by its *point of application*, its *magnitude*, and its *direction*. In this chapter we shall study the effect of forces on particles. The use of the word "particles" does not imply that we shall restrict our study to that of small corpuscles. It means that the size and shape of the bodies under consideration will not affect the solution of the problems treated in this chapter and that

FIG. 2.1   FIG. 2.2

all the forces acting on a given body will be assumed to have the same point of application. Each force will thus be completely defined by its magnitude and direction.

The magnitude of a force is characterized by a certain number of units; as was indicated in Sec. 1.3, the standard units used by American engineers to measure the magnitude of a force are the pound (lb) and its multiples, the kilopound (kip, or k), equal to 1,000 lb, and the ton, equal to 2,000 lb. The direction of a force is defined by the *line of action* and the *sense* of the force. The line of action is the infinite straight line along which the force acts; it is characterized by the angle it forms with some fixed axis (Fig. 2.1). The force itself is represented by a segment of that line; through the use of an appropriate scale, the length of this segment may be chosen to represent the magnitude of the force. Finally, the sense of the force should be indicated by an arrowhead. It is important, in defining a force, to indicate its sense. Two forces, such as those shown in Figs. 2.1 and 2.2, having the same magnitude and the same line of action but different sense, will have directly opposite effects on a particle.

Experimental evidence shows that two forces P and Q acting on a

10

particle A (Fig. 2.3a) may be replaced by a single force R which has the same effect on the particle (Fig. 2.3c).   This force is called the *resultant* of the forces P and Q and may be obtained, as shown in Fig. 2.3b, by constructing a parallelogram, using P and Q as two sides of the parallelogram.   *The diagonal that passes through A represents the resultant.*   This is known as the *parallelogram law* for the addition of two forces.   This law is based on experimental evidence; it cannot be proved or derived mathematically.

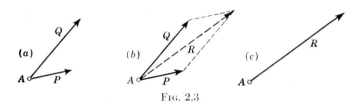

Fig. 2.3

It appears from the above that forces do not obey the rules of addition defined in ordinary arithmetic or algebra.   For example, two forces acting at right angle to each other, one of 4 lb and the other of 3 lb, add up to a force of 5 lb, *not* to a force of 7 lb.   Forces are not the only expressions which follow the parallelogram law of addition.   As we shall see later, *displacements, velocities, accelerations, momenta* are other examples of expressions possessing magnitude and direction and which are added according to the parallelogram law.   All these expressions are called *vectors*, while those quantities which do not have direction are called *scalars*.

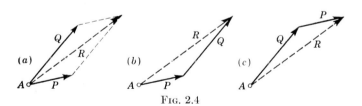

Fig. 2.4

From the parallelogram law, we can derive another useful method for determining the resultant of two forces, or two vectors.   This method, known as the *triangle rule*, is derived as follows: Consider Fig. 2.4a, where the resultant of the forces P and Q has been determined by the parallelogram law.   Since the side of the parallelogram opposite Q is equal to Q in magnitude and direction, we could draw only half of the parallelogram (Fig. 2.4b). The resultant may thus be found by *arranging P and Q in tip-to-tail fashion and then connecting the tail of P with the tip of Q.* In Fig. 2.4c, the other half of the parallelogram is considered, and, of course, the same resultant is found.

2.2. Addition of Concurrent Forces. Consider now the case when a particle A is acted upon by *three or more* forces contained in the same plane. Forces contained in the same plane are called *coplanar forces.* Since the forces considered here all pass through A, they are also said to be *concurrent.* The forces acting on A could be added by applying repeatedly the parallelogram law to successive pairs of forces until all the given forces were reduced to a single force. As we shall see, however, the resultant of three or more concurrent coplanar forces, or vectors, may be obtained more easily by extending the triangle rule. In Fig. 2.5a, three forces P, Q, and S are shown acting on the particle A. In Fig.

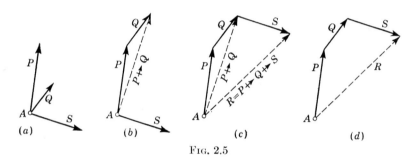

Fig. 2.5

2.5b, the forces P and Q are added by the triangle rule into their resultant $P \nrightarrow Q$ (where the sign $\nrightarrow$ denotes vector addition). In Fig. 2.5c, the resultant $P \nrightarrow Q$ is added to S; the total sum thus obtained is the resultant R of the original system. The determination of $P \nrightarrow Q$, however, could have been omitted and the resultant R could have been obtained directly, as shown in Fig. 2.5d, by *arranging the given forces in tip-to-tail fashion and connecting the tail of the first force with the tip of the last one.* This is known as the *polygon rule* for the addition of concurrent forces, or vectors. It should be noted that the order in which the forces, or vectors, are added is immaterial.

2.3. Resolution of a Force into Components. We have seen that two or more forces acting on a particle may be replaced by a single force which has the same effect on the particle. Conversely, a single force F acting on a particle may be replaced by two or more forces which, together, have the same effect on the particle. These forces are called the *components* of the original force F, and the process of replacing F by these forces is known as *resolving the force F into components.*

Clearly, for each force F there exist an infinite number of possible sets of components. Sets of *two components P and Q* are the most important as far as practical applications are concerned. But, even then, the number of ways in which a given force F may be resolved into two components

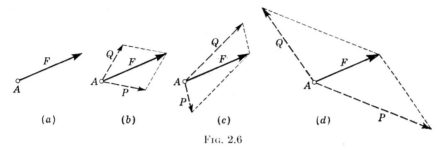

FIG. 2.6

is unlimited (Fig. 2.6). Two cases are of particular interest:

1. *One of the Two Components, P, Is Known.* The second component, Q, is obtained by applying the triangle rule and joining the tip of P to the tip of F (Fig. 2.7a); the magnitude and direction of Q are determined graphically or by trigonometry. Once Q has been determined, both components P and Q should be applied at A (Fig. 2.7b).

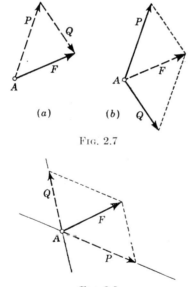

FIG. 2.7

FIG. 2.8

2. *The Line of Action of Each Component Is Known.* The magnitude and sense of the components are obtained by applying the parallelogram law and drawing lines, through the tip of F, parallel to the given lines of action (Fig. 2.8). This process leads to two well-defined components, P and Q, which may be determined graphically or by applying the law of sines.

SAMPLE PROBLEM 2.1

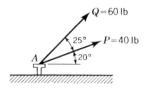

The two forces P and Q act on a bolt A. Determine their resultant.

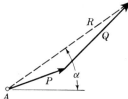

Graphical Solution. A parallelogram with sides equal to P and Q is drawn to scale. The magnitude and direction of the resultant are measured and found to be

$$R = 98 \text{ lb} \qquad \alpha = 35° \qquad \boldsymbol{R = 98 \text{ lb} \ \measuredangle \ 35°}$$

The triangle rule may also be used. Forces P and Q are drawn in tip-to-tail fashion. Again the magnitude and direction of the resultant are measured.

$$R = 98 \text{ lb} \qquad \alpha = 35° \qquad \boldsymbol{R = 98 \text{ lb} \ \measuredangle \ 35°}$$

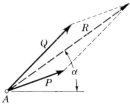

Trigonometric Solution. The triangle rule is again used; two sides and the included angle are known. We apply the law of cosines.

$$R^2 = P^2 + Q^2 - 2PQ \cos B$$
$$R^2 = (40 \text{ lb})^2 + (60 \text{ lb})^2$$
$$- 2(40 \text{ lb})(60 \text{ lb}) \cos 155°$$
$$R = 97.7 \text{ lb}$$

Now, applying the law of sines, we write

$$\frac{\sin A}{Q} = \frac{\sin B}{R}$$
$$\frac{\sin A}{60 \text{ lb}} = \frac{\sin 155°}{97.7 \text{ lb}}$$

Noting that $\sin 155° = \sin 25°$, and setting the slide rule as shown, we read

$$A = 15.0° \qquad \alpha = 20° + A = 35.0°$$
$$\boldsymbol{R = 97.7 \text{ lb} \ \measuredangle \ 35°}$$

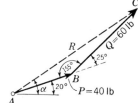

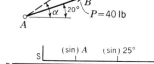

Alternate Trigonometric Solution. We construct the right triangle BCD and compute

$$CD = (60 \text{ lb}) \sin 25° = 25.4 \text{ lb}$$
$$BD = (60 \text{ lb}) \cos 25° = 54.4 \text{ lb}$$

Then, using triangle ACD, we obtain

$$\tan A = \frac{25.4 \text{ lb}}{94.4 \text{ lb}} \qquad A = 15.0°$$
$$R \sin A = 25.4 \qquad R = 97.7 \text{ lb}$$

Again,

$$\alpha = 20° + A = 35.0° \qquad \boldsymbol{R = 97.7 \text{ lb} \ \measuredangle \ 35°}$$

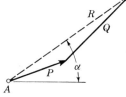

14

SAMPLE PROBLEM 2.2

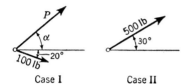

Case I   Case II

It is desired that the two forces shown in case I have the same effect as the single force shown in case II. Determine the magnitude and direction of the force P.

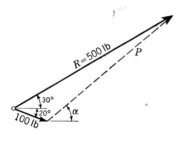

Graphical Solution. The resultant of the force P and the 100-lb force must equal the 500-lb force. We construct the triangle shown to scale and measure

$$P = 440 \text{ lb} \qquad \alpha = 40° \qquad \boldsymbol{P = 440 \text{ lb} \; \angle \; 40°}$$

Trigonometric Solution. The triangle rule may again be applied; two sides and the included angle are known. Using the law of cosines, we write

$$P^2 = (100 \text{ lb})^2 + (500 \text{ lb})^2 \\ - 2(100 \text{ lb})(500 \text{ lb}) \cos 50°$$

$$P = 442 \text{ lb}$$

Now, applying the law of sines, we have

$$\frac{\sin B}{100 \text{ lb}} = \frac{\sin 50°}{442 \text{ lb}} \qquad B = 10.0°$$

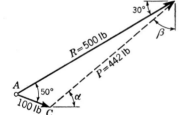

Considering the geometry of the problem, we find

$$\beta = 90° - 30° - B = 90° - 30° - 10.0° \\ = 50.0°$$

$$\alpha = 90° - \beta = 90° - 50.0° = 40.0°$$

$$\boldsymbol{P = 442 \text{ lb} \; \angle \; 40.0°}$$

Remark. The answers obtained by the graphical method are not exactly the same as those obtained by the trigonometric method. However, the differences are small (about 0.5 per cent); such accuracy is sufficient for almost all engineering purposes. The graphical solution is shown here greatly reduced in scale; such constructions should always be made as large as possible. The check that one solution provides for the other is of great advantage and should be used whenever possible. In many cases where an actual graphical solution is impractical, a freehand sketch will afford a check on the order of magnitude and hence will indicate any gross error in the trigonometric solution.

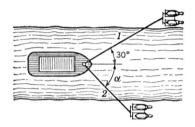

A canal barge is pulled by two horse teams. If the resultant of the forces exerted by the horses is a 500-lb force acting straight downstream, find (*a*) the tension in each of the ropes, knowing that $\alpha = 45°$, (*b*) the value of α such that the tension in rope *2* is minimum

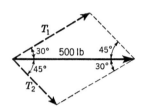

a. ***Tension for*** $\alpha = 45°$. *Graphical Solution.* The parallelogram law is used; the diagonal (resultant) is known to be equal to 500 lb and to be directed downstream. The sides are drawn parallel to the ropes. If the drawing is done to scale, we measure

$$T_1 = \textbf{370 lb} \qquad T_2 = \textbf{260 lb}$$

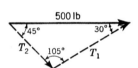

Trigonometric Solution. The triangle rule may be used. We note that the triangle shown represents half of the parallelogram shown above. Using the law of sines, we write

$$\frac{T_1}{\sin 45°} = \frac{T_2}{\sin 30°} = \frac{500 \text{ lb}}{\sin 105°}$$

or, since $\sin 105° = \sin 75°$,

$$\frac{T_1}{\sin 45°} = \frac{T_2}{\sin 30°} = \frac{500 \text{ lb}}{\sin 75°}$$

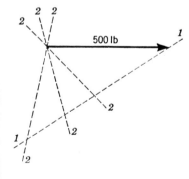

The values of T_1 and T_2 may be obtained in one setting of the slide rule.

$$T_1 = \textbf{366 lb} \qquad T_2 = \textbf{259 lb}$$

b. ***Value of*** α ***for Minimum*** T_2. To determine the value of α such that the tension in rope *2* is minimum, the triangle rule is again used. In the sketch shown, line *1-1* is the known direction of T_1. Several possible directions of T_2 are shown by the lines *2-2*. We note that the minimum value of T_2 occurs when T_1 and T_2 are perpendicular. The minimum value of T_2 is

$$T_2 = (500 \text{ lb}) \sin 30° = 250 \text{ lb}$$

Corresponding values of T_1 and α are

$$T_1 = (500 \text{ lb}) \cos 30° = 433 \text{ lb}$$

$$\alpha = 90° - 30° \qquad \alpha = \textbf{60°}$$

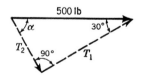

PROBLEMS†

2.1 and 2.2. Two forces F_1 and F_2 act on the particle A as shown. Determine the magnitude and direction of the resultant of these two forces graphically, using in each problem (*a*) the parallelogram law, (*b*) the triangle rule.

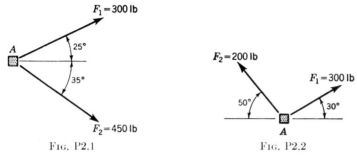

Fig. P2.1   Fig. P2.2

2.3. A transmission tower and portions of the cable it carries are shown. It is known that the tension in the cable to the left is 600 lb and the tension in the cable to the right is 700 lb. Both cables are attached to an insulator at point A. Determine graphically the magnitude and direction of the resultant force acting on the insulator.

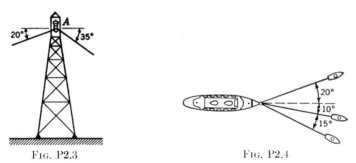

Fig. P2.3   Fig. P2.4

2.4. A disabled ocean liner is being towed by three tugboats as shown. The tension in each cable is 5,000 lb. (*a*) Determine graphically the resultant force acting on the bow of the liner. (*b*) If the tugboats cannot operate safely when the angle between any two of the cables is less than 10°, where should the tugboats be located in order to produce the largest resultant force parallel to the axis of the liner? What is the magnitude of this resultant?

2.5. When a certain airplane is in level flight, it is known that the lift provided by the wings is 6,000 lb and the thrust of the propeller is 1,500 lb. Determine by trigonometry the magnitude and direction of the resultant of these forces.

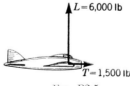

Fig. P2.5

† Answers to all even-numbered problems are given at the end of the book.

2.6. A rivet is acted upon by two forces as shown. Determine by trigonometry the magnitude and direction of the resultant force acting on the rivet.

2.7. Two men are pulling a block up an incline. One man pulls with a force $F_1 = 75$ lb and the other with a force $F_2 = 50$ lb. Determine the resultant force by trigonometry.

3,000 lb

400 lb

Fig. P2.6

Fig. P2.7

2.8. Solve Prob. 2.3 by trigonometry.

2.9. Two forces act on a bracket as shown. Determine by trigonometry the magnitude and direction of the force P so that the resultant of the two forces is a horizontal force of 400 lb.

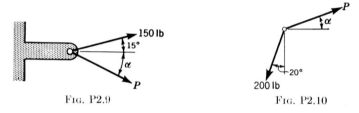

150 lb

15°

α

P

200 lb

P

α

20°

Fig. P2.9

Fig. P2.10

2.10. Determine by trigonometry the magnitude and direction of the force P so that the resultant of P and the 200-lb force is a vertical force of 500 lb directed upward.

2.11. A disabled automobile is being pulled by means of two ropes as shown. It is known that the tension in one rope is 150 lb. Determine the magnitude of the tension in the second rope so that the resultant force is parallel to the axis of the automobile. Check the answer graphically.

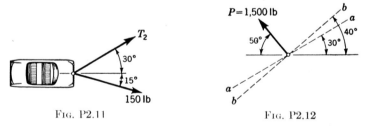

T_2

30°

15°

150 lb

$P = 1,500$ lb

b

a

50°

40°

30°

a

b

Fig. P2.11

Fig. P2.12

2.12. Resolve by trigonometry the force P into a component directed along the line aa and a component directed along the line bb.

2.4. Rectangular Components of a Force. In many problems it will be found desirable to resolve a force into two components which are perpendicular to each other. In Fig. 2.9, the force F has been resolved into a component F_x along the x axis and a component F_y along the y

axis. The parallelogram drawn to obtain the two components is a *rectangle*, and F_x and F_y are called *rectangular components*. Denoting by α the angle between F and the x axis, we write

$$F_x = F \cos \alpha \qquad F_y = F \sin \alpha \tag{2.1}$$

The x and y axes are usually chosen horizontal and vertical, respectively, as in Fig. 2.9; they may, however, be chosen in any two perpendicular directions, as shown in Fig. 2.10.

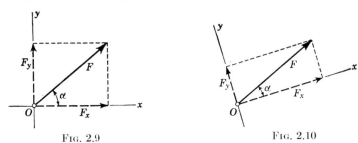

FIG. 2.9   FIG. 2.10

In determining the rectangular components of a force, the student should think of the construction lines shown in Figs. 2.9 and 2.10 as being *parallel* to the x and y axes, rather than *perpendicular* to these axes. This practice will help avoid mistakes in determining *oblique* components as in Sec. 2.3.

Example 1. An 800-lb force is exerted on a bolt A as shown in Fig. 2.11. Determine the horizontal and vertical components of the force.

It is seen from Fig. 2.12 that

$$F_x = (800 \text{ lb}) \cos 35° = 655 \text{ lb} \leftarrow$$
$$F_y = (800 \text{ lb}) \sin 35° = 459 \text{ lb} \uparrow$$

Note that, to be complete, the answer should include the *sense* of each component.

FIG. 2.11   FIG. 2.12

Example 2. A man pulls with a force of 75 lb on a rope attached to a building, as shown in Fig. 2.13. What are the horizontal and vertical components of the force exerted by the rope at point A?

It is seen from Fig. 2.14 that

$$F_x = (75 \text{ lb}) \cos \alpha \qquad F_y = (75 \text{ lb}) \sin \alpha$$

Observing that $AB = 25$ ft, we find from Fig. 2.13

$$\cos \alpha = \frac{20 \text{ ft}}{AB} = \frac{20 \text{ ft}}{25 \text{ ft}} = \tfrac{4}{5} \qquad \sin \alpha = \frac{15 \text{ ft}}{AB} = \frac{15 \text{ ft}}{25 \text{ ft}} = \tfrac{3}{5}$$

We thus obtain

$$F_x = (75 \text{ lb})\tfrac{4}{5} = 60 \text{ lb} \rightarrow \qquad F_y = (75 \text{ lb})\tfrac{3}{5} = 45 \text{ lb} \downarrow$$

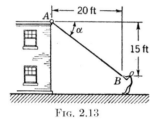

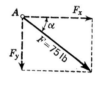

FIG. 2.13   FIG. 2.14

When a force is defined by its rectangular components F_x and F_y (see Fig. 2.9 or 2.10), the angle α defining its direction can be obtained by writing

$$\tan \alpha = \frac{F_y}{F_x} \tag{2.2}$$

The magnitude F of the force may be obtained by applying the Pythagorean theorem and writing

$$F = \sqrt{F_x^2 + F_y^2} \tag{2.3}$$

However, once α has been found, it is usually easier to determine the magnitude of the force by the process of solving one of the formulas (2.1) for F.

Example 3.   The horizontal and vertical components of a force F acting on a bolt A are, respectively, $F_x = 700$ lb and $F_y = 1,500$ lb (Fig. 2.15).   Determine the magnitude of the force and the angle α it forms with the horizontal.

Rather than α, we shall determine its complement β (Fig. 2.16) because β is smaller than 45° and because its tangent is more easily found on the slide rule.

We write

$$F_y \tan \beta = F_x$$
$$(1,500 \text{ lb}) \tan \beta = 700 \text{ lb} \tag{2.4}$$

and obtain

$$\beta = 25.0°$$

We then write

$$F \sin \beta = F_x$$
$$F \sin 25.0° = 700 \text{ lb} \tag{2.5}$$

and obtain

$$F = 1,656 \text{ lb}$$

The magnitude of the force is thus 1,656 lb, and the angle α it forms with the x axis is $\alpha = 90.0° - 25.0° = 65.0°$.

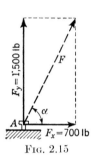

Fig. 2.15

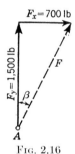

Fig. 2.16

Use of the Slide Rule. On most slide rules, β and F may be conveniently determined in the following way (Fig. 2.17):

FIRST STEP. Move the slide until one of the extremities of the trigonometric scale (in the present case the left one) coincides with the *larger* of the two components (1,500 lb) read on the D scale.

SECOND STEP. Move the indicator until the hairline coincides with the *smaller* of the two components (700 lb). Angle β may then be read *on the* T *scale* under the hairline since the rule is set to perform the product defined by Eq. (2.4).

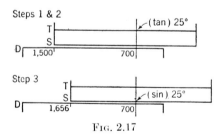

Fig. 2.17

THIRD STEP. Without touching the indicator, move the slide until angle β (25.0°) is read *on the* S *scale* under the hairline. The value of F (1,656 lb) may then be read on the D scale opposite one of the extremities of the trigonometric scale since the rule is set to perform the product defined by Eq. (2.5).

Remark. If the smaller of the two components is less than one-tenth of the larger one, the ST scale should be used in the second step, instead of the T scale, and the angle found will be less than 5.7°. The third step may then be omitted since, within the accuracy of the slide rule, the magnitude F of the force may be assumed equal to the larger of the two components (see Sample Prob. 2.4).

2.5. Addition of Forces by Summing x and y Components. It was seen in Sec. 2.1 that forces should be added according to the parallelogram law. From this law, two other methods, more readily applicable to the *graphical* solution of problems, were derived in Secs. 2.1 and 2.2: the triangle rule for the addition of two forces and the polygon rule for the addition of three or more forces. It was also seen that the force triangle used to define the resultant of two forces could be used to obtain a *trigonometric* solution.

When three or more forces are to be added, no practical trigonometric solution may be obtained from the force polygon which defines the resultant of the forces. In this case, an *analytic* solution of the problem may be obtained by first resolving each force into two rectangular components.

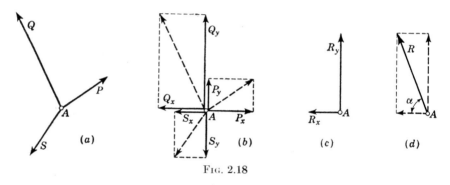

Fig. 2.18

In Fig. 2.18a, for example, three forces P, Q, and S are shown acting on a point A. In Fig. 2.18b, each of these forces has been replaced by its horizontal and vertical components; thus the forces of Fig. 2.18b produce the same effect on point A as the forces of Fig. 2.18a. Now the horizontal components may be added into a single force R_x. This is actually done by applying the parallelogram law; but since the forces considered lie in the same line, the actual computation reduces to a simple algebraic addition. Likewise, the vertical components may be reduced to a single force R_y. Thus the three given forces of Fig. 2.18a have been replaced by the horizontal force R_x and the vertical force R_y shown in Fig. 2.18c. These two forces are added vectorially into the resultant R of the given system (Fig. 2.18d) by applying the formulas of Sec. 2.4.

The procedure just described can be carried out most efficiently if the computations are arranged in a table. While it is the only practical analytic method for adding three or more forces, it is also often preferred to the trigonometric solution in the case of the addition of two forces.

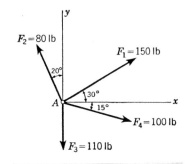

Four forces act on bolt A as shown. Determine the resultant of the forces on the bolt.

Solution. The x and y components of each force are determined by trigonometry as shown. The x components are now added algebraically to obtain R_x; the y components are added to obtain R_y. These additions are performed in tabular form as shown below.

Since several forces are involved, a sign convention must be chosen and used consistently throughout the problem. We choose the following: Components which have the same sense as the corresponding coordinate axis are positive. Thus, positive x components act to the right, and positive y components act upward. The signs are most easily and surely determined by referring directly to the sketch of the problem.

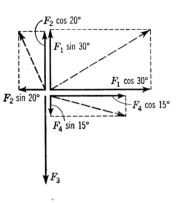

Force	Magnitude, lb	x component, lb	y component, lb
F_1	150	+129.9	+75.0
F_2	80	−27.4	+75.2
F_3	110	0	−110.0
F_4	100	+96.6	−25.9
		$R_x = +199.1$	$R_y = +14.3$
		$R_x = 199.1 \rightarrow$	$R_y = 14.3 \uparrow$

The magnitude and direction of the resultant may now be determined. In the triangle shown,

$$R_x \tan \alpha = R_y$$

$$(199.1 \text{ lb}) \tan \alpha = 14.3 \text{ lb}$$

The smaller component (14.3 lb) being less than one-tenth of the larger component (199.1 lb), we use the **ST** scale and read $\alpha = 4.1°$. Since within the accuracy of the slide rule the sine and tangent of this angle are equal, the magnitude of R may be assumed equal to the larger component,

$$R = 199.1 \text{ lb} \angle 4.1°$$

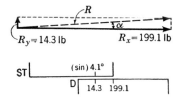

23

PROBLEMS

2.13. In removing a nail, a force of 200 lb is applied by a hammer in the direction shown. What are the horizontal and vertical components of this force?

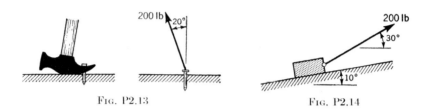

Fig. P2.13   Fig. P2.14

2.14. What are the components of the 200-lb force in directions parallel and perpendicular to the plane?

2.15. Determine the x and y components of each of the forces shown.

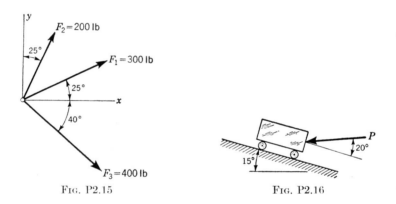

Fig. P2.15   Fig. P2.16

2.16. The force P must have a 40-lb component acting up the plane. Determine the magnitude of P and its component perpendicular to the plane.

2.17. Determine the horizontal and vertical components of the force F which acts along the line AB.

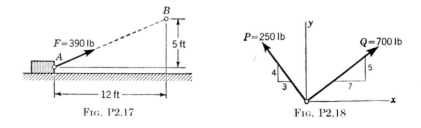

Fig. P2.17   Fig. P2.18

2.18. Determine the x and y components of each of the forces shown.

2.19 and 2.20. The x and y components of a force F are as shown. Determine the magnitude and direction of the force F.

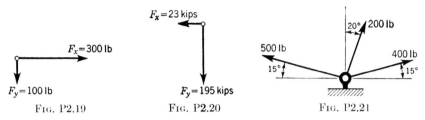

Fig. P2.19   Fig. P2.20   Fig. P2.21

2.21. A bolt is used to anchor three guy wires. The tension and the direction of each wire are shown. Determine the resultant of the forces acting on the bolt.

2.22. Using x and y components, solve part a of Prob. 2.4 analytically.

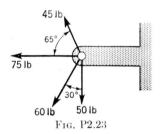

Fig. P2.23

2.23. Determine the resultant of the four forces which act on the bracket as shown.

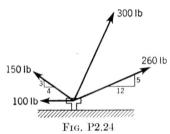

Fig. P2.24

2.24. A bolt is subjected to four forces as shown. The direction of the 300-lb force may be varied. If possible, determine the direction of the 300-lb force so that the resultant of the four forces is vertical.

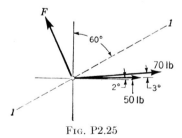

Fig. P2.25

2.25. The resultant of the three forces shown must be a 100-lb force directed to the right along line *1-1*. Determine the required magnitude and direction of the force F.

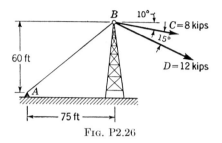

Fig. P2.26

2.26. Two cables which have known tensions are attached at point B. A third cable AB is used as a guy wire and is also attached at B. Determine the required tension in AB so that the resultant of the forces exerted by the three cables will be vertical.

2.27. Determine the resultant of the three forces of Prob. 2.15.

2.28. Determine the resultant of the two forces of Prob. 2.18.

2.6. Equilibrium of a Particle. In the preceding sections, we discussed the methods for determining the resultant of several forces acting on a particle. Although this has not occurred in any of the problems considered so far, it is quite possible for the resultant to be zero. In such a case, the net effect of the given forces is zero, and the particle is said to be in equilibrium. We thus have the following definition: *When the resultant of all the forces acting on a particle is zero, the particle is in equilibrium.*

A particle which is acted upon by two forces will be in equilibrium if

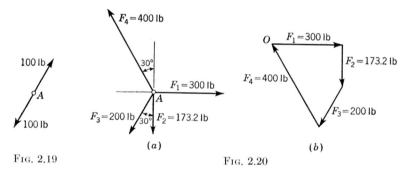

Fig. 2.19   Fig. 2.20

the two forces have same magnitude, same line of action, and opposite sense. The resultant of the two forces is then zero. Such a case is shown in Fig. 2.19.

Another case of equilibrium of a particle is represented in Fig. 2.20a, where four forces are shown acting on A. In Fig. 2.20b, the resultant of the given forces is determined by the polygon rule. Starting from point O with F_1 and arranging the forces in tip-to-tail fashion, we find that the tip of F_4 coincides with the starting point O. Thus the resultant R of the given system of forces is zero, and the particle is in equilibrium.

The closed polygon drawn in Fig. 2.20b provides a *graphical* expression of the equilibrium of A. To express *algebraically* that a particle is in equilibrium, we shall write that the two rectangular components R_x and R_y of the resultant are zero. Since R_x is equal to the sum ΣF_x of the x components of the given forces and R_y is equal to ΣF_y, we have the following necessary and sufficient conditions for the equilibrium of a particle:

$$\Sigma F_x = 0 \qquad \Sigma F_y = 0 \qquad (2.6)$$

Returning to the particle shown in Fig. 2.20a we check that the equilibrium conditions are satisfied.

$$\Sigma F_x = 300 \text{ lb} - (200 \text{ lb}) \sin 30° - (400 \text{ lb}) \sin 30°$$
$$= 300 \text{ lb} - 100 \text{ lb} - 200 \text{ lb} = 0$$
$$\Sigma F_y = -173.2 \text{ lb} - (200 \text{ lb}) \cos 30° + (400 \text{ lb}) \cos 30°$$
$$= -173.2 \text{ lb} - 173.2 \text{ lb} + 346.4 \text{ lb} = 0$$

2.7. Newton's First Law of Motion. In the latter part of the seventeenth century, Sir Isaac Newton formulated three fundamental laws upon which the science of mechanics is based. The first of these laws can be stated as follows:

If the resultant force acting on a particle is zero, the particle will remain at rest (if originally at rest) or will move with constant speed in a straight line (if originally in motion).

From this law and from the definition of equilibrium given in Sec. 2.6, it is seen that a particle in equilibrium either is at rest or is moving in a straight line with constant speed. In the following section, various problems concerning the equilibrium of a particle will be considered.

2.8. Problems Involving the Equilibrium of a Particle. Free-body Diagram. In practice, a problem in engineering mechanics is derived from an actual physical situation. A sketch showing the physical conditions of the problem is known as a *space diagram.*

The methods of analysis discussed in the preceding sections apply to a system of forces acting on a particle. A large number of problems involving actual structures, however, may be reduced to problems concerning the equilibrium of a particle. This is done by choosing a significant particle and drawing a separate diagram showing this particle and all the forces acting on it. Such a diagram is called a *free-body diagram.*

As an example, consider the heavy block, weighing 700 lb, shown in the space diagram of Fig. 2.21a. This block was lying between two buildings, and it is now being lifted onto a truck, which will remove it. The block is supported by a vertical cable, which is joined at A to the hooks of two chain hoists attached to the buildings at B and C. It is desired to determine the tension in each of the chains AB and AC.

In order to solve this problem, a free-body diagram must be drawn, showing a particle in equilibrium. Since we are interested in the chain tensions, the free-body diagram should include at least one of these tensions and, if possible, both tensions. Point A is seen to be a good free body for this problem. The free-body diagram of point A is shown in Fig. 2.21b. It represents point A and the three forces acting on A, namely, the 700-lb force exerted by the block and the two tensions T_{AB} and T_{AC}. The two tensions are shown acting away from point A. No other detail is included in the free-body diagram.

Since point A is in equilibrium, the three forces acting on it must form a closed triangle when drawn in tip-to-tail fashion. This *force triangle* has been drawn in Fig. 2.21c. The values of T_{AB} and T_{AC} may be found

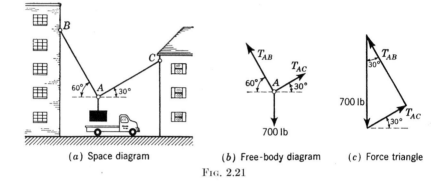

(*a*) Space diagram   (*b*) Free-body diagram   (*c*) Force triangle

Fig. 2.21

graphically if the triangle is drawn to scale, or they may be found by trigonometry. If the latter method of solution is chosen, we find, since the triangle is a right triangle,

$$T_{AB} = (700 \text{ lb}) \cos 30° = 606 \text{ lb}$$
$$T_{AC} = (700 \text{ lb}) \sin 30° = 350 \text{ lb}$$

When a particle is in *equilibrium under three forces*, the problem may always be solved by drawing a force triangle. However, this triangle will in general be oblique, and its trigonometric solution will include the use of the law of sines or the law of cosines.

When a particle is in *equilibrium under more than three forces*, the problem may be solved graphically by drawing a force polygon. If an analytic solution is desired, the *equations of equilibrium* given in Sec. 2.6 should be solved.

$$\Sigma F_x = 0 \qquad \Sigma F_y = 0 \qquad (2.6)$$

These equations may be solved for no more than *two unknowns;* similarly, the force triangle used in the case of equilibrium under three forces may be solved for two unknowns. The more common types of problems are those where the two unknowns represent (1) the two components (or the magnitude and direction) of a single force, (2) the magnitude of two forces each of known direction.

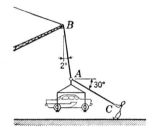

SAMPLE PROBLEM 2.5

In a ship-loading operation, a 3,500-lb automobile is supported by a cable. A rope is tied to the cable at A and pulled in order to center the automobile over its intended position. The angle between the cable and the vertical is 2°, while the angle between the rope and the horizontal is 30°. What is the tension in the rope?

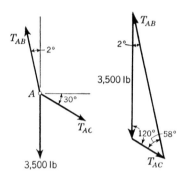

Solution. Point A is chosen as a free body, and the complete free-body diagram is drawn. T_{AB} is the tension in the cable AB, and T_{AC} is the tension in the rope. Drawing the force triangle and using the law of sines, we write

$$\frac{T_{AB}}{\sin 120°} = \frac{T_{AC}}{\sin 2°} = \frac{3,500 \text{ lb}}{\sin 58°}$$

$$T_{AB} = \textbf{3,570 lb} \qquad T_{AC} = \textbf{144 lb}$$

SAMPLE PROBLEM 2.6

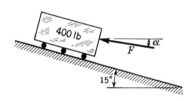

Determine the magnitude and direction of the smallest force F which will maintain the block in equilibrium. The block is placed on rollers so that the force between the block and the plane must be perpendicular to the plane.

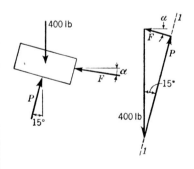

Solution. It is assumed that the block may be treated as a particle; the block is chosen as a free body. Three forces act on the free body; we draw a force triangle to express that the block is in equilibrium. Line 1-1 is the known direction of P. So that F will be a minimum, we choose its direction perpendicular to that of P. From the geometry of this triangle, we find

$$F = (400 \text{ lb}) \sin 15° = 103.6 \text{ lb} \qquad \alpha = 15°$$

$$F = \textbf{103.6 lb} \ \text{\ensuremath{\diagdown}}\ \textbf{15}°$$

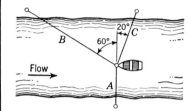

A small boat is moored by means of three ropes tied to posts on the banks of a stream. The stream flow exerts a force on the boat which acts directly downstream. The tensions in ropes A and B are measured and found to be $A = 120$ lb and $B = 80$ lb. Determine the magnitude of the force exerted by the flow and the tension in rope C.

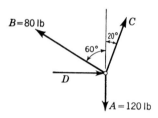

Solution. The boat is taken as a free body. It is acted upon by four forces directed as shown. Since the boat is in equilibrium, the resultant of these four forces is zero. Hence,

$$\Sigma F_x = 0 \qquad \Sigma F_y = 0$$

Each force is resolved into its x and y components; we obtain

$$A_x = 0$$

$$B_x = (80 \text{ lb}) \cos 30° = 69.3 \text{ lb} \leftarrow$$

$$C_x = C \sin 20° = 0.342C \rightarrow$$

$$D_x = D \rightarrow$$

$$A_y = 120 \text{ lb} \downarrow$$

$$B_y = (80 \text{ lb}) \sin 30° = 40 \text{ lb} \uparrow$$

$$C_y = C \cos 20° = 0.940C \uparrow$$

$$D_y = 0$$

In writing the equilibrium equations, components which act to the right or upward are assigned a positive sign; this is indicated by a small arrow before each equation

$$\xrightarrow{+} \Sigma F_x = 0: \qquad -69.3 \text{ lb} + 0.342C + D = 0$$

$$+\uparrow \Sigma F_y = 0: \quad -120 \text{ lb} + 40 \text{ lb} + 0.940C = 0$$

Solving these equations, we find

$$C = +85.1 \text{ lb} \qquad D = +40.2 \text{ lb}$$

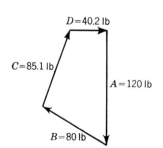

In drawing the free-body diagram, we assumed a sense for each unknown force. A positive sign in the answer indicates that the assumed sense is correct. The complete force polygon may be drawn to check the results.

SAMPLE PROBLEM 2.8

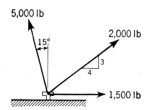

5,000 lb

2,000 lb

15°

3

4

1,500 lb

A bolt is used to anchor three guy wires as shown. The tension in each wire is given. Determine the magnitude and direction of the force exerted by the foundation on the bolt.

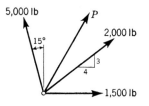

5,000 lb

P

2,000 lb

15°

3

4

1,500 lb

Solution. A free-body diagram of the bolt is drawn; the force exerted by the foundation is P. No attempt is made to guess the direction or sense of P (although in this case it is easily seen that P has a downward component). Since the bolt is in equilibrium, the resultant must be zero; therefore,

$$\Sigma F_x = 0 \qquad \Sigma F_y = 0$$

Positive sense is assumed to the right for the x components and upward for the y components. The components of the 2,000-lb force are computed directly from the given slope of the force.

$\overset{+}{\rightarrow} \Sigma F_x = 0:$
$\quad -(5,000 \text{ lb}) \sin 15° + (2,000 \text{ lb})\tfrac{4}{5} + 1,500 \text{ lb} + P_x = 0$
$\quad -1,294 \text{ lb} + 1,600 \text{ lb} + 1,500 \text{ lb} + P_x = 0$
$\quad +1,806 \text{ lb} + P_x = 0 \qquad P_x = -1,806 \text{ lb} = 1,806 \text{ lb} \leftarrow$

$+\uparrow \Sigma F_y = 0:$
$\quad +(5,000 \text{ lb}) \cos 15° + (2,000 \text{ lb})\tfrac{3}{5} + P_y = 0$
$\quad +4,830 \text{ lb} + 1,200 \text{ lb} + P_y = 0$
$\quad +6,030 \text{ lb} + P_y = 0 \qquad P_y = -6,030 \text{ lb} = 6,030 \text{ lb} \downarrow$

In solving the equations, both P_x and P_y were found to be negative. This indicated that their assumed directions were wrong. The magnitude and direction of P are now computed.

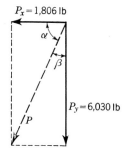

$P_x = 1,806$ lb

α

β

$P_y = 6,030$ lb

P

$$P_y \tan \beta = P_x$$

$$(6,030 \text{ lb}) \tan \beta = 1,806 \text{ lb}$$

$$\beta = 16.7° \qquad \alpha = 90° - 16.7° = 73.3°$$

$$P \sin \beta = P_x$$

$$P \sin 16.7° = 1,806 \text{ lb}$$

$$\mathbf{P = 6,300 \text{ lb} \nearrow 73.3°}$$

31

PROBLEMS

2.29 through 2.31. Two cables are tied together at C and loaded as shown.   Determine the tension in AC and BC.

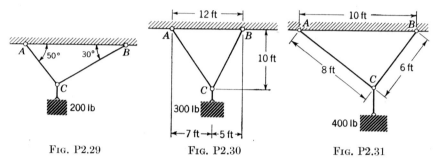

FIG. P2.29   FIG. P2.30   FIG. P2.31

2.32. A 500-lb block is supported by two cables as shown.   (*a*) For what value of α is the magnitude of the tension in cable B minimum?   (*b*) What are the corresponding values of the tension in cables A and B?

2.33. Two ropes are tied together at C.   If the maximum permissible tension in each rope is 75 lb, what is the maximum force F that may be applied?   In what direction must this maximum force act?

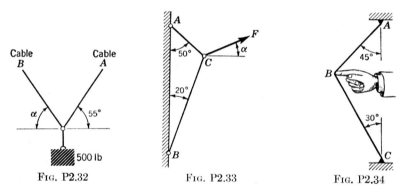

FIG. P2.32   FIG. P2.33   FIG. P2.34

2.34. A man stretches an elastic cord AC by applying his finger at B.   Determine the magnitude and direction of the force exerted by the man, knowing that the tension in both parts of the cord is 5 lb.

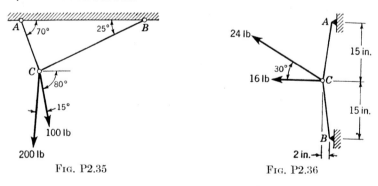

FIG. P2.35   FIG. P2.36

2.35 and 2.36. Two strings are tied together at C and loaded as shown. Determine the tension in AC and BC.

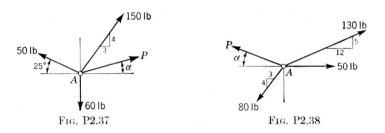

Fig. P2.37   Fig. P2.38

2.37 and 2.38. A particle A is in equilibrium under the action of the four forces shown. Determine the magnitude and direction of P.

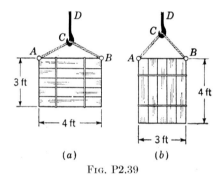

(a)   (b)

Fig. P2.39

2.39. A 1,500-lb crate is lifted by a crane cable CD. A cable sling ACB is 5 ft long and can be attached to the crate in each of the two ways shown. Determine the tension in the cable sling in each case.

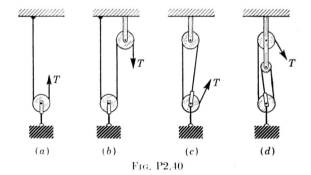

(a)   (b)   (c)   (d)

Fig. P2.40

2.40. A 600-lb weight is supported by several different rope-and-pulley arrangements as shown. Determine for each arrangement the tension in the rope. (The tension in the rope is the same on each side of a simple pulley. This can be proved by the methods treated in Chap. 3.)

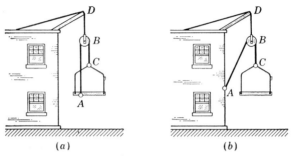

FIG. P2.41

2.41. A painter's scaffold can be supported in the two ways illustrated. Is one way better than the other? If the maximum permissible tension in rope ABC is 100 lb and the maximum permissible tension in rope BD is 150 lb, what is the greatest load that can be carried by each arrangement? (Neglect the effect of the horizontal distance from the building to the scaffold.)

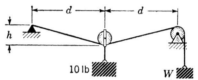

FIG. P2.42, P2.43, AND P2.44

2.42. In the diagram shown, $h = 5$ in., and $d = 12$ in. Determine the required value of W for equilibrium.

*2.43. If in the diagram shown $W = 80$ lb and $d = 20$ in., determine the value of h consistent with equilibrium.

*2.44. Express in terms of h the value of W required to maintain equilibrium, assuming $d = 12$ in. Explain the result obtained when $h = 0$.

FORCES IN SPACE

2.9. Rectangular Components of a Force in Space. The problems considered in the first part of this chapter involved only two dimensions; they could be formulated and solved in a single plane. In this section and in the remaining sections of the chapter, we shall discuss problems involving the three dimensions of space.

Consider a force F acting at the origin O of the system of rectangular coordinates x, y, z. To define the direction of F, we may draw the vertical plane $OBAC$ containing F and shown in Fig. 2.22a. This plane passes through the vertical y axis; its orientation is defined by the angle ϕ it forms with the xy plane, while the direction of F within the plane is defined by the angle θ_y that F forms with the y axis. The force F may be resolved into a vertical component F_y and a horizontal component F'; this operation, shown in Fig. 2.22b, is carried out inside plane $OBAC$ according to the rules developed in the first part of the chapter. We write

$$F_y = F \cos \theta_y \qquad F' = F \sin \theta_y \qquad (2.7)$$

But F' may be resolved into two rectangular components directed along the x and z axes, respectively. This operation, shown in Fig. 2.22c, is carried out inside the xz plane. We write

$$F_x = F' \cos \phi = F \sin \theta_y \cos \phi \\ F_z = F' \sin \phi = F \sin \theta_y \sin \phi \tag{2.8}$$

The given force F has thus been *resolved into three rectangular components* F_x, F_y, F_z, directed along the three axes of coordinates. These three component forces together produce the same effect as F.

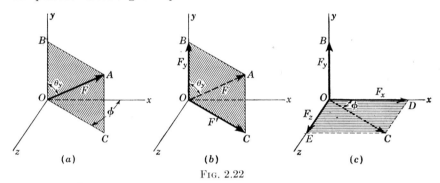

Fig. 2.22

Applying the Pythagorean theorem to the triangles OAB and OCD of Fig. 2.22, we write

$$F^2 = (OA)^2 = (OB)^2 + (BA)^2 = F_y^2 + F'^2 \\ F'^2 = (OC)^2 = (OD)^2 + (DC)^2 = F_x^2 + F_z^2$$

Eliminating F'^2 from these two equations and solving for F, we obtain the following relation between the magnitude and the rectangular components of the force F:

$$F = \sqrt{F_x^2 + F_y^2 + F_z^2} \tag{2.9}$$

The relationship existing between the force F and its three components F_x, F_y, F_z is more easily visualized if a "box" having F_x, F_y, F_z for edges is drawn as shown in Fig. 2.23. The force F is then represented by the diagonal OA of this box, which we shall refer to as the "force box" of F. In Fig. 2.23b, the right triangle OAB is shown again; this triangle was used to derive the first of the formulas (2.7): $F_y = F \cos \theta_y$. In Fig. 2.23a and c, two other right triangles have also been drawn: OAD and OAE. These triangles are seen to occupy in the force box positions comparable with that of triangle OAB. Denoting by θ_x and θ_z, respectively, the angles that F forms with the x and z axes, we may derive two formulas similar to $F_y = F \cos \theta_y$. We thus write

$$F_x = F \cos \theta_x \qquad F_y = F \cos \theta_y \qquad F_z = F \cos \theta_z \tag{2.10}$$

The three angles θ_x, θ_y, θ_z define the direction of the force F; they are more commonly used for this purpose than the angles θ_y and ϕ introduced at the beginning of this section. The cosines of θ_x, θ_y, θ_z are known as the direction cosines of the force F.

Formulas (2.10) may be readily used to find the components F_x, F_y, F_z of a force when its magnitude F and the angles θ_x, θ_y, θ_z are known. When the components F_x, F_y, F_z of a force are given, the magnitude F of the force is obtained from (2.9); the relations (2.10) may then be solved for the direction cosines, and the angles θ_x, θ_y, θ_z characterizing the direction of the force may be found.

The method we have described may also be used when the force F acts at a point M different from the origin of coordinates. The components F_x, F_y, F_z are then attached at M, and the angles θ_x, θ_y, θ_z are the angles that F forms with lines through M, parallel to the axes of coordinates.

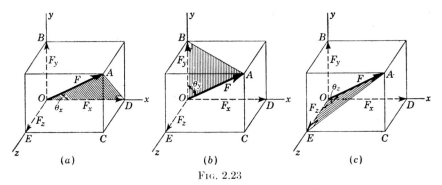

Fig. 2.23

Example 1. A 100-lb force forms angles of 60, 45, and 120°, respectively, with the x, y, and z axes. Find the components F_x, F_y, and F_z of the force.

Substituting $F = 100$ lb, $\theta_x = 60°$, $\theta_y = 45°$, $\theta_z = 120°$ into formulas (2.10), we write

$$F_x = (100 \text{ lb}) \cos 60° = +50.0 \text{ lb}$$
$$F_y = (100 \text{ lb}) \cos 45° = +70.7 \text{ lb}$$
$$F_z = (100 \text{ lb}) \cos 120° = -50.0 \text{ lb}$$

It would not be convenient here to indicate the sense of the components by means of an arrow as was done in two-dimensional problems. In all problems in space, the sense of the components will be specified by a sign, the plus sign indicating that the component has the same direction as the corresponding axis. The axes themselves will be oriented as shown in Figs. 2.22 and 2.23 whenever practical.

The angle a force forms with an axis should be measured from the positive side of the axis and will always be comprised between 0 and 180°. An angle θ_x smaller than 90° (acute) indicates that the force (assumed attached at O) is on the same side of the yz plane as the positive x axis;

cos θ_x and F_x will then be positive. An angle θ_x larger than 90° (obtuse) would indicate that the force is on the other side of the yz plane; cos θ_x and F_x would then be negative. In the present example θ_x and θ_y are acute, while θ_z is obtuse: consequently, F_x and F_y are positive, while F_z is negative.

It should also be observed that the values of the three angles θ_x, θ_y, θ_z are not independent. Substituting for F_x, F_y, F_z from (2.10) into (2.9), we find that the following identity must be satisfied:

$$\cos^2 \theta_x + \cos^2 \theta_y + \cos^2 \theta_z = 1 \tag{2.11}$$

In the present example, once the values $\theta_x = 60°$ and $\theta_y = 45°$ have been selected, the value of θ_z *must* be equal to 60 or 120° in order to satisfy identity (2.11).

Example 2. A force has the components $F_x = 20$ lb, $F_y = -30$ lb. $F_z = 60$ lb. Determine its magnitude F and the angles θ_x, θ_y, θ_z it forms with the axes of coordinates.

From formula (2.9) we obtain

$$F = \sqrt{F_x^2 + F_y^2 + F_z^2} = \sqrt{(20 \text{ lb})^2 + (-30 \text{ lb})^2 + (60 \text{ lb})^2}$$
$$= \sqrt{4{,}900} \text{ lb} = 70 \text{ lb}$$

The relations (2.10) may then be used to determine the angles θ_x, θ_y, θ_z. We shall write them first, however, in the following form:

$$\frac{\cos \theta_x}{F_x} = \frac{\cos \theta_y}{F_y} = \frac{\cos \theta_z}{F_z} = \frac{1}{F} \tag{2.12}$$

Formula (2.12) expresses more clearly the fact that F_x, F_y, F_z, and F are, respectively, proportional to cos θ_x, cos θ_y, cos θ_z, and 1; this formula is thus better adapted to the use of the slide rule.

Substituting the values of the components and of the magnitude of the force into (2.12), we obtain

$$\frac{\cos \theta_x}{20 \text{ lb}} = \frac{\cos \theta_y}{-30 \text{ lb}} = \frac{\cos \theta_z}{60 \text{ lb}} = \frac{1}{70 \text{ lb}}$$
$$\theta_x - 73.4° \qquad \theta_y = 115.4° \qquad \theta_z = 31.0°$$

Note that, F_y being negative, the value of θ_y must be larger than 90°; thus θ_y is equal not to 64.6° but to its supplement, 115.4°.

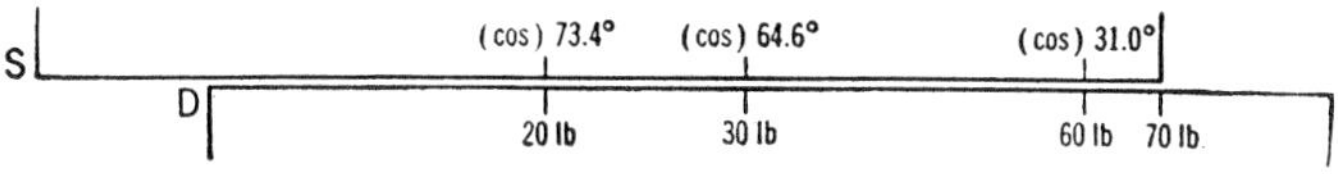

FIG. 2.24

Use of the Slide Rule. The angles θ_x, θ_y, θ_z defined by formula (2.12) are found on the slide rule by bringing one of the extremities of the S scale to coincide with F on the D scale. The values of θ_x, θ_y, θ_z are then read directly on the S scale (using angles corresponding to cosines) in front of F_x, F_y, F_z, respectively. The sketch of Fig. 2.24 shows the rule set to read the values corresponding to Example 2.

2.10. Components of Force and Components of Distance. Another method of defining the direction of a force F acting at the origin O of the system of coordinates is to specify a second point N through which the line of action of F passes (Fig. 2.25). Through N we may draw lines parallel to the axes of coordinates and thus define a new box; this box is called a "distance box" because its diagonal ON measures the distance d from O to N. The sides of the distance box, denoted, respectively, by d_x, d_y, d_z, are called *components of the distance d;* since, in the case considered, O is the origin of the system of coordinates, the components d_x,

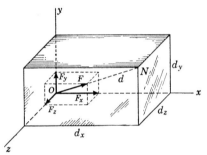

Fig. 2.25

d_y, d_z are also the coordinates of point N. Observing that the angles that ON forms with the axes of coordinates are θ_x, θ_y, θ_z, and proceeding as in Sec. 2.9, we write

$$d_x = d \cos \theta_x \qquad d_y = d \cos \theta_y \qquad d_z = d \cos \theta_z \qquad (2.13)$$

$$d = \sqrt{d_x^2 + d_y^2 + d_z^2} \qquad (2.14)$$

Dividing member by member the relations (2.10) and (2.13), we obtain

$$\frac{F_x}{d_x} = \frac{F_y}{d_y} = \frac{F_z}{d_z} = \frac{F}{d} \qquad (2.15)$$

Formula (2.15) states that the components and magnitude of the force F are, respectively, proportional to the components and magnitude of the distance d. This result could have been accepted intuitively by observing that the force box and the distance box have the same shape. It should be noted, however, that the dimensions of the force box are expressed in pounds, while the dimensions of the distance box are expressed in feet.

Suppose now that the magnitude F of a force acting at O is known and that the coordinates d_x, d_y, d_z of a point N on its line of action are also given. From (2.14) we may determine the distance d from O to N. Carrying F, d_x, d_y, d_z, and d into (2.15), we obtain the components F_x,

F_y, F_z by simple proportions. This computation, which is easily performed on the slide rule, has been carried out in Sample Prob. 2.9.

The relations (2.13) may also be written in the following form:

$$\frac{\cos \theta_x}{d_x} = \frac{\cos \theta_y}{d_y} = \frac{\cos \theta_z}{d_z} = \frac{1}{d} \tag{2.16}$$

Formula (2.16) may be used to obtain the angles θ_x, θ_y, θ_z on the slide
rule, directly from the distance d and its components d_x, d_y, d_z.

When the line of action of the force F is defined by two points M and
N, neither of which is at the origin (Fig. 2.26), the distance components
are equal to the difference between the coordinates of M and N. The
distance components should have the same sign as the corresponding force
components. The sign of d_x, therefore, will be positive if the x coordinate
increases when the line MN is described in the sense defined by F (from

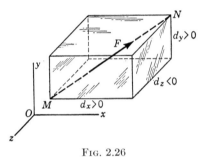

FIG. 2.26

M to N in the case represented in Fig. 2.26); it will be negative if the x
coordinate decreases. The signs of d_y and d_z are determined in a similar
way.

2.11. Addition of Concurrent Forces in Space. We shall determine the
resultant R of two or more forces in space by summing their rectangular
components. Graphical or trigonometric methods are generally not
practical in the case of forces in space.

The method followed here is similar to that used in Sec. 2.5 with
coplanar forces. First we resolve each of the given forces into rectangular
components F_x, F_y, F_z. Adding algebraically all x components, we obtain
the component R_x of the resultant; proceeding in the same manner with
the y and z components, we write

$$R_x = \Sigma F_x \qquad R_y = \Sigma F_y \qquad R_z = \Sigma F_z \tag{2.17}$$

The magnitude of the resultant and the angles θ_x, θ_y, θ_z it forms with the
axes of coordinates are obtained by the method of Sec. 2.10. We write

$$R = \sqrt{R_x^2 + R_y^2 + R_z^2} \qquad \frac{\cos \theta_x}{R_x} = \frac{\cos \theta_y}{R_y} = \frac{\cos \theta_z}{R_z} = \frac{1}{R} \tag{2.18}$$

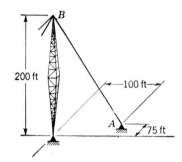

A tower guy wire is anchored by means of a bolt at A. The tension in the wire is 2,500 lb. Determine (*a*) the components F_x, F_y, F_z of the force acting on the bolt, (*b*) the angles θ_x, θ_y, θ_z defining the direction of the force.

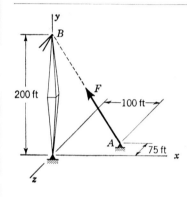

a. **Components of the Force.** The line of action of the force acting on the bolt passes through A and B; and the force is directed from A to B. The distance components are obtained by moving along the cable in the direction of the force, i.e., from A to B.

$$d_x = -100 \text{ ft} \qquad d_y = +200 \text{ ft} \qquad d_z = +75 \text{ ft}$$

The total distance from A to B is

$$d = \sqrt{d_x^2 + d_y^2 + d_z^2} = 236 \text{ ft}$$

Since the force components are proportional to the distance components, we write

$$\frac{F_x}{-100 \text{ ft}} = \frac{F_y}{+200 \text{ ft}} = \frac{F_z}{+75 \text{ ft}} = \frac{2,500 \text{ lb}}{236 \text{ ft}}$$

and obtain

$$F_x = -1{,}060 \text{ lb} \qquad F_y = +2{,}120 \text{ lb}$$
$$F_z = +794 \text{ lb}$$

b. **Direction of the Force.** Since the values of F_x, F_y, and F_z are known, we write

$$\frac{\cos \theta_x}{F_x} = \frac{\cos \theta_y}{F_y} = \frac{\cos \theta_z}{F_z} = \frac{1}{F}$$

$$\frac{\cos \theta_x}{-1{,}060 \text{ lb}} = \frac{\cos \theta_y}{+2{,}120 \text{ lb}} = \frac{\cos \theta_z}{+794 \text{ lb}} = \frac{1}{2{,}500 \text{ lb}}$$

$$\theta_x = 180° - 64.9° = \mathbf{115.1°} \qquad \theta_y = \mathbf{32.0°}$$
$$\theta_z = \mathbf{71.5°}$$

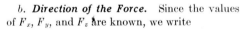

We may also consider the known distance components and write

$$\frac{\cos \theta_x}{d_x} = \frac{\cos \theta_y}{d_y} = \frac{\cos \theta_z}{d_z} = \frac{1}{d}$$

$$\frac{\cos \theta_x}{-100 \text{ ft}} = \frac{\cos \theta_y}{+200 \text{ ft}} = \frac{\cos \theta_z}{+75 \text{ ft}} = \frac{1}{236 \text{ ft}}$$

The same angles are obtained from these equations

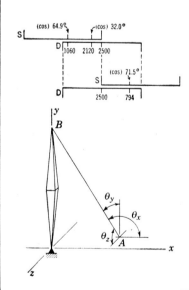

SAMPLE PROBLEM 2.10

In an attempt to move a wrecked railroad car, two cranes are used as shown. The cranes are oriented so that their booms lie in vertical planes perpendicular to the tracks. The tensions in the cables are

$$\text{Crane } A = 10 \text{ kips} \qquad \text{Crane } B = 15 \text{ kips}$$

What is the resultant force exerted on the car?

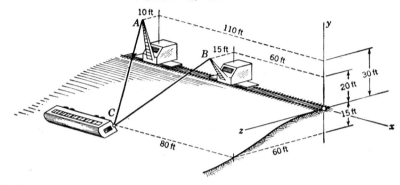

Solution. The tension in each cable will be resolved into x, y, and z components. We first determine the distance components of each force

For crane A (C to A): $d_x = -30$ ft $\quad d_y = +45$ ft $\quad d_z = -50$ ft $\quad d = 73.7$ ft
For crane B (C to B): $\quad d_x = +20$ ft $\quad d_y = +35$ ft $\quad d_z = -45$ ft $\quad d = 60.4$ ft

In order to determine the force components, it is necessary to express that force and distance components are proportional. This is most efficiently done in tabular form. The information entered in the table includes the components and the magnitude of the distances as well as the magnitude of the given forces. The force components are then found by proportions and added to obtain the components R_x, R_y, and R_z of the resultant.

Force	Distance components, ft			d, ft	Force components, kips			F, kips
	x	y	z		F_x	F_y	F_z	
Crane A........	-30	$+45$	-50	73.7	-4.07	$+6.11$	-6.78	10.0
Crane B........	$+20$	$+35$	-45	60.4	$+4.97$	$+8.69$	-11.17	15.0
					$R_x =$ $+0.90$	$R_y =$ $+14.80$	$R_z =$ -17.95	

The magnitude and direction of the resultant are now determined.

$$R = \sqrt{R_x^2 + R_y^2 + R_z^2} = \sqrt{(0.90)^2 + (14.80)^2 + (-17.95)^2} = \textbf{23.3 kips}$$

$$\frac{\cos \theta_x}{R_x} = \frac{\cos \theta_y}{R_y} = \frac{\cos \theta_z}{R_z} = \frac{1}{R}$$

$$\frac{\cos \theta_x}{+0.90 \text{ kip}} = \frac{\cos \theta_y}{+14.80 \text{ kips}} = \frac{\cos \theta_z}{-17.95 \text{ kips}} = \frac{1}{23.3 \text{ kips}}$$

$$\theta_x = \textbf{87.8}° \qquad \theta_y = \textbf{50.6}° \qquad \theta_z = 180° - 39.6° = \textbf{140.4}°$$

PROBLEMS

2.45 and 2.46. Determine F_x, F_y, and F_z for the force shown.

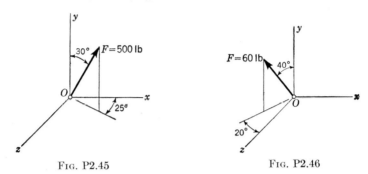

FIG. P2.45   FIG. P2.46

2.47. Determine the force components and the angles θ_x, θ_y, and θ_z for the force of Prob. 2.45.

2.48. A gun is aimed so that it will fire toward a point A which is 30° east of north and is 15 ft above the gun in elevation. The horizontal distance from the gun to point A is 50 ft. If at a given instant the recoil force of the gun is 80 lb, determine the x, y, and z components of the recoil force. (Assume the x axis is toward the east, the y axis is up, and the z axis is south.) Also, determine θ_x, θ_y, and θ_z.

2.49. A 700-lb force acts at the origin in a direction defined by the angles $\theta_x = 73.4°$, $\theta_y = 115.4°$, and $\theta_z = 149.0°$. Determine the x, y, and z components of the force.

2.50. A 500-lb force acts at the origin in a direction defined by the angles $\theta_y = 46.0°$ and $\theta_z = 80.0°$. It is also known that the x component of the force is positive. Determine the value of θ_x and the components of the force.

2.51. Cable AB is attached to a building and to a point on the ground as shown. If the tension in the cable is 350 lb, determine the components of the force exerted on the building at A.

2.52. The tension in cable BC is 450 lb. Determine the components of the force exerted on the building at C.

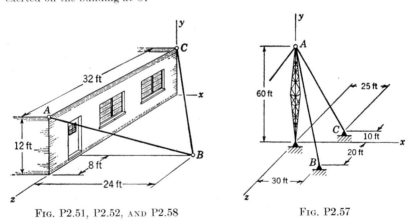

FIG. P2.51, P2.52, AND P2.58   FIG. P2.57

2.53. The components of a force are known to be $F_x = +175$ lb, $F_y = -125$ lb, and $F_z = -25$ lb. Determine the magnitude and direction of the force.

2.54. The components of a force are $F_x = +450$ lb, $F_y = -500$ lb, and $F_z = +250$ lb. Determine the magnitude and direction of the force.

2.55. Determine the angles θ_x, θ_y, and θ_z defining the direction of the force acting on point A in Prob. 2.51.

2.56. Determine the angles θ_x, θ_y, and θ_z defining the direction of the force acting on point C in Prob. 2.52.

2.57. Two guy wires AB and AC are attached to the top of a tower at A. The tension in AB is 600 lb, and the tension in AC is 800 lb. Determine the resultant of the two forces exerted by the cables on point A.

2.58. The tension in cable AB is 350 lb, and the tension in cable BC is 450 lb. Determine the vertical component of the resultant of the forces exerted by the cables on point B.

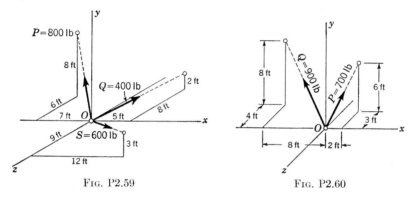

Fig. P2.59   Fig. P2.60

2.59. Determine the resultant of the three forces P, Q, and S.

2.60. Two forces P and Q act at point O as shown. A third force S, which also acts at point O, is then added. What must be the components of S if the resultant of all three forces is to be (a) 800 lb directed along the positive x axis, (b) 800 lb directed along the positive z axis, (c) zero?

2.12. Equilibrium of a Particle in Space. According to the definition given in Sec. 2.6, a particle A is in equilibrium if the resultant of all the forces acting on A is zero. The components R_x, R_y, R_z of the resultant are given by the relations (2.17); expressing that the components of the resultant are zero, we write

$$\Sigma F_x - 0 \qquad \Sigma F_y - 0 \qquad \Sigma F_z - 0 \qquad (2.19)$$

Formulas (2.19) represent the necessary and sufficient conditions for the equilibrium of a particle in space. They may be used to solve problems dealing with the equilibrium of a particle and involving no more than three unknowns.

To solve such problems, we first should draw a free-body diagram showing the particle in equilibrium and *all* the forces acting on it. We may then write the equations of equilibrium (2.19) and solve them for three unknowns. In the more common types of problems, these unknowns will represent (1) the three components of a single force or (2) the magnitude of three forces each of known direction.

SAMPLE PROBLEM 2.11

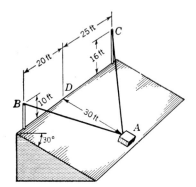

A 500-lb crate is held on a 30° incline by two ropes as shown. The crate is mounted on casters, and it may be assumed that the force which the incline exerts on the crate is perpendicular to the incline. Determine the magnitude of the force exerted by the incline and the tension in each rope.

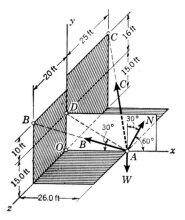

Solution. The crate is chosen as a free body; four forces act on the crate as shown. Three of these forces are unknown; their magnitudes are denoted, respectively, by B, C, and N; their sense is assumed as indicated on the free body.

The x, y, and z components of each force must now be expressed in terms of B, C, and N. The components of forces B and C are obtained by proportion. In the case of force N, it is noted that, since it lies in a vertical plane, its z component is zero and its x and y components are

$$N_x = N \sin 30° = +0.500N$$

$$N_y = N \cos 30° = +0.866N$$

Force	Distance components, ft			d, ft	Force components, lb			Force, lb
	x	y	z		F_x	F_y	F_z	
Cable AB.	-26	$+25$	$+20$	41.3	$-0.630B$	$+0.606B$	$+0.484B$	B
Cable AC.	-26	$+31$	-25	47.6	$-0.546C$	$+0.652C$	$-0.525C$	C
Incline....	....	....	....	....	$+0.500N$	$+0.866N$	....	N
Weight...	....	....	....	....	....	-500	....	-500

Equilibrium Equations. The equilibrium equations may be written directly by adding successively the force-components columns of the table.

$\Sigma F_x = 0:$ $\qquad\qquad -0.630B - 0.546C + 0.500N = 0$

$\Sigma F_y = 0:$ $\qquad\quad +0.606B + 0.652C + 0.866N - 500 = 0$

$\Sigma F_z = 0:$ $\qquad\qquad\qquad +0.484B - 0.525C = 0$

Solving these equations, we obtain

$$B = +158 \text{ lb} \qquad C = +146 \text{ lb} \qquad N = +358 \text{ lb}$$

PROBLEMS

2.61. A 300-lb weight is supported by three cables as shown. Determine the magnitude of the tension in each cable.

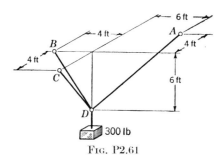

Fig. P2.61

2.62. Three cables are joined at point D, where an upward force of 500 lb is applied. Determine the magnitude of the tension in each cable.

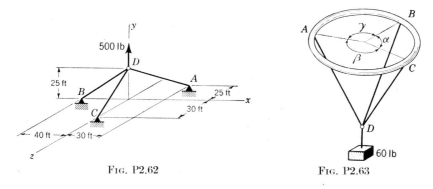

Fig. P2.62   Fig. P2.63

2.63. A 60-lb weight is hung by three strings which are attached to a ring and are tied together at D. The diameter of the ring is 24 in., and the length of each string is 20 in. If $\alpha = \beta = \gamma$, determine the tension in each string.

2.64. If, in Prob. 2.63, $\alpha = 80°$, $\beta = 130°$, and $\gamma = 150°$, determine the tension in each string.

2.65. In Prob. 2.62, determine the magnitude and direction of a horizontal force which must be applied at point D so that the tension in both DA and DC will be zero.

2.66. In Prob. 2.62, determine the magnitude and direction of a horizontal force which must be applied at point D so that the tension in both DB and DC will be zero.

2.67. Two wires are attached to the top of a pole. The direction and tension of each wire are known, and the force exerted by the pole on point A must be vertical. Determine the magnitude and direction of the horizontal force S which must be applied at A to maintain equilibrium.

2.68. A 500-lb weight is hung by means of two cables AC and BC, which are attached to the top of vertical posts. A horizontal force P, perpendicular to the plane containing the posts, holds the weight in the position shown. Determine the magnitude of P and the tension in each cable.

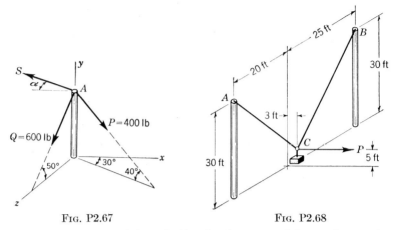

FIG. P2.67   FIG. P2.68

2.69. A 20-lb instrument is hung inside a box by means of three strings, as shown. If the instrument hangs directly in the center of the box and the strings are tied together at a point D, 3 in. below the top of the box, determine the tension in each string.

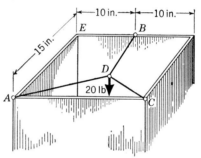

FIG. P2.69

2.70. Same as Prob. 2.69 assuming that string BD is removed and replaced by a string between D and E.

2.71. Same as Prob. 2.69 assuming that point D is located only $\frac{1}{2}$ in. from the top of the box.   (Explain why this arrangement results in higher tensions.)

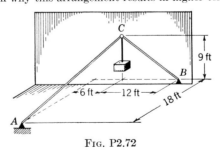

FIG. P2.72

2.72. Two poles are used to support a 400-lb load which hangs very close to a smooth wall.   It is known that the force exerted on point C by a pole must be directed along the pole and that the force exerted by the wall on point C must be perpendicular to the wall.   Determine the force exerted by the wall and the force exerted by each pole.

3. Statics of Rigid Bodies
in Two Dimensions

EQUIVALENT SYSTEMS OF FORCES

3.1. Rigid Bodies. External and Internal Forces. In the preceding chapter it was assumed that each of the bodies considered could be treated as a single particle. Such a view, however, is not always possible, and a body, in general, should be treated as a combination of a large number of particles. The size of the body will have to be taken into consideration, as well as the fact that forces will act on different particles and thus will have different points of application.

Most of the bodies considered in elementary mechanics are assumed to be *rigid*, a *rigid body* being defined as one which does not deform. Actual structures and machines, however, are never absolutely rigid and deform under the loads to which they are subjected. But these deformations are usually small and do not appreciably affect the conditions of equilibrium or motion of the structure under consideration. They are important, though, as far as the resistance of the structure to failure is concerned, and are considered in the study of mechanics of materials.

Forces acting on rigid bodies may be separated into two groups: (1) *external forces;* (2) *internal forces.*

1. The *external forces* represent the action of other bodies on the rigid body under consideration. They are entirely responsible for the external behavior of the rigid body. They will either cause it to move or assure that it remains at rest. We shall be concerned only with external forces in this chapter and in Chaps. 4 and 5.

2. The *internal forces* are the forces which hold together the particles forming the rigid body. If the rigid body is structurally composed of several parts, the forces holding the component parts together are also defined as internal forces. Internal forces will be considered in Chaps. 6 and 7.

As an example of external forces, we shall consider the forces acting on a disabled truck that men are pulling forward by means of a rope attached to the front bumper (Fig. 3.1). The external forces acting on the truck are shown in a *free-body diagram* (Fig. 3.2). Let us first consider the *weight W.* Although it embodies the effect of the earth's pull on each of the particles forming the truck, the weight may be represented by the single force *W*. The *point of application* of this force, i.e., the point at which the force acts, is defined as the *center of gravity* of the truck. It will be seen in Chap. 5 how centers of gravity may be determined. The weight *W* tends to make the truck move vertically downward. In fact, it would actually cause the truck to move downward, i.e., to fall, if it were not for the presence of the ground. The ground opposes the downward motion of the truck by means of the reactions R_1 and R_2. These forces are exerted *by* the ground *on* the truck and must therefore be included among the external forces acting on the truck.

The men pulling on the rope exert the force *F*. The point of application of *F* is on the front bumper. The force *F* tends to make the truck move forward in a straight line and does actually make it move, since no external force opposes this motion. (Rolling resistance has been neglected here for simplicity.) This forward motion of the truck, during

FIG. 3.1

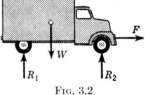

FIG. 3.2

which all straight lines remain parallel to themselves (the floor of the truck remains horizontal, and its walls remain vertical), is known as a *translation*. The force *F* might cause the truck to move differently if the conditions of the problem were changed. For example, if the front wheels were blocked, the force *F*, if large enough, could cause the rear of the truck to rise and the entire truck to pivot about the front axle. Such a motion is a *rotation*. It may be concluded, therefore, that each of the *external forces* acting on a *rigid body* is capable, if unopposed, of imparting to the rigid body a motion of translation or rotation, or both.

3.2. Principle of Transmissibility. Equivalent Forces. The *principle of transmissibility* states that the conditions of equilibrium or of motion of a rigid body will remain unchanged if a force *F* acting at a given point of the rigid body is replaced by a force *F′* of same magnitude and same direction, but acting at a different point, *provided that the two forces have the same line of action* (Fig. 3.3). The two forces *F* and *F′* have the same effect on the rigid body and are said to be *equivalent*. This principle, which states in fact that the action of a force may be *transmitted* along its line of action, is based on experimental evidence. It *cannot* be derived from the properties established so far in this text and must therefore be accepted as an experimental law.

It was indicated in Chap. 2 that the forces acting on a particle are vectors. These vectors have a well-defined point of application, namely, the particle itself, and are therefore called *fixed*, or *bound*, *vectors*. In the case of forces acting on a rigid body, however, the point of application of the force does not matter, as long as the line of action remains unchanged. In other words, forces acting on a rigid body are vectors which may be allowed to slide along their line of action; such vectors are called *sliding vectors*.

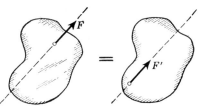

Fig. 3.3

Returning to the example of the truck, we first observe that the line of action of the force F is a horizontal line passing through both the front and the rear bumper of the truck (Fig. 3.4). Using the principle of transmissibility, we may therefore replace F by an *equivalent force* F'

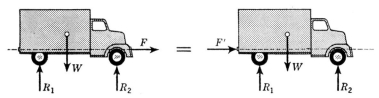

Fig. 3.4

acting on the rear bumper. In other words, the conditions of motion are unaffected, and all the other external forces acting on the truck (W, R_1, R_2) remain unchanged if the men push on the rear bumper instead of pulling on the front bumper.

The principle of transmissibility and the concept of equivalent forces have limitations, however. Consider, for example, a short bar AB acted upon by equal and opposite axial forces P_1 and P_2, as shown in Fig. 3.5a. According to the principle of transmissibility, the force P_2 may be replaced by a force P'_2 having same magnitude, same direction, and same line of action, but acting at A instead of B (Fig. 3.5b). The forces P_1 and P'_2 acting on the same particle may be added according to the rules of Chap. 2, and, being equal and opposite, their sum is found equal to zero. The original system of forces shown in Fig. 3.5a is thus equivalent to no force at all (Fig. 3.5c) from the point of view of the external behavior of the bar.

Consider now the two equal and opposite forces P_1 and P_2 acting on the bar AB as shown in Fig. 3.5d. The force P_2 may be replaced by a force P_2' having same magnitude, same direction, and same line of action, but acting at B instead of A (Fig. 3.5e). The forces P_1 and P_2' may then be added, and their sum is found again to be zero (Fig. 3.5f). From the point of view of the mechanics of rigid bodies, the systems shown in Fig. 3.5a and d are thus equivalent. But the *internal forces* and *deformations* produced by the two systems are clearly different. The bar of Fig. 3.5a is in *tension* and, if not absolutely rigid, will increase in length slightly; the bar of Fig. 3.5d is in *compression* and, if not absolutely rigid, will decrease in length slightly. Thus, while the principle of transmis-

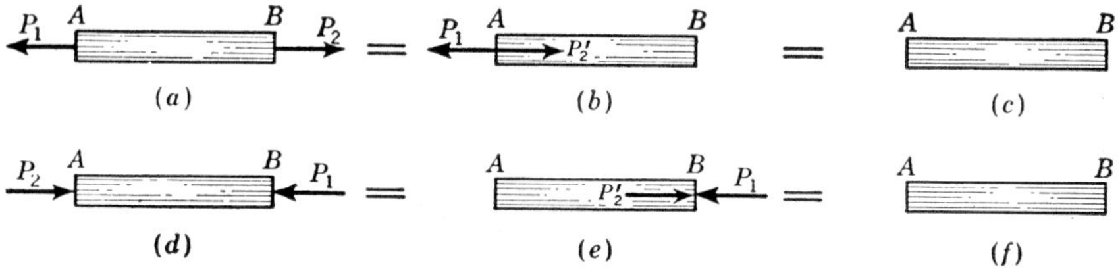

FIG. 3.5

sibility may be used freely to determine the conditions of motion or equilibrium of rigid bodies and to compute the external forces acting on these bodies, it should be avoided, or at least used with care, in determining internal forces and deformations.

3.3. Two-dimensional Structures.
The remarks made in the two preceding sections apply to rigid bodies and to all types of external forces acting on such bodies. For the rest of this chapter, however, we shall be concerned only with two-dimensional structures. By a two-dimensional structure we mean a flat structure which has length and breadth but no depth or, more generally, a structure which contains a plane of symmetry.

All forces acting on these structures will be assumed in the plane of the structure itself, or, more generally, it will be assumed that they may be reduced to forces in the plane of symmetry of the structure. Two-dimensional structures and coplanar forces may be readily represented on a sheet of paper or on a blackboard. Their analysis is therefore considerably simpler than that of three-dimensional structures and forces.

3.4. Moment of a Force about an Axis.
It was established in Sec. 3.2 that, from the point of view of the mechanics of rigid bodies, two forces F and F' are equivalent if they have same magnitude, same direction, and same line of action (Fig. 3.6). On the other hand, a force F'' of same magnitude and same direction, but having a different line of action, will not be equivalent to either F or F'. True, all three forces will tend to give to the rigid body the same motion of *translation*, but F'' would make it *rotate* differently about an axis through A, perpendicular to the plane of the figure.

The tendency of a force to make a rigid body rotate about an axis is

measured by the moment of the force about that axis.   The *moment*
M_A *of the force F about an axis through A*, or, for short, the *moment of F
about A*, is defined as the product of the magnitude F of the force and of
the perpendicular distance d from A to the line of action of F:

$$M_A = Fd \tag{3.1}$$

Since a force is expressed in lb and a distance in ft or in., the moment
of a force will be expressed in lb-ft or lb-in.   The moment of a force
has not only a magnitude but also a sense, just as the components of a
force have magnitude and sense.   The x component of a force may be
either to the right or to the left, and the y component may be either up
or down.   Similarly, the moment of a force may be either *clockwise* $\rangle$ or
counterclockwise $\rangle$.   It is seen that the moment M_A of F about A in
Fig. 3.6 is clockwise, while the moment M_B of F about B is counterclockwise.

Since the forces F and F' shown in Fig. 3.6 have the same magnitude,
the same sense, and the same line of action, the moment of F' about A

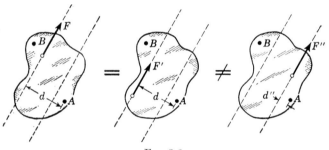

Fig. 3.6

will also be Fd and its sense will be clockwise.   Both forces have the
same moment about A.   Clearly they would have *the same moment about
any other axis*.   It may thus be stated that *two equivalent forces have the
same components F_x and F_y and the same moment about any axis.*   On
the other hand, the moment of F'' about A is different; it is equal to Fd''.

A force acting on a rigid body is completely defined (except for its
exact position on its line of action) if its components F_x and F_y and its
moment M_A about A are known (in magnitude and sense).   The magnitude F of the force and its direction may be determined from the components F_x and F_y by the methods of Chap. 2, while the perpendicular
distance d from A to the line of action may be obtained by forming the
quotient of M_A over F.   The line of action itself will be drawn on one side
of A or the other, depending upon the sense of F and upon the sense of
the moment.

3.5. Varignon's Theorem.   An important theorem of statics is due to
the French mathematician Varignon (1654–1722).   It states that *the*

moment of a force about any axis is equal to the sum of the moments of its components about that axis.

To prove this statement, consider a force F acting at point A and the components F_1 and F_2 of the force F in any two directions (Fig. 3.7). We have already made use of the fact, in Chap. 2, that the sum of the components of two forces F_1 and F_2 in any direction is equal to the component of their resultant F in that direction. Considering now the

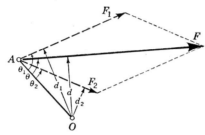

FIG. 3.7

moments of F, F_1, and F_2 about an axis through O, and denoting respectively by d, d_1, and d_2 the perpendicular distances from O to the lines of action of F, F_1, and F_2, we propose to prove that

$$Fd = F_1 d_1 + F_2 d_2 \qquad (3.2)$$

Denoting respectively by θ, θ_1, and θ_2 the angles that the line AO forms with F, F_1, and F_2, we have

$$d = (AO) \sin \theta \qquad d_1 = (AO) \sin \theta_1 \qquad d_2 = (AO) \sin \theta_2$$

Equation (3.2), which we wish to prove, may thus be written

$$F(AO) \sin \theta = F_1(AO) \sin \theta_1 + F_2(AO) \sin \theta_2$$

or
$$F \sin \theta = F_1 \sin \theta_1 + F_2 \sin \theta_2 \qquad (3.3)$$

But $F \sin \theta$ represents the component of F in the direction perpendicular to AO, and the two terms in the right-hand member represent the components of F_1 and F_2 in the same direction. Thus, Eq. (3.3) simply states that the sum of the components of F_1 and F_2 in the direction perpendicular to AO is equal to the component of their resultant F in the same direction. Since this statement was verified in Chap. 2, Eqs. (3.3) and (3.2) must be correct and the theorem is proved.

Varignon's theorem is very useful in the computation of moments of forces. Through a judicious choice of components, it is possible to simplify many problems. Two ways in which this may be done are indicated in Sample Probs. 3.2 and 3.3.

It should be noted that, in adding two moments, the sense (counterclockwise or clockwise) of each moment must be taken into account. In any given problem, either clockwise or counterclockwise will be defined as positive and the other as negative.

SAMPLE PROBLEM 3.1

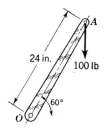

A 100-lb vertical force is applied to the end of a lever which is attached to a shaft at O. Determine (a) the moment of the 100-lb force about O; (b) the magnitude of the horizontal force applied at A which creates the same moment about O; (c) the smallest force applied at A which creates the same moment about O; (d) how far from the shaft a 240-lb vertical force must act to create the same moment about O; (e) whether the forces obtained in parts b, c, and d are equivalent to the original force.

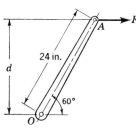

a. Moment about O. The perpendicular distance from O to the line of action of the 100-lb force is

$$d = (24 \text{ in.}) \cos 60° = 12 \text{ in.}$$

The moment about O is

$$M_O = Fd = (100 \text{ lb})(12 \text{ in.})$$
$$M_O = \textbf{1,200 lb-in.}$$

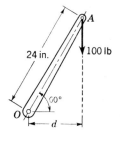

b. Horizontal Force. In this case, we have

$$d = (24 \text{ in.}) \sin 60° = 20.8 \text{ in.}$$

Since the moment about O must be 1,200 lb-in., we write

$$M_O = Fd$$
$$1,200 \text{ lb-in.} = F(20.8 \text{ in.}) \qquad F = \textbf{57.8 lb}$$

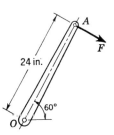

c. Smallest Force. Since $M_O = Fd$, the smallest value of F occurs when d is maximum. We choose F perpendicular to OA and find $d = 24$ in.; thus

$$M_O = Fd$$
$$1,200 \text{ lb-in.} = F(24 \text{ in.}) \qquad F = \textbf{50 lb}$$

d. 240-lb Vertical Force. In this case $M_O = Fd$ yields

$$1,200 \text{ lb-in.} = (240 \text{ lb})d \qquad d = 5 \text{ in.}$$

but $\qquad OB \cos 60° = d \qquad OB = \textbf{10 in.}$

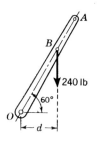

e. None of the forces considered in parts b, c, and d is equivalent to the original 100-lb force. Although they have the same moment about O, they have different x and y components. In other words, although each force tends to rotate the shaft in the same manner, each causes the lever to pull on the shaft in a different way.

SAMPLE PROBLEM 3.2

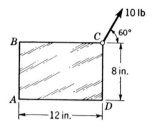

A 10-lb force acts on the corner of a 12- by 8-in. plate as shown. Determine the moment M_A of the force about A.

Solution. Resolving the force into its x and y components, we write

$$F_x = (10 \text{ lb}) \cos 60° = 5 \text{ lb}$$

$$F_y = (10 \text{ lb}) \sin 60° = 8.66 \text{ lb}$$

The moment of F_x about A is

$$(5 \text{ lb})(8 \text{ in.}) = 40 \text{ lb-in.} \text{)}$$

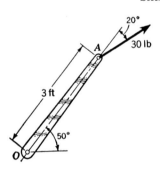

The moment of F_y about A is

$$(8.66 \text{ lb})(12 \text{ in.}) = 104 \text{ lb-in.} \text{)}$$

Taking) as positive, we apply Varignon's theorem and write

$$M_A = +(104 \text{ lb-in.}) - (40 \text{ lb-in.}) = +64 \text{ lb-in.}$$

$$M_A = \textbf{64 lb-in.)}$$

SAMPLE PROBLEM 3.3

A 30-lb force acts on the end of the 3-ft lever as shown. Determine the moment of the force about the axle through O.

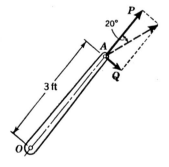

Solution. The force is replaced by two components, one component P in the direction of OA and one component Q perpendicular to OA. Since O is on the line of action of P, the moment of P about O is zero and the moment of the 30-lb force reduces to the moment of Q.

$$Q = (30 \text{ lb}) \sin 20° = 10.26 \text{ lb}$$

$$M_O = Q(3 \text{ ft}) = (10.26 \text{ lb})(3 \text{ ft})$$

$$M_O = \textbf{30.8 lb-ft)}$$

PROBLEMS

3.1. A 40-lb force is applied at the end B of a post which is embedded in the ground at A. Determine the moment of the force about A when $\alpha = 15°$.

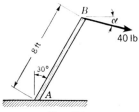

FIG. P3.1

3.2. Determine the maximum moment about A which can be caused by the 40-lb force of Prob. 3.1. In what direction should the force act?

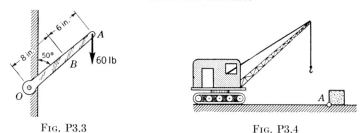

FIG. P3.3   FIG. P3.4

3.3. A 60-lb force is applied to the lever OA as shown. Determine (a) the moment of the 60-lb force about O, (b) the smallest force applied at B which creates the same moment about O.

3.4. A block of granite in the shape of a cube (each side $= 6$ ft) is to be turned over counterclockwise by pulling on it with a crane. Where should the cable be attached and what should be the direction of the force if the moment of the force about A is to be maximum?

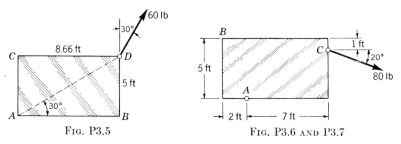

FIG. P3.5   FIG. P3.6 AND P3.7

3.5. Compute the moment of the 60-lb force about A (a) by using the definition of the moment of a force, (b) by resolving the force into components along BD and CD, (c) by resolving the force into components along AD and in the direction perpendicular to AD.

3.6. Determine the moment of the 80-lb force about A.

3.7. Determine the moment of the 80-lb force about B.

3.8. Determine the moment of the 200-lb force about A.

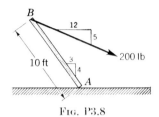

Fig. P3.8

3.9. A force F of components F_x and F_y acts at a point of coordinates x and y. Find the expression for the moment of F about the origin O of the system of coordinates.

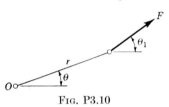

Fig. P3.10

3.10. A force F acts at a point of coordinates r and θ as shown. The force forms an angle θ_1 with a line parallel to the horizontal reference axis. Show that the moment of the force about the origin O is $Fr \sin(\theta_1 - \theta)$, positive counterclockwise.

3.11. The line of action of a force of magnitude P passes through the two points A (x_1,y_1) and B (x_2,y_2). If the force is directed from A to B, determine the moment of the force about the origin.

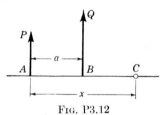

Fig. P3.12

3.12. Two forces P and Q have parallel lines of action and act at A and B, respectively. The distance between A and B is a. Find the distance x from A to the point C about which both forces have the same moment. Check the formula obtained by assuming $a = 10$ in. and (a) $P = 20$ lb up, $Q = 10$ lb up; (b) $P = 10$ lb up, $Q = 20$ lb up; (c) $P = 20$ lb up, $Q = 10$ lb down; (d) $P = 10$ lb up, $Q = 20$ lb down.

3.6. Moment of a Couple.

Two forces having same magnitude, parallel lines of action, and opposite sense are said to form a couple. Two such forces are shown acting on a rigid body in Fig. 3.8.

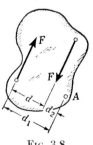

Fig. 3.8

Clearly, the sums of the x components and of the y components of the two forces are zero. The sum of the moments of the two forces about an axis through a point A, however, is not zero. Thus, the effect of the couple on the rigid body is not zero. While the two forces will not move the body away, they will tend to make it turn.

Denoting by d_1 and d_2 the perpendicular distances from A to the two lines of action, and taking clockwise as positive, we write the sum M of the moments of the two forces about A as follows,

$$+\!\!\rotatebox[origin=c]{0}{$\curvearrowright$}\ M = Fd_1 - Fd_2$$
$$= F(d_1 - d_2)$$

or, noting that $d_1 - d_2$ is equal to the distance d between the lines of action of the two forces,

$$M = Fd\ \rotatebox[origin=c]{0}{$\curvearrowright$}$$

The sum M is called the *moment of the couple*. It may be observed *that M does not depend upon the choice of A; M* will have the same magnitude and same sense regardless of the location of A. This may be checked by repeating the above derivation, choosing A to the left of the couple, and then between the two forces forming the couple. We state therefore:

The moment M of a couple is constant. Its magnitude is equal to the product Fd of the common magnitude F of the two forces and of the distance d between their lines of action. The sense of M (clockwise or counterclockwise) is obtained by direct observation.

3.7. Equivalent Couples. Consider the three couples shown in Fig. 3.9, which are made to act successively on the same corner plate. As seen in the preceding section, the only motion a couple may impart to a rigid body is a rotation. Each of the couples shown will cause the plate

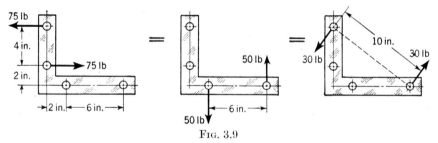

Fig. 3.9

to rotate counterclockwise. Since the product Fd is found to be 300 lb-in. in each case, we may expect the three couples to have the same effect on the corner plate.

As reasonable as this conclusion may appear, we should not accept it hastily. While intuitive feeling is of great help in the study of mechanics, it should not be accepted as a substitute for logical reasoning. Before stating that two systems (or groups) of forces have the same effect on a rigid body, we should prove that fact on the basis of the experimental evidence introduced so far. This evidence consists of the parallelogram law for the addition of two forces (Sec. 2.1) and of the principle of transmissibility (Sec. 3.2). Therefore, we shall state that *two systems of forces are equivalent* (i.e., they have the same effect on a rigid body) *if we can transform one of them into the other by means of one or several of the following operations:* (1) replacing two forces acting on the same particle by their resultant; (2) resolving a force into two components; (3) canceling two equal and opposite forces acting on the same particle; (4) attaching to the same particle two equal and opposite forces; (5) moving a force along its line of action. Each of these operations is easily justified on the basis of the parallelogram law or the principle of transmissibility.

Let us now prove that *two couples having the same moment (same magnitude and same sense) are equivalent.* Consider the couples shown in Fig. 3.10a and d; they are both clockwise, and we shall assume that they have equal moments:

$$Fd = F'd' \tag{3.4}$$

To prove that they are equivalent, we shall show that the F couple of Fig. 3.10a may be transformed into the F' couple of Fig. 3.10d by means of the operations listed above.

Denoting by A, B, C, D the points of intersection of the lines of action of the two couples, we first slide the forces of the F couple until they are

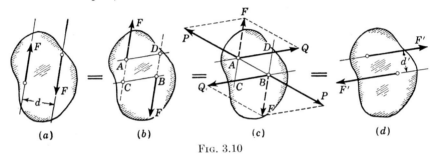

(a)   (b)   (c)   (d)

Fig. 3.10

attached, respectively, at A and B, as shown in Fig. 3.10b. Each of the two forces is then resolved into a component P along line AB and a component Q along AD or BC (Fig. 3.10c). The two forces P have same magnitude and same line of action, but opposite sense; they may be moved along their common line of action until they are applied at the same point and then canceled. Thus the F couple reduces to the Q couple.

We shall show now that the forces Q are equal to the forces F'. The moment of the Q couple may be obtained by computing the moment about B of the force Q attached at A; similarly, the moment of the F couple is the moment about B of the force F attached at A. But, by Varignon's theorem, the moment of F is equal to the sum of the moments of its components P and Q. Since the moment of P about B is zero, the moment of the Q couple must be equal to the moment of the F couple. Recalling (3.4), we write

$$Qd' = Fd = F'd' \qquad \text{and} \qquad Q = F'$$

Thus the forces Q and F' are equal, and the F couple of Fig. 3.10a is equivalent to the F' couple of Fig. 3.10d.

The property we have just established is very important for the correct understanding of the mechanics of rigid bodies. It indicates that, when a couple acts on a rigid body, it does not matter where the two forces forming the couple act, or what magnitude and direction they have. The only thing which counts is the *moment* of the couple (magnitude and sense). Couples with the same moment will have the same effect on the rigid body.

3.8. Addition of Couples. Consider two couples acting on the same rigid body, as shown in Fig. 3.11. Since a couple is completely defined by its moment, the couple formed by the forces Q may be replaced by a couple of same moment, formed by two forces Q' which have the same lines of action as the forces P. The magnitude Q' of the new forces must

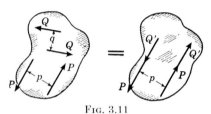

FIG. 3.11

be such that $Q'p = Qq$. The forces Q' may be added to the forces P to form a single couple of moment

$$M = (P + Q')p = Pp + Q'p = Pp + Qq$$

The moment M is thus found to be the sum of the moments Pp and Qq of the two original couples. It should be noted that, if the two couples have opposite senses, the moments should be subtracted from each other.

We state: *Two couples may be replaced by a single couple of moment equal to the algebraic sum of the moments of the given couples.*

3.9. Resolution of a Given Force into a Force Acting at a Given Point and a Couple. Consider a force F acting at point B on a rigid body, as shown in Fig. 3.12a. Suppose that for some reason we would rather have it acting at point A. We know that we can move F along its line of action (principle of transmissibility); but we cannot move it to a point A away from the original line of action without modifying the action of F on the rigid body.

We may attach, however, two forces to point A: one of same magnitude and direction as F, and another equal and opposite (Fig. 3.12b). As indicated in Sec. 3.7, this operation does not modify the action of the original force on the rigid body. We observe that two of the three forces shown form a couple of moment $M = Fd$. Since this couple may be replaced by any other couple of same moment (Sec. 3.7), we may represent it by the symbol $\supsetneq$ placed at any convenient location. The force and the couple, however, are usually grouped as shown in Fig. 3.12c.

The result we have obtained may be stated as follows: *Any force F acting on a rigid body may be moved to any given point A, provided that a couple is added; the moment of the couple must equal the moment of F (in its original position) about A.* The couple will then impart to the rigid body the same motion of rotation about A that the force F produced before it was transferred to A. In the following sections we shall refer

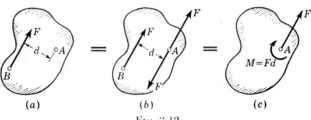

Fɪɢ. 3.12

to this combination as a *force-couple system*. The location of the couple is immaterial, but the force F should not be moved from A. If it were to be moved again, a new couple should be determined.

The transformation we have described may be performed in reverse. That is, *a force F acting at A and a couple of moment M may be combined into a single resultant force F.* This is done by moving the force F until its moment about A becomes equal to the moment M of the couple to be eliminated. The magnitude and direction of F are unchanged, but its new line of action will be at a distance $d = M/F$ from A. An example of such a transformation is given in Fig. 3.13. Part a of the figure shows the head of a bolt which is subjected to the combined action of a 600-lb-in. clockwise couple and of a 50-lb vertical downward force through the

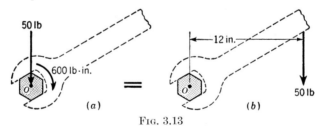

Fɪɢ. 3.13

center O of the head. The force-couple system may be replaced by a single 50-lb force located 12 in. to the right of O (Fig. 3.13b). In this new position, the 50-lb force has a clockwise moment of 600 lb-in. about O. Figure 3.13a gives a good representation of the action to which the head of the bolt is subjected, while Fig. 3.13b suggests a simple way of exerting this action. The wrench was sketched to help visualize the action exerted on the bolt. This is particularly useful in Fig. 3.13b; it was not strictly necessary, however, to suggest an actual contact between the 50-lb force and the bolt.

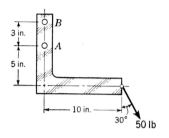

A 50-lb force is applied to a corner plate as shown. Determine (a) an equivalent force-couple system at A, (b) the smallest forces acting at A and B which form a couple equivalent to the couple found in part a.

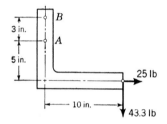

a. Force-couple System at A. We resolve the 50-lb force into x and y components

$$F_x = (50 \text{ lb}) \sin 30° \qquad F_x = \textbf{25.0 lb} \rightarrow$$

$$F_y = (50 \text{ lb}) \cos 30° \qquad F_y = \textbf{43.3 lb} \downarrow$$

These components may be moved to A if a couple is added, of moment M_A equal to the moment about A of the components in their original position. Choosing clockwise positive, we obtain

$$M_A = +(43.3 \text{ lb})(10 \text{ in.}) - (25.0 \text{ lb})(5 \text{ in.})$$

$$M_A = \textbf{308 lb-in.} \downarrow$$

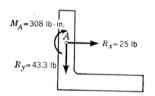

b. Forces Forming the Couple. Forces forming the couple found in part a must be equal and opposite. Since we wish to determine the smallest forces, we make the distance between the forces maximum by choosing the forces in a direction perpendicular to AB. Then

$$308 \text{ lb-in.} = F(3 \text{ in.}) \qquad F = \textbf{102.7 lb}$$

Remark. The forces found in part b are equivalent only to the 308-lb-in. couple of the force-couple system found in part a; they are not therefore equivalent to the original 50-lb force. If the force components omitted in part b are added to the 102.7-lb forces, we again have a system of forces equivalent to the original 50-lb force.

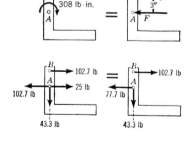

SAMPLE PROBLEM 3.5

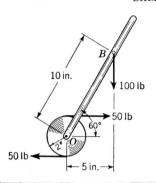

Replace the couple and force shown by an equivalent single force applied to the lever. Determine the distance from the shaft to the point of application of this equivalent force.

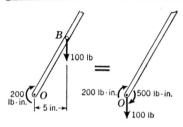

Solution. First the given force and couple are replaced by an equivalent force-couple system at O. We move the 100-lb force to O and at the same time add a couple of moment equal to the moment about O of the force in its original position, namely,

$$(100 \text{ lb})(5 \text{ in.}) = 500 \text{ lb-in.}$$

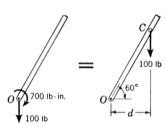

This couple is added to the 200-lb-in. clockwise couple formed by the two 50-lb forces, and a 700-lb-in. couple is obtained. We now move the 100-lb force to the right a distance d such that the moment of the force about O is 700 lb-in.

$$700 \text{ lb-in.} = (100 \text{ lb})d \qquad d = 7 \text{ in.}$$

The equivalent single force or resultant is attached at point C, where its line of action intersects the lever.

$$(OC) \cos 60° = 7 \text{ in.} \qquad \mathbf{OC = 14\ in.}$$

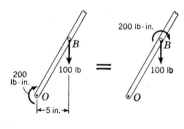

Alternate Solution. Since the effect of a couple does not depend on its location, the 200-lb-in. couple may be moved to B; we obtain a force couple at B directly. The 100-lb force may now be moved from B to the right a distance d' such that the moment of the force about B is 200 lb-in.

$$200 \text{ lb-in.} = (100 \text{ lb-in.})d' \qquad d' = 2 \text{ in.}$$

Again the point of intersection of the lever and of the line of action of the force is determined.

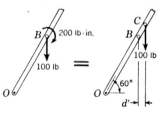

$$(BC) \cos 60° = 2 \text{ in.} \qquad BC = 4 \text{ in.}$$

$$OC = OB + BC = 10 \text{ in.} + 4 \text{ in.}$$

$$\mathbf{OC = 14\ in.}$$

PROBLEMS

3.13. The two couples shown are applied to a 6- by 8-in. plate. Prove that their sum is zero (a) by adding their moments, (b) by combining P_1 and Q_1 into their resultant R_1, combining P_2 and Q_2 into their resultant R_2, and showing that R_1 and R_2 are equal and opposite and have the same line of action.

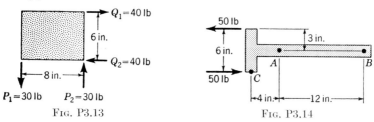

FIG. P3.13 FIG. P3.14

3.14. A couple formed by two 50-lb forces is applied to a T-shaped plate as shown. Determine an equivalent couple which is formed by (a) vertical forces acting at A and B, (b) the smallest possible forces acting at A and C.

3.15. A multiple-drilling machine is set up to drill simultaneously four holes in a plate at A, B, C, and D. Each drill exerts a 15-lb-in. couple on the plate. Determine the smallest forces applied at E and F which would produce the same effect on the plate.

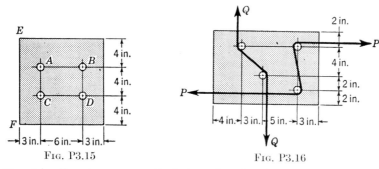

FIG. P3.15 FIG. P3.16

3.16. Four 1-in.-diameter pegs are attached to a board as shown. Two strings are passed around the pegs and pulled with forces $P = 5$ lb and $Q = 8$ lb. Determine the resultant couple on the plate.

3.17. Replace each of the forces considered in Sample Prob. 3.1 by a force acting on the shaft O and a couple.

3.18. A column, 1 ft wide, carries a 500-lb load as shown. Reduce the load to an axial load along AB and a couple.

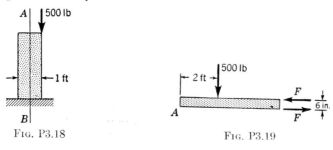

FIG. P3.18 FIG. P3.19

3.19. Determine the magnitude of the two forces F which, together with the 500-lb force, form a system equivalent to a single force through A.

3.20. A 50-lb force is applied to a bent bar as shown. Determine an equivalent force-couple system (*a*) at A and (*b*) at B.

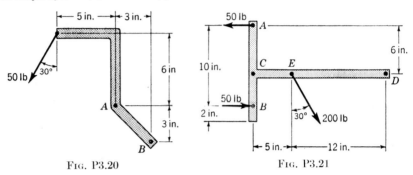

FIG. P3.20　　　　　　　　　　FIG. P3.21

3.21. Replace the force and couple shown by a single force applied at a point located on the line CD. Determine the distance from C to the point of application of this force.

3.22. The rod is fastened to the plate by means of two rivets A and B, 2 in. apart. Replace the 100-lb force by (*a*) an equivalent force-couple system at A, (*b*) an equivalent system formed by two parallel forces at A and B.

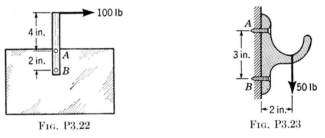

FIG. P3.22　　　　　　　　　　FIG. P3.23

3.23. A hook is held by screws at A and B. (*a*) Replace the 50-lb load shown by an equivalent force-couple system at B. (*b*) Find two horizontal forces at A and B forming a couple equivalent to the couple found in part *a*.

3.24. A beam is loaded as shown. Assuming $a = 4$ ft, $b = 8$ ft, and $P = 1$ kip, replace the load by an equivalent system formed (*a*) by a force at A and a couple, (*b*) by two vertical forces, one applied at A and the other at B.

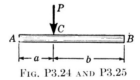

FIG. P3.24 AND P3.25

3.25. A load P is applied to a beam AB at a point C as shown. Find the vertical forces F_A and F_B, applied, respectively, at A and B, forming a system equivalent to P.

3.10. Reduction of a System of Coplanar Forces to One Force and One Couple. Resultant of a System of Coplanar Forces. Consider a system of coplanar forces F_1, F_2, F_3, etc., acting on a rigid body as shown in Fig.

3.14a. As seen in Sec. 3.9, F_1 may be moved and attached to a given point A if a couple of moment M_1, equal to the moment of F_1 about A, is added to the original system of forces. Repeating this procedure with F_2, F_3, etc., we obtain the system shown in Fig. 3.14b. Since the forces act now on the same particle A, they may be added vectorially and replaced by their resultant R as shown in Fig. 3.14c. On the other hand, the couples may be replaced by a single couple of moment M equal to the algebraic sum of the moments M_1, M_2, M_3, etc. Any system of coplanar forces, however complex, may thus be reduced to an *equivalent force-couple system acting at a given point A.*

In the general case, when the force R is different from zero, the system obtained may be reduced further to a *single force R,* called the *resultant* of the given system (Fig. 3.14d). This is done, as indicated in Sec. 3.9,

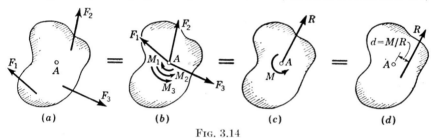

FIG. 3.14

by moving R until its moment about A becomes equal to M, thus eliminating the need for a couple. The distance from A to the line of action of R is $d = M/R$.

When R is equal to zero, the force-couple system reduces to the couple of moment M. Thus, the given system of forces is reduced to a *single couple*, called the *resultant couple* of the system.

To summarize, *any given system of coplanar forces may be reduced to a single force or a single couple*, as the case may be. The only exception is when both R and M are zero. Then, the system exerts no action on the rigid body, and the rigid body is said to be in *equilibrium*. This very particular case is of great practical interest and will be considered under Equilibrium of Rigid Bodies later in this chapter.

In practice, the reduction of a system of coplanar forces to a force R at A and a couple will be considerably simplified if the given forces F_1, F_2, F_3, etc., are resolved into their x and y components as shown in Fig. 3.15a. The sums ΣF_x and ΣF_y of the components of the given forces will yield, respectively, the components R_x and R_y of the force R. Besides, by using Varignon's theorem, the moments of the given forces about A may be determined more conveniently from the components F_x and F_y than from the forces F themselves; the sum ΣM_A of these moments is equal to the moment M of the couple. It is advisable to arrange the computations in tabular form as shown in Sample Probs. 3.7 and 3.8

and to sketch the force R_x, the force R_y, and the couple of moment M to which the given system of forces is reduced (Fig. 3.15b).   The component forces R_x and R_y may then be added vectorially, and a force-couple system at A is obtained.

If the given system is to be reduced to a single force (i.e., to its resultant), the following method may be used: The forces R_x and R_y are moved to a point B located on the line of action of R_x at a distance $d_x = M/R_y$ from A, as shown in Fig. 3.15c.   The moment of R_x about A is still zero, but the moment of R_y about A is now equal to M.   Thus the couple is eliminated, and the given system reduces to the two forces R_x and R_y attached at B.   These components may then be added vectorially, and the resultant R is obtained.

The forces R_x and R_y could also have been moved to point C, located on the line of action of R_y at a distance $d_y = M/R_x$ from A, as shown in Fig. 3.15d.   The couple is eliminated, since the moment of R_x about A

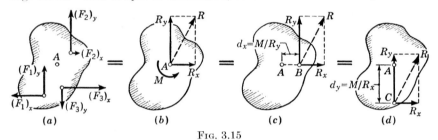

FIG. 3.15

is equal to M, and the given system reduces to the forces R_x and R_y at C, which may again be added vectorially.

3.11. Equivalent Systems of Coplanar Forces.   We have seen in the preceding section that any system of coplanar forces acting on a rigid body may be reduced to a force-couple system at a given point A.   This equivalent force-couple system characterizes completely the action exerted by the given system on the rigid body.   *Two systems of coplanar forces are equivalent, therefore, if they may be reduced to the same force-couple system at A.*   Referring to Fig. 3.15b and recalling that R_x, R_y, and M are obtained, respectively, by summing the x components, the y components, and the moments about A of the forces of the system considered, we state: *Two systems of coplanar forces are equivalent if, and only if, the sums of the x components, of the y components, and of the moments about A of their forces are, respectively, equal.*

The above statement has a simple physical significance.   It means that two systems of coplanar forces are equivalent if they tend to impart to the rigid body (1) the same translation in the x direction, (2) the same translation in the y direction, and (3) the same rotation about a fixed point A.   Note that it is sufficient to establish the last property with respect to *one point only.*   The property, however, holds with respect to *any point* if the two systems are equivalent.

SAMPLE PROBLEM 3.6

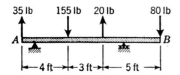

A 12-ft beam is subjected to the forces shown. Reduce the given system of forces to (a) an equivalent force-couple system at A, (b) an equivalent force-couple system at B, (c) a single force or resultant.

Note. Since the reactions at the supports are not included in the given system of forces, the given system will not maintain the beam in equilibrium.

---

a. Force-couple System at A. We choose positive senses for the force-couple system as shown. Adding the components of the given forces and the moments about A of the given forces, we obtain

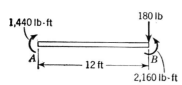

$$\xrightarrow{+} R_x = 0$$

$$+\uparrow R_y = +35 \text{ lb} - 155 \text{ lb} + 20 \text{ lb} - 80 \text{ lb}$$
$$= -180 \text{ lb}$$

$$+\curvearrowleft M_A = +(155 \text{ lb})(4 \text{ ft}) - (20 \text{ lb})(7 \text{ ft})$$
$$+ (80 \text{ lb})(12 \text{ ft}) = +1,440 \text{ lb-ft}$$

The negative sign indicates that the 180-lb force acts in a direction opposite to that assumed. The actual force-couple system is as shown.

$$R = 180 \text{ lb} \downarrow \qquad M_A = 1,440 \text{ lb-ft} \curvearrowright$$

b. Force-couple System at B. We shall find a force couple at B equivalent to the force-couple system at A determined in part *a*. The 180-lb force may be moved to B provided we add a couple of moment equal to the moment about B of the force in its original position, namely,

$$(180 \text{ lb})(12 \text{ ft}) = 2,160 \text{ lb-ft} \curvearrowright$$

The 1,440-lb-ft couple may be moved to B without changing its effect on the beam. Adding the two couples now at B, we obtain a 720-lb-ft counterclockwise couple.

$$R = 180 \text{ lb} \downarrow \qquad M_B = 720 \text{ lb-ft} \curvearrowright$$

c. Single Force or Resultant. Using the results of part *a*, we move the 180-lb force to the right through a distance d chosen so that the moment of the force about A is 1,440 lb-ft. We write

$$1,440 \text{ lb-ft} = (180 \text{ lb})d \qquad d = 8 \text{ ft}$$

$$R = 180 \text{ lb} \downarrow \qquad d = 8 \text{ ft}$$

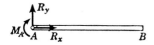

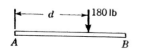

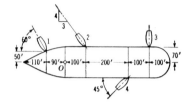

Four tugboats are used to bring an ocean liner to its pier. Each tugboat exerts a 5,000-lb force in the direction shown. Determine (a) the equivalent force-couple system at the foremast O, (b) the point on the hull where a single, more powerful tugboat should push to produce the same effect as the original four tugboats.

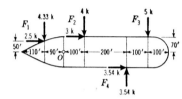

a. Force-couple System at O. Each of the given forces is resolved into components in the free-body diagram (kip units are used). For convenience the components and their moments about O are recorded in a table, from which R_x, R_y, and M are then obtained

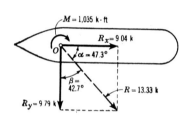

Force	$F_x \xrightarrow{+}$, kips	$F_y +\uparrow$, kips	$M_O +\downarrow$, kip-ft
F_1	+2.50		+ 125
		−4.33	− 390
F_2	+3.00		+ 210
		−4.00	+ 400
F_3	0		0
		−5.00	+2,000
F_4	+3.54		− 248
		+3.54	−1,062
	$R_x = \Sigma F_x$ $= +9.04$ $= 9.04 \rightarrow$	$R_y = \Sigma F_y$ $= -9.79$ $= 9.79 \downarrow$	$M = \Sigma M_O$ $= +1,035$ $= 1,035)$

The force components are combined to yield a force-couple system equivalent to the original system.

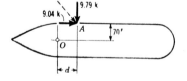

R = **13.33 kips** ⦨ **47.3°** M = **1,035 kip-ft** $)$

b. Single Tugboat. The force exerted by a single tugboat must be equivalent to the force-couple system found in part *a* and thus equal to 13.33 kips. Since this force acts on the hull at a point A, we resolve it into components at A. The distance d must be such that the total moment about O is 1,035 kip-ft.

1,035 kip-ft = (9.04 kips)(70 ft) + (9.79 kips)d

d = 41.1 ft

R = **13.33 kips** ⦨ **47.3°** d = **41.1 ft**

SAMPLE PROBLEM 3.8

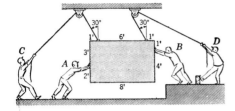

In order to move a 173-lb crate, two men push on it while two other men pull on it by means of ropes. The force exerted by man A is 150 lb, and that exerted by man B is 50 lb; both forces are horizontal. Man C pulls with a force equal to 80 lb and man D with a force equal to 120 lb. Both cables form an angle of 30° with the vertical. Determine the resultant of all forces acting on the crate.

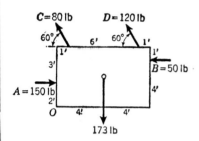

Solution. The forces acting on the crate are shown in the free-body diagram. We shall first determine the equivalent force-couple system at some convenient point, for instance, the lower left corner O. Each of the given forces is resolved into components, and the moment about O is computed for each component.

Force	$F_x \xrightarrow{+}$, lb	$F_y +\uparrow$, lb	$M_O +\downarrow$, lb-ft
W	0	−173	+692
A	+150	0	+300
B	− 50	0	−200
C	− 40		−200
		+ 69.3	− 69
D	− 60		−300
		+103.9	−727
	$R_x = \Sigma F_x$ $= 0$	$R_y = \Sigma F_y$ $= 0$	$M = \Sigma M_O$ $= -504$ $= 504 \,\rangle$

The force-couple system at O is found to consist of a force equal to zero and a counterclockwise couple. The given system of forces reduces to a resultant couple which may be represented anywhere on the crate.

$$R = 0 \qquad M = \textbf{504 lb-ft} \,\rangle$$

We note that the crate is not in equilibrium under the action of the given forces. While the given forces do not tend to move the crate horizontally or vertically, they do tend to rotate the crate in a counterclockwise sense.

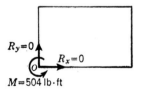

PROBLEMS

3.26. A 12-ft beam is loaded in the various ways represented in the figure. Find two loadings which are equivalent.

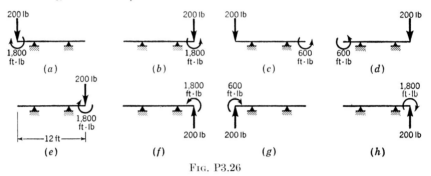

Fig. P3.26

3.27. A truss is loaded as shown. Find the resultant of the loads and the distance from its line of action to point A.

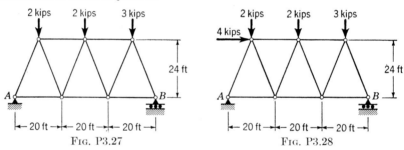

Fig. P3.27   Fig. P3.28

3.28. A truss is loaded as shown. Find the resultant of the loads and the point where its line of action intersects line AB.

3.29. Two parallel forces P and Q are applied at the ends of a beam AB of length L. Find the distance x from A to the line of action of their resultant.

3.30. Reduce the system of belt tensions shown to an equivalent force-couple system at O.

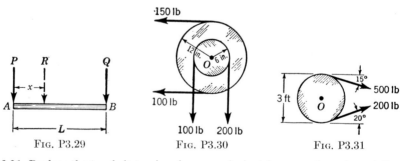

Fig. P3.29   Fig. P3.30   Fig. P3.31

3.31. Replace the two belt tensions by an equivalent force-couple system at O.

3.32 and 3.33. Four forces act as shown on the beam. Determine (a) the equivalent force-couple system at C, (b) the resultant of the system and the distance from A to its line of action.

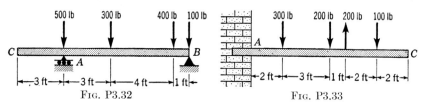

FIG. P3.32

FIG. P3.33

3.34. What additional vertical force P should be applied at the extremity C of the beam considered in Prob. 3.33 to transform the system of loads shown into a system equivalent to (a) a single couple, (b) a single force applied at A?

3.35 and 3.36. An angle bracket is subjected to the system of forces shown. Find the resultant of the system and the point of intersection of its line of action with (a) line AB and (b) line BC.

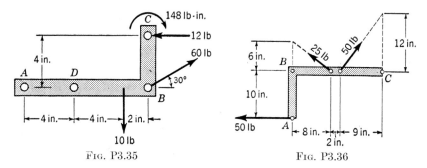

FIG. P3.35

FIG. P3.36

***3.37.** Find the resultant of the forces acting on the truss, and determine the distance from A (a) to the line of action of the resultant, (b) to the point where the line of action intersects AH.

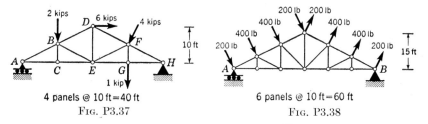

4 panels @ 10 ft = 40 ft

FIG. P3.37

6 panels @ 10 ft = 60 ft

FIG. P3.38

***3.38.** A roof structure is subjected to the wind loading shown. (a) Find the equivalent force-couple system at A. (b) Determine the resultant of the wind loading and its line of action.

EQUILIBRIUM OF RIGID BODIES

3.12. Rigid Body in Equilibrium. *A rigid body is said to be in equilibrium when the external forces acting on it form a system of forces equivalent to zero,* i.e., a system which has no resultant and no resultant couple. The necessary and sufficient conditions for the equilibrium of a rigid body may thus be expressed analytically by writing

$$\Sigma F_x = 0 \qquad \Sigma F_y = 0 \qquad \Sigma M_A = 0 \qquad (3.5)$$

Since the direction of the axes of coordinates and the location of point A may be chosen arbitrarily, Eqs. (3.5) indicate that the external forces acting on the rigid body do not impart to the body any motion of translation and do not make it rotate about any point. The action of any individual external force is thus canceled by the action of the other forces of the system, and the external forces are said to be *balanced*.

3.13. Free-body Diagram. In solving a problem concerning the equilibrium of a rigid body, it is essential to consider *all* the forces acting on the body; it is equally important to exclude any force which is not directly applied on the body. Omitting a force or adding an extraneous one would destroy the conditions of equilibrium. Therefore, the first step in the solution of the problem should consist in drawing a *free-body diagram* of the rigid body under consideration. Free-body diagrams have already been used on many occasions in Chaps. 2 and 3. However, in view of their importance to the solution of equilibrium problems, we shall summarize here the various steps which must be followed in drawing a free-body diagram.

First, a clear decision is made regarding the choice of the free body to be used. This body is then detached from the ground and separated from any other body. The contour of the body thus isolated is sketched.

All external forces are then indicated. These forces represent the action exerted *on* the free body *by* the ground and the bodies which have been detached; they should be applied at the various points where the free body was supported by the ground or connected to the other bodies. The *weight* of the free body should also be included among the external forces, since it represents the attraction exerted by the earth on the various particles forming the free body. As will be seen in Chap. 5, the weight should be applied at the center of gravity of the body. When the free body is made of several parts, the forces the various parts exert on each other should *not* be included among the external forces. These forces are internal forces as far as the free body is concerned.

The magnitude and direction of the *known external forces* should be clearly marked on the free-body diagram. Care should be taken to indicate the sense of the force exerted *on* the free body, not that of the force exterted *by* the free body. Known external forces generally include the *weight* of the free body and *forces applied* for a given purpose.

Unknown external forces usually consist of the *reactions* through which the ground and other bodies oppose a possible motion of the free body. Reactions are exerted at the points where the free body is *supported* or *connected* to other bodies. They may be divided into three groups, corresponding to three types of *supports*, or *connections:*

1. *Reactions Equivalent to a Force with Known Line of Action.* Supports and connections causing reactions of this group include *rollers,* *rockers, smooth surfaces, short links,* and *cables.* Each of these supports

and connections can prevent motion in one direction only. They are shown in Fig. 3.16, together with the reaction they produce. Reactions of this group involve *one unknown*, namely, the magnitude of the reaction; this magnitude should be denoted by an appropriate letter. The line of action of the reaction is known and should be indicated clearly in the free-body diagram. The sense of the reaction must be as shown in Fig.

Support or connection	Reaction	Number of unknowns
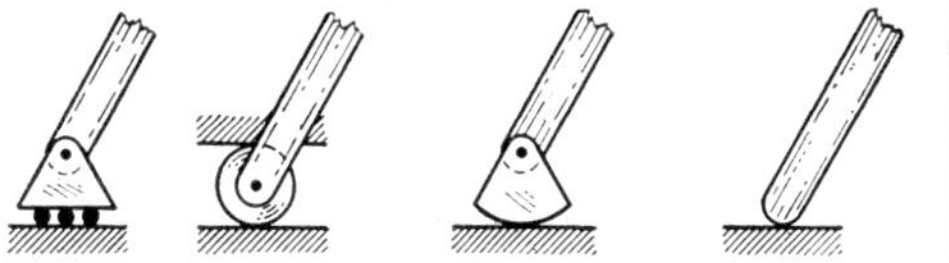 Rollers Rocker Smooth surface	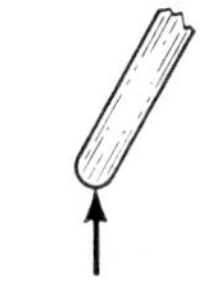 Force with known line of action	1
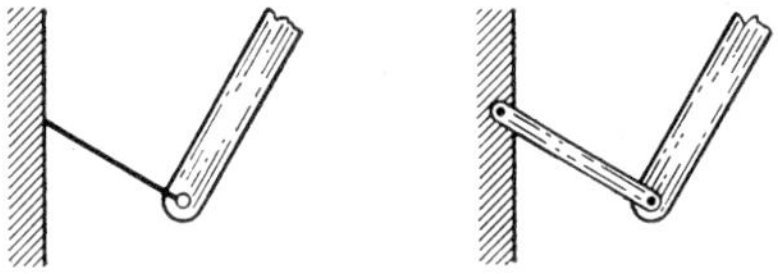 Short cable Short link	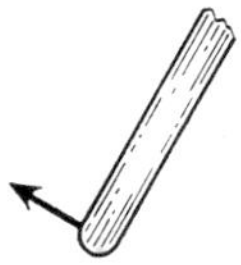 Force with known line of action	1
Smooth pin or hinge Rough surface	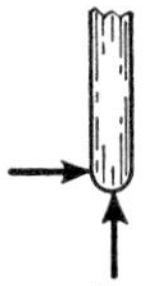 Force of unknown direction	2
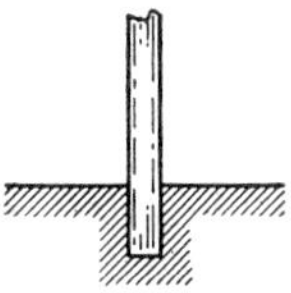 Fixed support	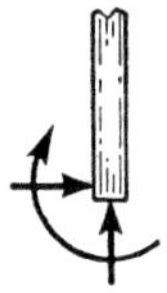 Force and couple	3

FIG. 3.16. Reactions at supports and connections.

3.16 in the case of a smooth surface (away from the surface) or of a cable (tension in the direction of the cable). The reaction may be directed either way in the case of double-track rollers and links. Single-track rollers and rockers are generally assumed to be reversible, and thus the corresponding reactions will also be directed either way.

2. *Reactions Equivalent to a Force of Unknown Direction.* Supports and connections causing reactions of this group include *smooth pins, hinges,* and *rough* surfaces. They can prevent translation of the free

body in all directions, but they cannot prevent the body from rotating about the connection. Reactions of this group involve *two unknowns* and are usually represented by their x and y components. In the case of a rough surface, the component normal to the surface must be directed away from the surface.

3. *Reactions Equivalent to a Force and a Couple.* These reactions are caused by *fixed supports* which oppose any motion of the free body. Fixed supports actually produce forces over the entire surface of contact; these forces, however, form a system which may be reduced to a force and a couple. Reactions of this group involve *three unknowns*, namely, the two components of the force and the moment of the couple.

When the sense of an unknown force or couple is not clearly apparent, no attempt should be made at determining it. Instead, the sense of the force or couple should be arbitrarily assumed; the sign of the answer obtained will indicate whether the assumption is correct or not.

The free-body diagram should also include dimensions, since these may be needed in the computation of moments of forces. Any other detail, however, should be omitted.

3.14. Problems Involving the Equilibrium of a Rigid Body. We saw in Sec. 3.12 that the conditions for the equilibrium of a rigid body may be expressed analytically by writing the three equations

$$\Sigma F_x = 0 \qquad \Sigma F_y = 0 \qquad \Sigma M_A = 0 \qquad \textbf{(3.5)}$$

where A is any point. These equations may be solved for no more than three unknowns.

We saw in Sec. 3.13, on the other hand, that unknown forces usually consist of reactions. The number of unknowns corresponding to a given reaction was seen to depend upon the type of support or connection causing that reaction. Referring to Sec. 3.13, we check that the equilibrium equations (3.5) may be used to determine the reactions of two rollers and one cable, or of one fixed support, or of one smooth pin and one roller, etc.

Consider, for instance, the truss shown in Fig. 3.17a, which is subjected to the given forces P, Q, and S. The truss is held in place by a smooth pin at A and a roller at B. The pin prevents point A from moving by exerting a force of components A_x and A_y on the truss; the roller keeps the truss from rotating about A by exerting the vertical force B. The free-body diagram of the truss is shown in Fig. 3.17b; it includes the reactions A_x, A_y, and B as well as the applied forces P, Q, S, and the weight W of the truss. Expressing that the sum of the moments about A of all the forces shown in Fig. 3.17b is zero, we write the equation $\Sigma M_A = 0$, which may be solved for B since it does not contain A_x or A_y. Expressing, then, that the sum of the x components and the sum of the y components of the forces are zero, we write the equations $\Sigma F_x = 0$ and $\Sigma F_y = 0$, which may be solved for A_x and A_y, respectively.

Additional equations could be obtained by expressing that the sum of the moments of the external forces about points other than A is zero. We could write, for instance, $\Sigma M_B = 0$. Such a statement, however, does not contain any new information, since it has already been established that the system of the forces shown in Fig. 3.17b is equivalent to zero. The additional equation *is not independent* and cannot be used to determine a fourth unknown. It will be useful, however, for checking the solution obtained from the original three equations of equilibrium.

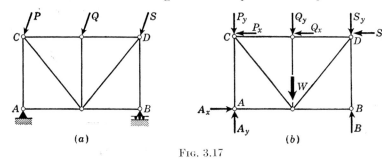

(a)   (b)

Fig. 3.17

While the three equations of equilibrium cannot be *augmented* by additional equations, any of them may be *replaced* by another equation. Thus, an alternate system of equations of equilibrium is

$$\Sigma F_x = 0 \qquad \Sigma M_A = 0 \qquad \Sigma M_B = 0 \qquad (3.6)$$

where the line AB is chosen in a direction different from the y direction (Fig. 3.17b). These equations are sufficient conditions for the equilibrium of the truss. The first two equations indicate that the external forces must reduce to a single vertical force at A. Since the third equation requires that the moment of this force be zero about a point B which is not on its line of action, the force must be zero and the rigid body is in equilibrium.

A third possible set of equations of equilibrium is

$$\Sigma M_A = 0 \qquad \Sigma M_B = 0 \qquad \Sigma M_C = 0 \qquad (3.7)$$

where the points A, B, and C are not in a straight line (Fig. 3.17b). The first equation requires that the external forces reduce to a single force at A; the second equation requires that this force pass through B; the third, that it pass through C. Since the points A, B, C are not in a straight line, the force must be zero and the rigid body is in equilibrium.

The equation $\Sigma M_A = 0$, which expresses that the sum of the moments of the forces about pin A is zero, possesses a more definite physical meaning than either of the other two equations (3.7). These two equations express a similar idea of balance, but with respect to points about which the rigid body is not actually hinged. They are, however, as useful as the first equation, and our choice of equilibrium equations should not be unduly influenced by the physical meaning of these equations. Indeed, it will be desirable in practice to choose equations of equilibrium containing only one unknown, since this eliminates the necessity of solving simultaneous equations.   Equations containing only one unknown may be obtained by summing moments about the point of intersection of the lines of action of two unknown forces or, if these forces are parallel, by summing components in a direction perpendicular to their common direction.   In the case of the truss of Fig. 3.18, for example, which is held by rollers at A and B and a short link at D, the reactions at A and B may be eliminated by summing x components.   The reactions at A and D

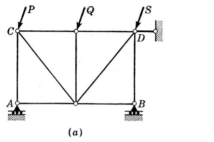 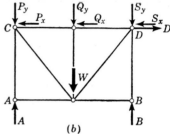

(a)   (b)

FIG. 3.18

will be eliminated by summing moments about C and the reactions at B and D by summing moments about D.   The equations obtained are

$$\Sigma F_x = 0 \qquad \Sigma M_C = 0 \qquad \Sigma M_D = 0$$

Each of these equations contains only one unknown.

3.15. Statically Indeterminate Reactions. Unstable Rigid Bodies. In each of the two examples considered in the preceding section (Figs. 3.17 and 3.18), the reactions to be determined involved *three unknowns;* these unknowns were obtained by solving the three equations of equilibrium.   Besides, the types of supports used were such that equilibrium

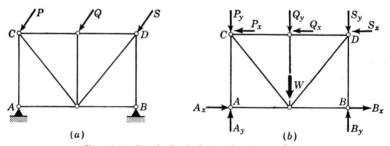

(a)   (b)

FIG. 3.19. Statically indeterminate reactions.

could be maintained under the given loads or under any other loading conditions.   In such cases, the reactions are said to be *statically determinate* and the rigid body is said to be *stable.*

Consider now the truss shown in Fig. 3.19a, which is held by smooth pins at A and B.   We note from the free-body diagram of Fig. 3.19b that the reactions involve *four unknowns*. Since, as was pointed out in Sec. 3.14, only three independent equilibrium equations are available, there are *more unknowns than equations* and all the unknowns cannot be determined. While the equations $\Sigma M_A = 0$ and $\Sigma M_B = 0$ yield the vertical components B_y and A_y, respectively, the equation $\Sigma F_x = 0$ gives only the sum $A_x + B_x$ of the horizontal components of the reactions at A and B. The components A_x and B_x are said to be *statically indeterminate*. They could be determined by considering the deformations they produce, but this method is beyond the scope of statics and belongs to the study of mechanics of materials.

The supports used to hold the truss shown in Fig. 3.20a consist of rollers at A and B. The corresponding reactions, shown in Fig. 3.20b, involve *two unknowns*. Since three equations of equilibrium must still be satisfied, there are *fewer unknowns than equations* and one of the equilibrium equations will not be satisfied. While the equations $\Sigma M_A = 0$ and

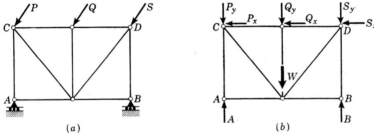

(a)   (b)

FIG. 3.20. Unstable rigid body.

$\Sigma M_B = 0$ can be satisfied by a proper choice of reactions at A and B, the equation $\Sigma F_x = 0$ will not be satisfied unless the sum of the horizontal components of the applied forces happens to be zero. The physical significance of this result is clear: equilibrium cannot be maintained under general loading conditions, and the truss moves. The truss is said to be *unstable*.

It should be noted that a rigid body may be unstable even when the reactions involve three or more unknowns. *Instability will occur whenever an equation of equilibrium cannot be satisfied.* Consider, for example, the truss shown in Fig. 3.21a, which is held by rollers at A, B, and E, to which correspond three unknown vertical reactions. From the free-body diagram of Fig. 3.21b, we find that the equation $\Sigma F_x = 0$ will not be satisfied unless the sum of the horizontal components of the applied forces happens to be zero. This kind of instability is due to the location of the supports, rather than to their type or number, and is known as *geometric instability*. Since, in the case considered, only two equilibrium equations are left for determining the three unknowns, the reactions will be statically indeterminate. Under general loading conditions, geometric instability is thus accompanied by indeterminacy. Another example of geometric instability and indeterminacy is provided by the truss shown in Fig. 3.22. This truss is held by a smooth pin at A and by rollers at B and C, which altogether involve four unknowns. Choosing the equilibrium equations $\Sigma M_A = 0$, $\Sigma F_x = 0$, and $\Sigma F_y = 0$, we find that the first equation cannot be satisfied under general loading conditions, while the other two yield only the sums $A_x + B$ and $A_y + C$. The examples of Figs. 3.21 and 3.22 lead us to conclude that *geometric instability occurs when the supports, although providing a sufficient number of unknowns, are arranged in such a way that the reactions must be either concurrent or parallel.*

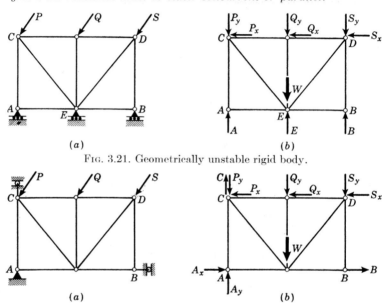

(a)   (b)

FIG. 3.21. Geometrically unstable rigid body.

(a)   (b)

FIG. 3.22. Geometrically unstable rigid body.

Supports involving statically indeterminate reactions should be used with care in the *design* of structures, and only with a full knowledge of the problems they may cause. On the other hand, the *analysis* of structures possessing statically indeterminate reactions often may be partially carried out by the methods of statics. In the case of the truss of Fig. 3.19, for example, the vertical components of the reactions at A and B were obtained from the equilibrium equations.

For obvious reasons, supports causing instability should be avoided in the design of stationary structures. However, an unstable structure will not necessarily collapse; under particular loading conditions, equilibrium may be maintained. For example, although unstable, the trusses of Figs. 3.20 and 3.21 will be in equilibrium if the applied forces P, Q, and S are vertical. Besides, structures which are designed to move *should* be unstable. A railroad car, for instance, would be of little use if it could not be made unstable by releasing its brakes.

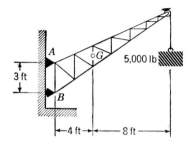

A fixed crane weighs 2,000 lb and is used to lift a load of 5,000 lb. It is held in place by a smooth pin at A and a rocker at B. The center of gravity is located at G. Determine the components of the reactions at A and B.

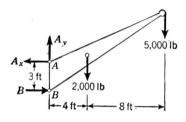

Solution. A free-body diagram of the crane is drawn. Since the reaction at a smooth pin is a force of unknown direction, the reaction at A is represented by its components A_x and A_y. Since the reaction at a rocker is perpendicular to the rocker surface, the reaction at B will be horizontal. We assume that A_x, A_y, and B act in the directions shown on the free-body diagram.

Determination of B. We express that the sum of the moments of all external forces about point A is zero. The equation obtained will contain neither A_x nor A_y since the moments of these forces about A are zero. We write

$$+\circlearrowleft \ \Sigma M_A = 0: \quad (2,000 \text{ lb})(4 \text{ ft}) + (5,000 \text{ lb})(12 \text{ ft}) - B(3 \text{ ft}) = 0$$

$$B = +22,700 \text{ lb} \qquad B = 22,700 \text{ lb} \rightarrow$$

Since the result is positive, the reaction is directed as assumed.

Determination of A_x. The value of A_x is determined by expressing that the sum of the horizontal components of all external forces is zero. We write

$$\xrightarrow{+} \ \Sigma F_x = 0: \quad B - A_x = 0 \qquad 22,700 \text{ lb} - A_x = 0$$

$$A_x = +22,700 \text{ lb} \qquad A_x = 22,700 \text{ lb} \leftarrow$$

Determination of A_y. The sum of the vertical components must also equal zero.

$$+\uparrow \ \Sigma F_y = 0: \quad A_y - 2,000 \text{ lb} - 5,000 \text{ lb} = 0$$

$$A_y = +7,000 \text{ lb} \qquad A_y = 7,000 \text{ lb} \uparrow$$

From the components A_x and A_y, we find that the reaction at A is 23,700 lb $\measuredangle$ 17.2°.

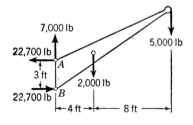

Check. The values obtained for the reactions may be checked by recalling that the sum of the moments of all external forces about any point must be zero. For example, considering point B, we write

$$+\circlearrowleft \ \Sigma M_B = (2,000 \text{ lb})(4 \text{ ft}) + (5,000 \text{ lb})(12 \text{ ft})$$
$$- (22,700 \text{ lb})(3 \text{ ft})$$
$$= 0$$

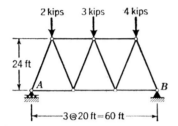

2 kips 3 kips 4 kips

24 ft

A

B

3 @ 20 ft = 60 ft

Three loads are applied to a truss as shown. The truss is supported by a roller at A and by a smooth pin at B. Determine the reactions at A and B.

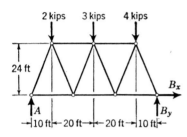

2 kips 3 kips 4 kips

24 ft

B_x

A

B_y

10 ft — 20 ft — 20 ft — 10 ft

Solution. A free-body diagram of the truss is drawn. The reaction at A is vertical and is denoted by A. The reaction at B is represented by components B_x and B_y. Each component is assumed to act in the direction shown.

Equilibrium Equations. We write the following three equilibrium equations and solve for the reactions indicated:

$\xrightarrow{+} \Sigma F_x = 0$: $\qquad\qquad\qquad B_x = 0 \qquad$ **$B_x = 0$**

$+\downarrow \Sigma M_A = 0$: (2 kips)(10 ft) + (3 kips)(30 ft) + (4 kips)(50 ft) $- B_y$(60 ft) = 0

$$B_y = +5.17 \text{ kips} \qquad \textbf{\textit{B}}_y = \textbf{5.17 kips} \uparrow$$

$+\uparrow \Sigma M_B = 0$: A(60 ft) $-$ (2 kips)(50 ft) $-$ (3 kips)(30 ft) $-$ (4 kips)(10 ft) = 0

$$A = +3.83 \text{ kips} \qquad \textbf{\textit{A}} = \textbf{3.83 kips} \uparrow$$

Check. The results are checked by adding the vertical components of all the external forces.

$$+\uparrow \Sigma F_y = +5.17 \text{ kips} + 3.83 \text{ kips} - 2 \text{ kips} - 3 \text{ kips} - 4 \text{ kips} = 0$$

Remark. In this problem the reactions at both A and B are vertical; however, these reactions are vertical for different reasons. At A, the truss is supported by a roller; hence the reaction cannot have any horizontal component. At B, the horizontal component of the reaction is zero because it must satisfy the equilibrium equation $\Sigma F_x = 0$ and none of the other forces acting on the truss has a horizontal component.

We could have noticed at first glance that the reaction at B was vertical and dispensed with the horizontal component B_x. This, however, is a bad practice. In following it, we would run the risk of forgetting the component B_x when the loading conditions require such a component (i.e., when a horizontal load is included). Also, the component B_x was found to be zero by using and solving an equilibrium equation, $\Sigma F_x = 0$. By setting B_x equal to zero immediately, we might not realize that we actually make use of this equation and thus might lose track of the number of equations available for solving the problem.

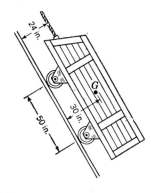

A loading car is at rest on a track forming an angle of 25° with the vertical. The gross weight of the car and its load is 5,500 lb, and it is applied at a point 30 in. from the track, halfway between the two axles. The car is held by a cable attached 24 in. from the track. Determine the tension in the cable and the reaction at each wheel.

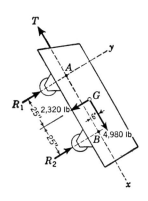

Solution. A free-body diagram of the car is drawn. The reaction at each wheel is perpendicular to the track, and the tension T is parallel to the track. For convenience, we choose the x axis parallel to the track and the y axis perpendicular to the track. The 5,500-lb weight is then resolved into x and y components

$$W_x = (5,500 \text{ lb}) \cos 25° = 4,980 \text{ lb} \searrow$$

$$W_y = (5,500 \text{ lb}) \sin 25° = 2,320 \text{ lb} \swarrow$$

Equilibrium Equations. We take moments about A to eliminate T and R_1 from the computation.

$$+\!\!\downarrow \ \Sigma M_A = 0: \quad (2,320 \text{ lb})(25 \text{ in.}) + (4,980 \text{ lb})(6 \text{ in.}) - R_2(50 \text{ in.}) = 0$$

$$R_2 = +1,758 \text{ lb} \qquad R_2 = \textbf{1,758 lb} \nearrow$$

Now, taking moments about B to eliminate T and R_2 from the computation, we write

$$+\!\!\uparrow \ \Sigma M_B = 0: \quad (2,320 \text{ lb})(25 \text{ in.}) - (4,980 \text{ lb})(6 \text{ in.}) - R_1(50 \text{ in.}) = 0$$

$$R_1 = +562 \text{ lb} \qquad R_1 = \textbf{562 lb} \nearrow$$

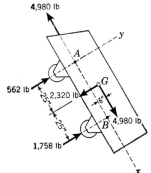

The value of T is found by writing

$$\searrow +\Sigma F_x = 0: \quad +4,980 \text{ lb} - T = 0$$
$$T = +4,980 \text{ lb} \qquad T = \textbf{4,980 lb} \nwarrow$$

The computed values of the reactions are shown in the adjacent sketch.

Check. The computations are verified by writing

$$\nearrow +\Sigma F_y = +562 \text{ lb} + 1,758 \text{ lb} - 2,320 \text{ lb}$$
$$= 0$$

A check could also have been obtained by computing moments about any point except A or B.

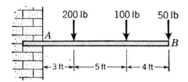

A cantilever beam is loaded as shown. The beam is fixed at the left end and free at the right end. Determine the reaction at the fixed end.

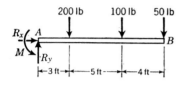

Solution. The portion of the beam which is embedded in the wall is subjected to a large number of forces. These forces, however, are equivalent to a force of components R_x and R_y and a couple of moment M. The assumed directions of R_x, R_y, and M are shown on the free body.

Equilibrium Equations

$$\xrightarrow{+} \Sigma F_x = 0: \qquad\qquad R_x = 0 \qquad R_x = 0$$

$$+\uparrow \Sigma F_y = 0: \qquad\qquad R_y - 200 \text{ lb} - 100 \text{ lb} - 50 \text{ lb} = 0$$

$$R_y = +350 \text{ lb} \qquad R_y = \textbf{350 lb} \uparrow$$

$$+\!\!\downarrow \Sigma M_A = 0: \quad +(200 \text{ lb})(3 \text{ ft}) + (100 \text{ lb})(8 \text{ ft}) + (50 \text{ lb})(12 \text{ ft}) - M = 0$$

$$M = +2,000 \text{ lb-ft} \qquad M = \textbf{2,000 lb-ft} \,\rotatebox{0}{\textgravedbl}$$

The reaction at the fixed end consists of a vertical upward force of 350 lb and of a 2,000-lb-ft counterclockwise couple.

Check. The results may be checked by computing moments about any point. Choosing point B, we write

$$+\!\!\downarrow \Sigma M_B = +R_y(12 \text{ ft}) - M - (200 \text{ lb})(9 \text{ ft}) - (100 \text{ lb})(4 \text{ ft}) = 0$$

$$= +(350 \text{ lb})(12 \text{ ft}) - 2,000 \text{ lb-ft} - 1,800 \text{ lb-ft} - 400 \text{ lb-ft} = 0$$

PROBLEMS

3.39. A man raises a 12-ft joist weighing 20 lb by pulling on a rope.   Find the tension T in the rope and the reaction at A.

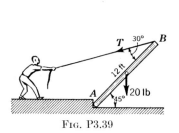

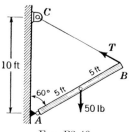

Fig. P3.39   Fig. P3.40

3.40. A 10-ft boom, weighing 50 lb, is hinged at A and attached to a cable at B. Find the tension T in the cable and the reaction at A.

3.41. A load W is supported by a pulley as shown.   Prove that, if the pulley is in equilibrium, the tensions T_1 and T_2 are both equal to $W/2$.

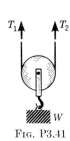

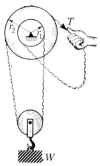

Fig. P3.41   Fig. P3.42

3.42. The chain hoist shown may be used to raise a weight W by pulling on the free chain with a smaller force T.   (a) Derive an expression for T in terms of W, r_1, and r_2.   (b) If $W = 3$ tons, $r_1 = 7$ in., and $r_2 = 7.5$ in., determine the required value of T.

3.43. Two links AB and CD are connected to a bell crank as shown.   The tension in link AB is 100 lb.   Determine the tension in CD and the reaction at shaft O.

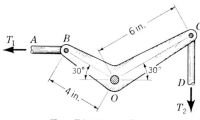

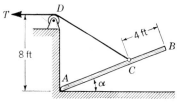

Fig. P3.43 and P3.44   Fig. P3.45

3.44. Find the maximum pull which may be safely exerted by link AB on the bell crank if the maximum allowable value for the reaction at the shaft O is 500 lb.

3.45. A 12-ft beam weighs 350 lb and is held in various positions by a cable attached at point C.   Determine the tension T in the cable and the reaction at A when $\alpha = 30°$.

3.46. Solve Prob. 3.45 when $\alpha = 60°$.

3.47. A man holds a 3-ft wooden bar at both ends while another man tightens screws into the bar with a screw driver, applying a couple of 10 lb-ft. Find the smallest forces that the first man may apply to hold the bar in place while a screw is being tightened (*a*) in the middle of the bar, (*b*) 1 ft from the end of the bar.

3.48. Two external shafts of a gearbox carry torques as shown. Determine the vertical forces which must be exerted by the bolts at A and B to maintain the gearbox in equilibrium.

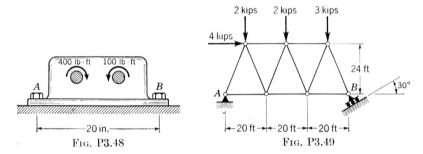

Fig. P3.48   Fig. P3.49

3.49. Determine the reactions at A and B for the truss and loading shown. Note that the roller rests on a 30° incline.

3.50. Determine the reactions at A and B for the truss of Prob. 3.49 if the horizontal 4-kip load is directed to the left.

3.51. Determine the reactions at A and B for the truss of Prob. 3.49 if the horizontal 4-kip load is removed.

3.52. Determine the reactions at A and B for the truss and loading of Prob. 3.49 if the roller at B rests on a horizontal plane.

3.53. A light bar AD is suspended from a cable BE and supports a 600-lb load at its mid-point C. The extremities A and D of the bar are in contact with smooth, vertical walls. Determine the tension in cable BE and the reactions at A and D.

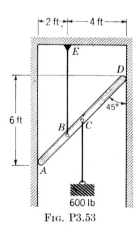

Fig. P3.53

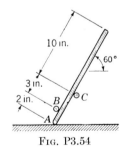

Fig. P3.54

3.54. A slender rod, 15 in. long, weighs 5 lb and is lodged between two smooth pegs as shown. If the surface at A is also smooth, determine the reactions at A, B, and C.

3.55. A truss ABC is loaded as shown. Determine the reactions at A and B for each of the three types of supports indicated.

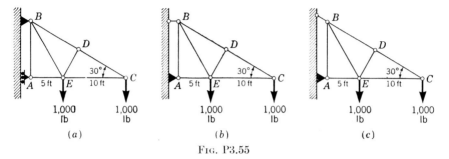

FIG. P3.55

3.56. The crane supports a 500-lb load.   Find the reactions for each of the three types of supports shown.

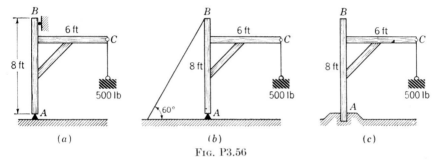

FIG. P3.56

3.57. Determine the reactions at the points of support of the angle bracket of Prob. 3.35, assuming in turn the following types of connections: (*a*) a pin in a fitted hole at *A* and a pin in a horizontal slot at *D*, (*b*) a pin in a horizontal slot at *A* and a pin in a fitted hole at *D*, (*c*) a rivet at *D*.

3.58. Determine the reactions at the points of support of the angle bracket of Prob. 3.36, assuming in turn the following types of connections: (*a*) a pin in a fitted hole at *B* and a pin in a horizontal slot at *C*, (*b*) a pin in a horizontal slot at *B* and a pin in a fitted hole at *C*, (*c*) a rivet at *B*.

3.59. A *T*-shaped bracket supports a 50-lb load.   Determine the reactions at *B* and *C*.

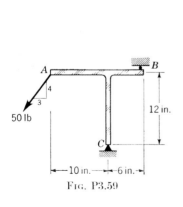

FIG. P3.59

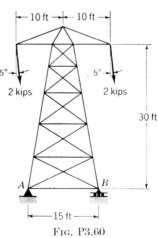

FIG. P3.60

3.60. A transmission tower carries two wires. Each of the wires is known to exert a 2-kip force on its insulator directed as shown. The weight of the tower is 4 kips. Determine the reactions at A and B.

3.61. Determine the reactions at A and B for the beam of Prob. 3.32.

3.62. Determine the reaction at A for the beam of Prob. 3.33.

3.63. Determine the reactions at A and H for the truss of Prob. 3.37.

3.64. Determine the reactions at A and B for the roof structure of Prob. 3.38.

3.65. A pole is driven into the ground, leaving a length L aboveground. If the portion aboveground weighs W, determine the reaction at A.

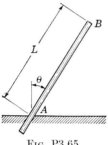

FIG. P3.65

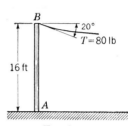

FIG. P3.66

3.66. Determine the reaction at the base of a 16-ft telephone pole weighing 300 lb and used to hold the end of a line. The tension in the line is 80 lb, and, at the point of support, the line forms an angle of 20° with the horizontal.

3.67. A workbench seat ABC is held in the position shown by a vertical bar DE and supports a 175-lb man. (a) Determine the reaction at A. (b) If the inside diameter of the collar is slightly larger than the bar, the collar will bear only at points G and H. Determine the horizontal forces developed at G and H.

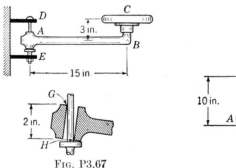

FIG. P3.67

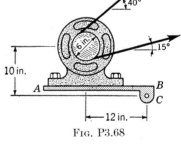

FIG. P3.68

3.68. In the pivoted motor mount, or Rockwood drive, the weight of the motor is used to maintain tension in the drive belt. When the motor is at rest, the tensions T_1 and T_2 may be assumed equal. The weight of the motor is 175 lb, and the diameter of the drive pulley is 6 in. Assuming that the weight of the platform AB is negligible, determine the tension in the belt and the reaction at C when the motor is at rest.

*3.69. Two wheels A and B, weighing 20 lb and 10 lb, respectively, are connected by a weightless rod 40 in. long and allowed to roll on 45° inclines. Determine the distance x corresponding to equilibrium.

*3.70. Find the angle θ for which the boom AB is in equilibrium. Neglect the weight of the boom.

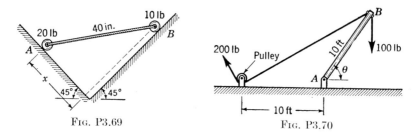

FIG. P3.69　　　　　　　　　　FIG. P3.70

3.71. A plate is to be held by three links. Two links *EF* and *GH* are located as shown. The third link *CD* is to be vertical and located at a distance *x* from corner *B*. Determine the distance *x* for which the plate is geometrically unstable.

3.72. The plate shown weighs 50 lb. If link *CD* is located so that $x = 15.2$ in., compute the reactions at each link. Explain the large numerical values obtained.

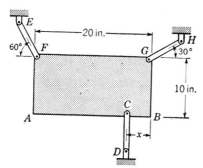

FIG. P3.71 AND P3.72

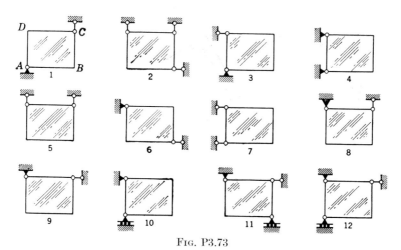

FIG. P3.73

3.73. Twelve identical rectangular plates, 2 by 3 ft, weighing 100 lb each, are held in a vertical plane as shown. All connections consist of smooth pins, rollers, or short links. Determine in each case whether (*a*) the reactions are statically determinate or indeterminate, (b) the plate is stable or unstable (specify if geometrically unstable), (c) equilibrium is maintained under the given loading. Also, wherever possible, compute the reactions.

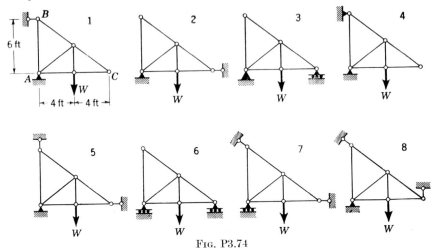

FIG. P3.74

3.74. A small truss is supported in eight different ways as shown. All connections consist of smooth pins, rollers, or short links. For each structure, answer the questions listed in Prob. 3.73, and, wherever possible, compute the reactions, assuming $W = 10$ kips.

3.16. Equilibrium of a Two-force Body. A particular case of equilibrium which is of considerable interest is that of a rigid body subjected to two forces. Such a body is commonly called a *two-force body*. We

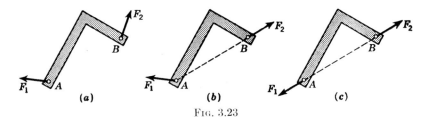

FIG. 3.23

shall show that, *if a two-force body is in equilibrium, the two forces must have same magnitude, same line of action, and opposite sense.*

Consider a corner plate subjected to two forces F_1 and F_2 acting at A and B, respectively (Fig. 3.23a). If the plate is to be in equilibrium, the sum of the moments of F_1 and F_2 about any axis must be zero. First, we sum moments about A: since the moment of F_1 is obviously zero, the moment of F_2 must also be zero and the line of action of F_2 must pass through A (Fig. 3.23b). Summing moments about B, we prove similarly that the line of action of F_1 must pass through B (Fig. 3.23c). Both forces have the same line of action (line AB). From the equation $\Sigma F_x = 0$ or $\Sigma F_y = 0$, it is seen that they must have also same magnitude but opposite sense.

If several forces act at two points A and B, the forces acting at A may be replaced by their resultant F_1 and those acting at B by their resultant F_2. Thus a two-force body may be more generally defined as *a rigid body subjected to forces acting at only two points*. The resultants F_1 and F_2 then must have same line of action, same magnitude, and opposite sense.

Although problems dealing with the equilibrium of two-force bodies may be solved by the general methods studied in the preceding sections, it is sometimes desirable to make use of the property we have just established to simplify certain problems so that simple trigonometric or geometric relations can be used to solve them.

3.17. Equilibrium of a Three-force Body.   Another case of equilibrium that is of great interest is that of a *three-force body*, i.e., a rigid body subjected to three forces or, more generally, *a rigid body subjected to forces*

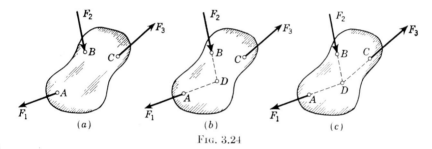

Fig. 3.24

acting at only three points.   Consider a rigid body subjected to a system of forces which may be reduced to three forces F_1, F_2, and F_3 acting at A, B and C, respectively (Fig. 3.24a). We shall show that, if the body is in equilibrium, *the lines of action of the three forces must be either concurrent or parallel.*

Since the rigid body is in equilibrium, the sum of the moments of F_1, F_2, and F_3 about any axis must be zero.   Assuming that the lines of action of F_1 and F_2 intersect, and denoting their point of intersection by D, we sum moments about D (Fig. 3.24b); since the moments of F_1 and F_2 about D are zero, the moment of F_3 about D must also be zero and the line of action of F_3 must pass through D (Fig. 3.24c).   The three lines of action are concurrent.   The only exception occurs when none of the lines intersect; the lines of action must then be parallel.

Although problems concerning three-force bodies may be solved by the general methods studied in Secs. 3.12 to 3.15, the property we have just established may be used to solve these problems either graphically or from simple trigonometric or geometric relations.

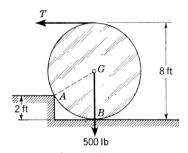

A 500-lb cylindrical tank, 8 ft in diameter, is to be raised over a 2-ft obstruction. A cable is wrapped around the tank and pulled horizontally as shown. The corner of the obstruction at A is rough. Find the required tension in the cable and the reaction at A.

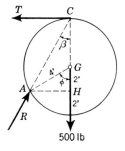

Solution. When the tank is just about to be raised, there is no force acting at B. Since the corner at A is rough, the reaction R is of unknown magnitude and direction. The only other forces acting on the tank are its 500-lb weight and the tension T in the cable. The tank is thus a three-force body, and the three forces must be concurrent. The reaction R, therefore, will pass through the point of intersection C of the lines of action of the 500-lb weight and the tension T.

We compute

$$\cos \phi = \frac{GH}{AG} = \frac{2 \text{ ft}}{4 \text{ ft}} = 0.500 \qquad \phi = 60°$$

Since β is the corresponding inscribed angle, we find

$$\beta = \frac{\phi}{2} = 30°$$

A force triangle is drawn as shown, and we compute

$$T = (500 \text{ lb}) \tan 30° \qquad T = \textbf{288 lb}$$

$$R = \frac{500 \text{ lb}}{\cos 30°} = 577 \text{ lb} \qquad R = \textbf{577 lb} \measuredangle \textbf{60°}$$

Remark. It should be noted that R is not normal to the surface of the tank. Therefore, the surfaces of the obstruction and of the tank must be rough if the tank is to be raised in the described manner. This point is discussed fully in Chap. 8.

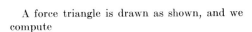

PROBLEMS

3.75. Using the method of Sec. 3.17, solve Prob. 3.39.

3.76. Using the method of Sec. 3.17, solve Prob. 3.40.

3.77. Using the method of Sec. 3.17, solve Prob. 3.43.

3.78. Using the method of Sec. 3.17, solve Prob. 3.44.

3.79. Using the method of Sec. 3.17, solve Prob. 3.45.

3.80. Using the method of Sec. 3.17, solve Prob. 3.59.

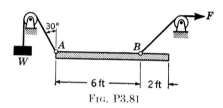

Fig. P3.81

3.81. A uniform beam 8 ft long weighs 600 lb. It is held by two cables as shown; the cable attached at A forms an angle of 30° with the vertical. If the beam is to be horizontal, determine the direction of the cable attached at B and the magnitude of F and W.

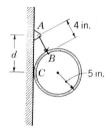

Fig. P3.82

3.82. A thin ring, of radius 5 in., weighs 3 lb and is held against a smooth wall by a 4-in. string AB. Determine the angle the string forms with the wall and the tension in the string. Also find the distance d and the reaction between the wall and the ring.

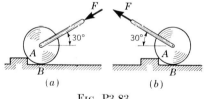

Fig. P3.83

3.83. A 600-lb roller, 2 ft in diameter, is used on a lawn. Determine the force F required to make it roll over a 3-in. obstruction (a) if the roller is pushed as shown, (b) if the roller is pulled as shown.

3.84. A 12-ft ladder, weighing 80 lb, leans against a smooth, vertical wall. The lower end of the ladder rests on rough ground, 4 ft away from the wall. Determine the reaction at both ends.

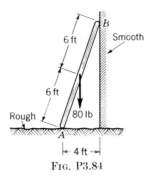

FIG. P3.84

*3.85. A slender rod of length L and weight W is lodged between a smooth wall and a smooth peg. Determine the angle θ between the rod and the wall for equilibrium.

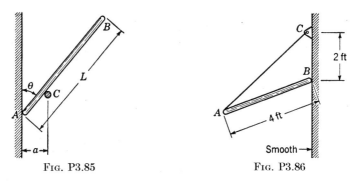

FIG. P3.85   FIG. P3.86

*3.86. A 4-ft rod, of uniform cross section, is held in equilibrium as shown, with one end against a smooth, vertical wall and the other end attached to a cord. Find the length of the cord.

GRAPHICAL METHODS

*3.18. A Graphical Method for the Reduction of a System of Forces.
A system of coplanar forces acting on a rigid body may be reduced graphically to one force or one couple by making use of the principle of transmissibility and the parallelogram law. Consider, for instance, the three forces F_1, F_2, and F_3 (Fig. 3.25a). The forces F_1 and F_2 may be moved along their lines of action until they act at the same point A (Fig. 3.25b). They may then be added into their resultant $R_{1,2}$ (Fig. 3.25c). The forces $R_{1,2}$ and F_3 may in turn be moved along their lines of action until they act at the same point B (Fig. 3.25d) and added into their resultant $R_{1,2,3}$ (Fig. 3.25e). If there were more than three forces, it would be possible to repeat this procedure until all the forces were added together.

This method is simple to understand and easy to remember; yet it is not always practical. Indeed, the construction may become quite cumbersome if many forces are involved. Besides, lines of action will perhaps intersect off the paper; and, obviously, the method fails completely if all the forces are parallel. We shall consider next another method for the graphical reduction of a system of forces, which is less direct but more effective.

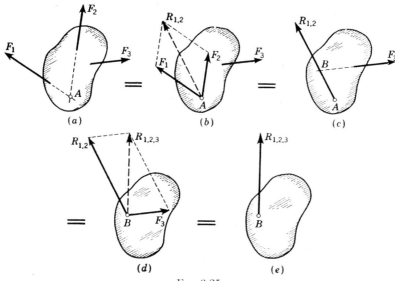

(a)   (b)   (c)

(d)   (e)

Fig. 3.25

*3.19. Resultant of a System of Forces by the Method of the Force Polygon and String Polygon.

Consider four forces F_1, F_2, F_3, and F_4 acting on a rigid body (Fig. 3.26a). We draw the lines of action of the forces, extending them as far as possible on one side of the rigid body to divide the space outside the rigid body into four distinct regions. We write the letter a in one of these regions, and, moving clockwise around the body, we write successively b, c, d, and finally e in the region from which we started. The line of action of F_1, which separates regions a and b, will be referred to as *line ab*. The lines of action of F_2, F_3, and F_4 will be denoted similarly by bc, cd, and de, each time reading the letters clockwise around the body. This is *Bow's notation*.

We shall now draw the four given forces in tip-to-tail fashion in a separate diagram (Fig. 3.26b). The tail of the first force is denoted by A and its tip, which is also the tail of the second force, by B; C, D, and E are defined in a similar way. We shall refer to each of these forces by the names of the points they join, naming first the letter corresponding to the tail and last the letter corresponding to the tip. Thus, the four given forces will be called AB, BC, CD, and DE, respectively.

Comparing the two figures we have drawn (Fig. 3.26a and b), we note that a correspondence exists between *regions* in Fig. 3.26a and *points* in Fig. 3.26b. Each force *joins two points* in Fig. 3.26b, while its line of action *separates two regions* of corresponding names in Fig. 3.26a; thus, to the force AB joining points A and B corresponds the line of action ab

separating regions a and b; to the force BC corresponds the line bc, to CD corresponds cd, and to DE corresponds de.

The magnitude, direction, and sense of the resultant are easily obtained by joining points A and E in Fig. 3.26b. We shall see next how the line of action of the resultant AE may be determined by using the two figures simultaneously. We note that, according to the notation used, this line will be named ae.

We choose an arbitrary point O, called a *pole* (Fig. 3.26d), and draw lines from O to each of the vertices of the force polygon. The lines OA, OB, OC, OD, and OE are called *rays*. We may now resolve each of the original forces AB, BC, CD, and DE into components along the rays (Fig. 3.26f). We write

$$AB = AO \nrightarrow OB \qquad BC = BO \nrightarrow OC$$
$$CD = CO \nrightarrow OD \qquad DE = DO \nrightarrow OE$$

We note that the components OB and BO have same magnitude and direction, but opposite sense. Indeed, OB is a force with tail at O and tip at B, while BO has tail at B and tip at O. When all the components are added together, OB and BO cancel, and so do OC and CO, and OD and DO. Only AO and OE remain and add up into the resultant AE (Fig. 3.26h). Algebraically, this is expressed as follows:

$$AE = AB \nrightarrow BC \nrightarrow CD \nrightarrow DE$$
$$= AO \nrightarrow OB \nrightarrow BO \nrightarrow OC \nrightarrow CO \nrightarrow OD \nrightarrow DO \nrightarrow OE$$
$$= AO \nrightarrow OE$$

This construction is obviously not necessary to determine the magnitude and direction of AE. If, however, we repeat it, taking into account the lines of action of the forces as well as their magnitude, this construction enables us to determine the line of action of the resultant. We choose an arbitrary point (point 1) on line ab (Fig. 3.26c) and draw from point 1 a line parallel to ray OA. This line, which separates region a from a central region o, is called the *string oa*. From point 1, we also draw *string ob* parallel to ray OB; this string will intersect line bc at point 2. From point 2, we draw *string oc* parallel to ray OC and determine its point of intersection with cd (point 3). From point 3, we draw *string od* parallel to OD and determine its point of intersection with de (point 4). Finally, we draw *string oe* through point 4 in a direction parallel to OE, thus completing a polygon called the *string polygon*, or *funicular polygon* (from *funiculus*, Latin for "string"). The first string (oa) and the last string (oe) intersect at point 5.

We now move force F_1 (i.e., force AB) along its line of action until it acts at point 1 and resolve it into its components AO and OB (Fig. 3.26e), using the force triangle 1 of Fig. 3.26f. We similarly attach force BC at point 2, force CD at point 3, and force DE at point 4 and resolve them into components, using the force triangles 2, 3, and 4. The components

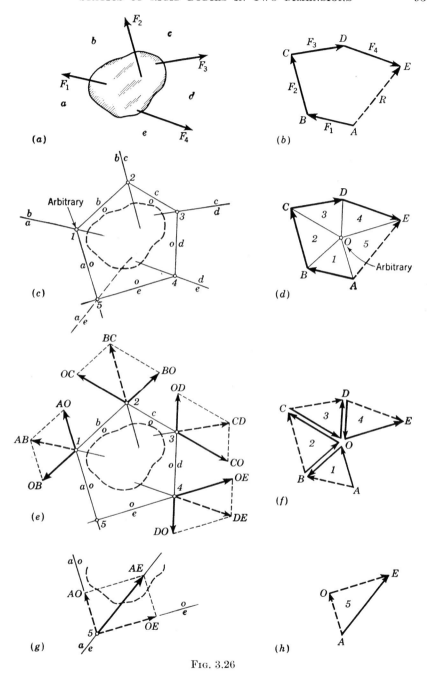

Fɪɢ. 3.26

OB and *BO*, being equal and opposite and having the same line of action *ob*, will cancel, and so will *OC* and *CO*, and *OD* and *DO*. The system of forces reduces to *AO* and *OE*. These forces are moved along their respective lines of action (Fig. 3.26*g*) until they act at point *5*. They may then be added into the resultant *AE*, using the force triangle *5* of Fig. 3.26*h*. The line of action of the resultant is the line *ae* drawn through point *5* in a direction parallel to *AE*.

Once the construction has been understood, it may be reduced to a few steps. Since the magnitude and direction of the resultant are obtained from the force polygon, the string polygon will be used to determine only its line of action. The necessary steps are the following:

1. Denote the various regions defined by the lines of action of the given forces, using lower-case letters and moving clockwise around the rigid body (Fig. 3.26*a*).

2. Draw the force polygon, using capital letters corresponding to the lower-case letters used in step 1, and determine the magnitude, direction, and sense of the resultant (Fig. 3.26*b*).

3. Choose an arbitrary pole *O* (either inside or outside the force polygon), and draw rays from *O* to each of the vertices of the force polygon (Fig. 3.26*d*).

4. Starting from an arbitrary point on the line of action *ab*, draw the string polygon, each string parallel to the corresponding ray. Through the point of intersection of the first and last strings (here *oa* and *oe*), draw a line parallel to the resultant; this is the line of action of the resultant (Fig. 3.26*c*).

The shape of the string polygon depends upon the choice of the pole, and care should be taken to choose the pole so that no string will be parallel to the line of action it is supposed to intersect. The size of the polygon generally depends upon the choice of its first vertex (unless all forces are parallel). The line of action of the resultant does not, however, depend upon the choice of the pole or of the first vertex.

It may happen that *the resultant of the force polygon is zero*. In this case, the first and last vertices of the force polygon (here *A* and *E*) coincide. The first and last rays (here *OA* and *OE*) also coincide, and the corresponding two strings (here *oa* and *oe*) have same direction. Two cases may be distinguished:

1. *The Two Strings Coincide.* The forces they carry (here *AO* and *OE*) may be canceled, and the given system of forces reduces to zero. The rigid body is in equilibrium (see Sec. 3.20).

2. *The Two Strings Are Parallel and Distinct.* The given system reduces to the two forces they carry, i.e., to a couple. The moment of this resultant couple is equal to the product of the common ray *OA* and the perpendicular distance between the two parallel strings (see Sample Prob. 3.15).

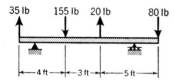

A 12-ft beam is subjected to the forces shown. Determine graphically the resultant of the given system of forces. *Note.* This problem is the same as Sample Prob. 3.6. Again the reactions at the supports are not included in the given system of forces.

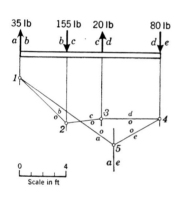
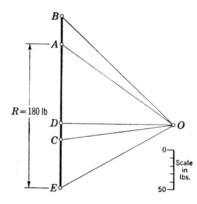

Solution. 1. Moving clockwise around the beam, we write the lower-case letters a, b, c, d, and e. Note that a and e are written in the same region.

2. Using the corresponding capital letters, we draw the force polygon $ABCDE$. Since all the forces are vertical, the polygon reduces to a vertical line. The resultant AE is directed downward, and its magnitude is 180 lb.

3. We choose an arbitrary pole O and draw rays OA, OB, OC, OD, and OE.

4. We choose an arbitrary point 1 on line ab and draw the following strings:
From point 1 on ab, we draw string oa parallel to OA.
From point 1 on ab, we draw string ob parallel to OB and obtain point 2 on bc.
From point 2 on bc, we draw string oc parallel to OC and obtain point 3 on cd.
From point 3 on cd, we draw string od parallel to OD and obtain point 4 on de.
From point 4 on de, we draw string oe parallel to OE.

5. The line of action ae of the resultant passes through the point of intersection (point 5) of strings oa and oe. Since the resultant is vertical (see step b), we draw the line of action of the resultant ae vertically through point 5.

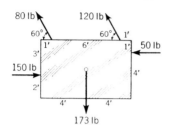

Determine graphically the resultant of the forces acting on the crate considered in Sample Prob. 3.8. The free-body diagram obtained in Sample Prob. 3.8 is repeated here for convenience.

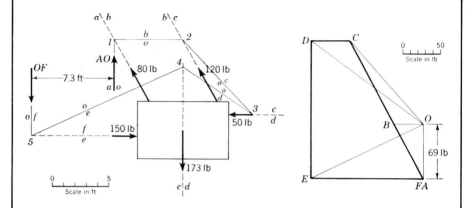

Solution. 1. Moving clockwise around the crate, we write the lower-case letters *a*, *b*, *c*, *d*, *e*, and *f*.

2. Using the corresponding capital letters, we draw the force polygon *ABCDEF* and note that *F* coincides with *A*. The polygon is closed, and the resultant *AF* is zero. The given forces must thus reduce either to a couple or to zero.

3. We choose pole *O* and draw the various rays; the rays *OA* and *OF* coincide.

4. Starting from an arbitrary point *1* on line *ab*, we draw the string polygon, obtaining successively the vertices *2*, *3*, *4*, and *5*. The strings *oa* and *of* are parallel but distinct, and the forces *AO* and *OF* that they carry have the same magnitude and opposite sense. The system of forces thus reduces to a counterclockwise couple. The moment of the couple is obtained by multiplying the common magnitude

$$AO = OF = 69 \text{ lb}$$

of the forces *AO* and *OF* by the perpendicular distance between strings *oa* and *of* (7.3 ft); the moment is found to be 504 lb-ft ↺.

PROBLEMS

3.87. Solve Prob. 3.21 graphically.
3.88. Solve Prob. 3.28 graphically.
3.89. Solve Prob. 3.27 graphically.
3.90. Solve Prob. 3.32*b* graphically.
3.91. Solve Prob. 3.33*b* graphically.
3.92. Solve Prob. 3.36 graphically.
3.93. Solve Prob. 3.35 graphically.
3.94. Solve Prob. 3.38*b* graphically.
3.95. Solve Prob. 3.37 graphically.

3.96. Determine graphically the distance from the left end of the beam to the line of action of the resultant of the loads shown.

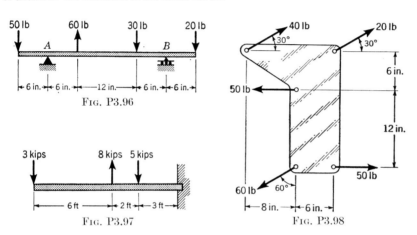

Fig. P3.96

Fig. P3.97

Fig. P3.98

3.97 and 3.98. Determine graphically the resultant of the force system shown.

*3.20. Equilibrium of a Rigid Body by the Method of the Force Polygon and String Polygon.

We saw in Sec. 3.19 that, when a rigid body is in equilibrium, the force polygon is closed and the first and last strings of the string polygon coincide. Consider, for example, a rigid body in equilibrium under four forces. The corresponding string polygon and force polygon are shown in Fig. 3.27. Note that, since the force polygon is closed, the same letter *A* is used to denote the tail of the first force and the tip of the last force. Similarly, the first and last regions that we meet while moving clockwise around the rigid body we denote by a single letter *a* and not by two different letters *a* and *e* as we did in Sec. 3.19 when the rigid body was not in equilibrium.

Problems concerning the equilibrium of rigid bodies usually call for the determination of two unknown forces.† The force polygon, therefore,

---

† If three forces are unknown, their lines of action must be known. Two of the forces may then be replaced by a single force applied at the point of intersection of their lines of action.

cannot be drawn completely at the outset of the solution; one of its vertices is unknown, and the object of the solution is to determine this vertex graphically. The exact procedure to follow varies from one prob-

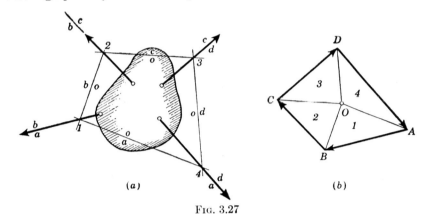

(a)   (b)

Fig. 3.27

lem to another, and the student is advised to turn now to the Sample Problems. A general outline of the method is described here for later reference.

1. The lines of action of all external forces are named according to Bow's notation, moving clockwise around the rigid body. If necessary, the lines of action of some of the forces are extended to the other side of the body, so that all known forces may be denoted by successive letters (see Sample Prob. 3.16).

2. The force polygon is drawn, starting with the known forces. All the vertices of the force polygon may be plotted except one.

3. A pole O is chosen, and all the rays corresponding to known vertices are drawn.

4. Next, we draw the string polygon, choosing the first vertex on the line of action of one of the two unknown forces, and ending with the vertex located on the second unknown force. The last side of the string polygon is obtained by joining the first and last vertices. It should be noted that, if a force is unknown in magnitude and direction, the string polygon *must* be started at the point of application of that force (see Sample Prob. 3.17).

5. We draw a ray from pole O in a direction parallel to the last side of the string polygon, thus defining the unknown vertex of the force polygon. The force polygon may now be completed and the unknown forces determined.

Note that, if a rigid body is in equilibrium under three nonparallel forces, the unknown forces may be determined more conveniently by observing that the lines of action of the three forces must be concurrent (Sec. 3.17).

Determine graphically the reactions at the points of support of the truss shown.

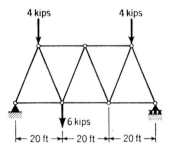

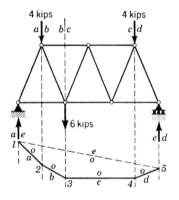

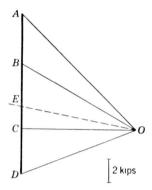

Solution. 1. The truss is drawn to scale, and the lines of action of the given loads and of the two unknown reactions are named according to Bow's notation, moving clockwise around the truss. The line of action of the 6-kip load has been extended to the other side of the truss, so that all known forces may be denoted by successive letters.

2. The force polygon is drawn, starting with load AB and proceeding with loads BC and CD. The reaction DE at the roller is vertical, and so must be the reaction EA at the pin, since all applied loads are vertical. The location of point E, however, is not known, and the force polygon is incomplete.

3. A pole O is chosen, and the rays OA, OB, OC, and OD are drawn.

4. The string polygon is drawn. Point *1* is chosen on the line of action ea of one of the unknown reactions, and strings oa, ob, oc, and od are drawn in directions parallel, respectively, to the known rays OA, OB, OC, and OD. The vertices *2*, *3*, *4*, and *5* are thus successively obtained. The last string oe may then be drawn by joining point *1* and point *5*.

5. Ray OE is drawn from O in a direction parallel to string oe, thus defining point E. The force polygon is completed, and the reactions are measured on the force polygon. They are found to be

$$DE = 6 \text{ kips} \uparrow \qquad EA = 8 \text{ kips} \uparrow$$

SAMPLE PROBLEM 3.17

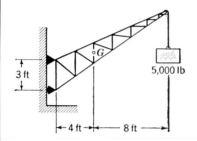

A fixed crane weighs 2,000 lb and is used to lift a load of 5,000 lb. The center of gravity of the crane is located at G. Determine graphically the reactions at the points of support.

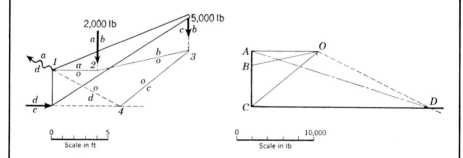

Solution. 1. A free-body diagram of the crane is drawn to scale. The lines of action of the given load, of the weight of the crane, and of the two unknown reactions are named according to Bow's notation, moving clockwise around the crane.

2. The force polygon is drawn, starting with the 2,000-lb weight AB and proceeding with the 5,000-lb load BC. The reaction CD at the rocker is horizontal, but its magnitude is not known, and point D cannot be plotted. The reaction DA at the pin is unknown in magnitude and in direction and cannot be drawn. The force polygon is incomplete.

3. A pole O is chosen, and the rays OA, OB, and OC are drawn.

4. The string polygon is drawn. The line of action da of the reaction at the pin is not known, except for the fact that it passes through the pin. We must then choose the first vertex of the string polygon at the pin. If the string polygon were started at any other point, we would eventually have to find the point of intersection of a string with line da. This would be impossible since line da is not known. Having thus chosen point 1 at the pin, we draw strings oa, ob, and oc in directions parallel, respectively, to the known rays OA, OB, and OC. The vertices 2, 3, and 4 are obtained, respectively, on lines ab, bc, and cd. The last string od may then be drawn by joining point 1 and point 4.

5. We draw ray OD from O in a direction parallel to string od, and since CD must be horizontal, we determine the vertex D of the force polygon. Side DA may now be drawn to complete the force polygon. The reactions CD and DA are determined (magnitude and direction) from the force polygon. We find

$$CD = \textbf{22,700 lb} \rightarrow \qquad DA = \textbf{23,700 lb} \;\nwarrow\, \textbf{17°}$$

102

PROBLEMS

3.99. Determine graphically the reactions for the truss of Prob. 3.27.

3.100. Determine graphically the reactions for the truss of Prob. 3.28.

3.101. Determine graphically the reactions for the beam of Prob. 3.96.

3.102. Determine graphically the reactions for the beam of Prob. 3.32.

3.103. Solve Prob. 3.51 graphically.

3.104. Solve Prob. 3.50 graphically.

3.105. Determine graphically the reactions for the truss of Prob. 3.38.

3.106. Solve Prob. 3.60 graphically.

3.107. Solve Prob. 3.55 graphically.

3.108. Solve Prob. 3.56a and b graphically.

*__3.109.__ Solve Prob. 3.68 graphically. (*Hint.* Since the belt tensions are known to be equal, the direction of their resultant may be found. The problem will then involve only three unknowns.)

*__3.110.__ Solve Prob. 3.54 graphically. (*Hint.* Start the string polygon at the point of intersection of the lines of action of two of the unknown forces.)

*__3.111.__ Solve Prob. 3.53 graphically (see hint of Prob. 3.110).

4. Statics of Rigid Bodies in Three Dimensions

4.1. Moment of a Force about an Axis. When the moment of a force about an axis was defined in Chap. 3, all the forces considered were contained in the plane of the figure and their moments were computed about axes perpendicular to that plane. In space, however, the forces generally are not contained in a plane perpendicular to the axis about which their

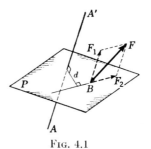

Fig. 4.1

moment is to be determined. The definition of the moment of a force given in Sec. 3.4 needs therefore to be extended.

Consider a force F applied at B and an axis AA' (Fig. 4.1). We resolve F into two perpendicular components F_1 and F_2; the component F_1 is chosen in a direction parallel to AA', and the component F_2 lies in a plane P perpendicular to AA' and passing through B. (We say that F_2 is the *projection* of F on P.) If F acted on a rigid body, only its component F_2 would tend to make the body rotate about the axis AA'. Therefore, *the moment of F about the axis AA' is defined as the moment of F_2 about that axis*. It is equal to the product $F_2 d$, where d is the perpendicular distance from the axis AA' to the line of action of F_2. The sense of the moment (clockwise or counterclockwise) is determined from the point of view of an observer located at A' and looking toward A. The moment of F about the axis AA' (directed from A to A') shown in Fig. 4.1 is thus counterclockwise.

It should be noted that the moment of a force F about an axis AA' is zero if the line of action of F either intersects the axis or is parallel to it. In the first case, the line of action of the projection F_2 of F also intersects the axis (Fig. 4.2), and, in the second case, the magnitude of F_2 is zero (Fig. 4.3). In both cases the moment of F_2, and thus the moment of F, is zero.

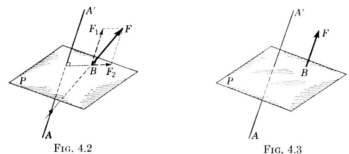

FIG. 4.2   FIG. 4.3

Consider now a force F acting on the corner B of a rectangular box of sides a, b, and c (Fig. 4.4). The force may impart to the body a motion of translation in the x, y, or z directions, or a motion of rotation about the x, y, or z axes, or a combination of all these motions. The ability of the force to produce a translation is measured by its components F_x, F_y, F_z; its ability to produce a rotation about any of the coordinate axes is measured by its moment about that axis. The moments of F about the x, y, and z axes are denoted, respectively, by M_x, M_y, and M_z.

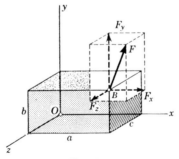

FIG. 4.4

According to the definition given above for the moment of a force, the moment M_x of F about the x axis will be obtained by projecting F on the yz plane and computing the moment of its projection about the x axis. This is done in Fig. 4.5a, which shows the yz plane as an observer located along the positive half of the x axis and looking toward O would see it. It will generally be found convenient to carry out the actual computation of M_x by using Varignon's theorem and computing the moments of the components F_y and F_z about O. Figure 4.5b shows the projection of F on the zx plane, as seen by an observer located along the positive half of the y axis and looking toward O. The moment of this projection about the y axis is the moment M_y of F about that axis. Figure 4.5c shows the projection of F on the xy plane, as seen by an observer located along the positive half of the z axis and looking toward O. The moment of this projection about the z axis is the moment M_z of F about that axis. In the case considered here, the moments M_x, M_y, and M_z are, respectively, clockwise, clockwise, and counterclockwise. For convenience, we shall adopt a common sign convention for the three moments, and we shall observe this convention throughout the present chapter: counterclockwise will be positive; clockwise will be negative.

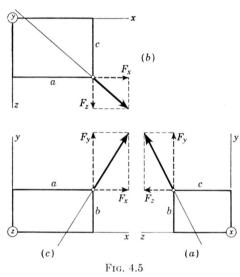

Fig. 4.5

In the case considered here, the moments M_x, M_y, and M_z are, respectively, negative, negative, and positive.

4.2. Couples in Space. A *couple* was defined in Sec. 3.6 as the combination of two forces having same magnitude, parallel lines of action, and opposite sense. It was shown in Sec. 3.7 that the action a couple exerts on a rigid body depends only upon the moment M of the couple, which is equal to the product Fd of the magnitude F of the forces and the distance d between their lines of action. In the case of a couple in space, however, *the plane in which the couple acts* should be specified (Fig. 4.6a). Since the couple may be replaced by any other couple of same moment acting in the same plane, it will be found convenient to represent a couple in space by a *vector* perpendicular to the plane of the couple and of magnitude equal to the moment M of the couple (Fig. 4.6b). The sense of this vector, called a *couple vector*, is such that a man located at the tip of the vector will see the couple acting counterclockwise. The sense of the couple vector may also be found by applying the *right-hand rule:* Close your right hand, and hold it so that your fingers are curled in the sense defined by the couple; your thumb will indicate the sense of the couple vector. Note that the symbol $)$ is added to the couple vector to distinguish it from vectors representing forces.

The point of application of the couple vector may be chosen anywhere in the plane of the couple. In fact, it may be chosen anywhere in space since, as will be seen below, only the *orientation* of the plane of the couple matters. (In other words, two couples of same moment and acting in parallel planes are equivalent.) Because of this fact, couple vectors are said to be *free vectors*, as opposed to *bound* vectors, which have well-defined points of application, and *sliding* vectors, which have well-defined lines of action. The point of application of the couple vector, therefore, may be chosen at the origin of the system of coordinates (Fig. 4.6c). Furthermore, the couple vector M may be resolved into component

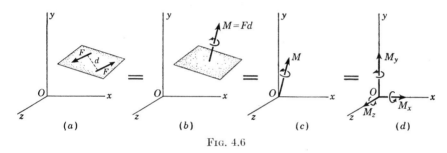

Fig. 4.6

vectors of magnitude M_x, M_y, M_z, directed along the axes of coordinates (Fig. 4.6d). The vector directed along the x axis represents a couple of moment M_x acting in the yz plane; similarly, the other two vectors represent couples of moments M_y and M_z acting, respectively, in the zx and xy planes.

The representation of a couple by means of a vector is convenient. This representation, however, should be *justified*, i.e., we should show that couples possess all the characteristics of vectors (see Sec. 2.1). We already know that couples have magnitude and direction; we shall show now that couples may be added by adding the corresponding couple vectors according to the parallelogram law.†

Consider two couples of moment M_1 and M_2 acting, respectively, in planes P_1 and P_2; these couples may be represented by the couple vectors shown in Fig. 4.7a. Each of these couples may also be represented by two forces of arbitrary magnitude F. The distance d_1 between the forces forming the first couple and the distance d_2 between the forces forming

† Some expressions have magnitude and direction yet do not obey the parallelogram law of addition, for example, the finite rotations of a rigid body.

the second couple should satisfy the equations

$$M_1 = Fd_1 \qquad M_2 = Fd_2 \tag{4.1}$$

One force in each couple may be chosen along the line of intersection AA' of the two planes, one in the sense AA', the other in the opposite sense (Fig. 4.7b). The forces along AA' cancel each other, and the given couples thus reduce to the forces along BB' and CC'. These two forces form a couple acting in the plane P defined by BB' and CC' and may be represented by a couple vector perpendicular to P, of magnitude $M - Fd$ (Fig. 4.7c).

To show that the couple vector M may be obtained by adding vectorially M_1 and M_2, we draw M_1 and M_2 in tip-to-tail fashion in a plane parallel to plane ABC of Fig. 4.7b and join the tail of M_1 to the tip of M_2 (Fig. 4.7d). The triangle obtained is similar to triangle ABC since the sides M_1 and M_2 are, respectively, perpendicular to the sides AB and

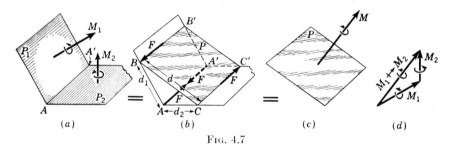

FIG. 4.7

AC, and since, according to (4.1), they are proportional to d_1 and d_2. The resultant of M_1 and M_2, represented by the third side of the triangle of Fig. 4.7d, must therefore be perpendicular to BC and be proportional to d; its magnitude is thus $Fd = M$. We conclude that *the resultant of M_1 and M_2 is the couple vector M*.

We note that, if forces of magnitude F' different from F are used to represent the couples of Fig. 4.7a, new distances d_1' and d_2' are obtained and the resultant couple, which has the same moment M, is found to act in a plane P' parallel to the plane P of Fig. 4.7c. Clearly, this new couple is equivalent to the couple of Fig. 4.7c. Since, by an appropriate choice of the forces F', the plane P' may be chosen at any distance from P, we conclude that *couples of same moment and acting in parallel planes are equivalent*. Couples acting in parallel planes may thus be moved freely from one plane to another and added as if they were coplanar.

Summarizing the results obtained, we conclude that *couples in space may be truly represented by vectors*. These vectors, called couple vectors, may be added or resolved according to the parallelogram law; they are *free vectors* and may be applied at any point.

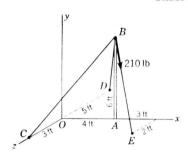

A 6-ft pole AB is held by three guy wires as shown. Determine the moment about each of the coordinate axes of the force exerted by wire BE on point B. The tension T in wire BE is known to be 210 lb.

Solution. The force T exerted by BE is first resolved into components. The components and magnitude of the distance BE (with sense from B to E) are

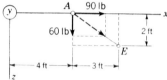

$$d_x = +3 \text{ ft} \quad d_y = -6 \text{ ft} \quad d_z = +2 \text{ ft} \quad d = 7 \text{ ft}$$

Therefore,

$$\frac{T_x}{+3 \text{ ft}} = \frac{T_y}{-6 \text{ ft}} = \frac{T_z}{+2 \text{ ft}} = \frac{210 \text{ lb}}{7 \text{ ft}}$$

$$T_x = +90 \text{ lb} \quad T_y = -180 \text{ lb} \quad T_z = +60 \text{ lb}$$

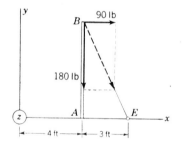

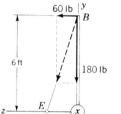

The projections of T on the three coordinate planes are now sketched. Using Varignon's theorem, we write

$$+\!\!\gamma \quad M_x = +(60 \text{ lb})(6 \text{ ft}) = +360 \text{ lb-ft}$$

$$+\!\!\gamma \quad M_y = -(60 \text{ lb})(4 \text{ ft}) = -240 \text{ lb-ft}$$

$$+\!\!\gamma \quad M_z = -(180 \text{ lb})(4 \text{ ft}) - (90 \text{ lb})(6 \text{ ft})$$

$$= -1,260 \text{ lb-ft}$$

Alternate Solution. The computation of M_z may be simplified by moving the projection of T along its line of action to the point where it intersects the x axis; the moment of T_x about the z axis is now zero. We obtain

$$+\!\!\gamma \quad M_z = -(180 \text{ lb})(7 \text{ ft}) = -1,260 \text{ lb-ft}$$

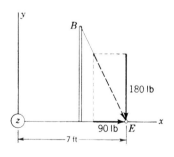

SAMPLE PROBLEM 4.2

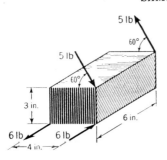

Two couples act on a rectangular box as shown. Replace these two couples by a single equivalent couple.

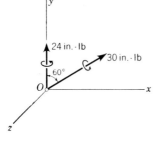

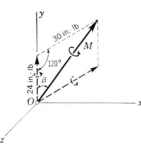

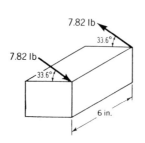

Solution. Each of the given couples is represented by a couple vector which is perpendicular to the plane of the couple and of a magnitude equal to the moment of the couple. The sense of each vector is obtained by applying the right-hand rule, and for convenience both couple vectors are attached at the origin.

The single couple equivalent to the two given couples will be represented by the resultant of the two couple vectors. The magnitude of the resultant couple vector M is obtained from the law of cosines.

$$M^2 = (24)^2 + (30)^2 - (2)(24)(30) \cos 120°$$

$$M = 46.9 \text{ lb-in.}$$

The angle β that the resultant couple vector forms with the vertical is obtained from the law of sines,

$$\frac{\sin \beta}{30 \text{ lb-in.}} = \frac{\sin 120°}{46.9 \text{ lb-in.}} \qquad \beta = 33.6°$$

The single couple equivalent to the two original couples is therefore a couple of moment $M = 46.9$ lb-in., acting in a plane parallel to the z axis and forming an angle of 33.6° with the horizontal plane. This couple may be formed in many ways, for example, by the two 7.82-lb forces shown.

110

PROBLEMS

4.1. Three forces act on a rectangular box as shown. Determine the moment of each force about each of the coordinate axes.

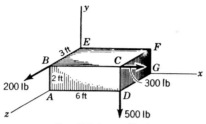

Fig. P4.1 and P4.2

4.2. Determine the moment of each force about (*a*) edge *AD*, (*b*) edge *GF*, (*c*) edge *BC*, and (*d*) a line joining corners *A* and *C*.

4.3. In Prob. 2.51, determine the moment about each of the coordinate axes of the 350-lb force exerted on the building by cable *AB*.

4.4. In Prob. 2.52, determine the moment about each of the coordinate axes of the 450-lb force exerted on the building by cable *BC*.

4.5. A vertical force *P* = 50 lb is applied to a crank. Determine the moment of *P* about each of the coordinate axes when θ = 60°.

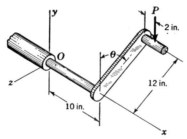

Fig. P4.5 and P4.6

4.6. Determine the moment of the force *P* = 50 lb about each of the coordinate axes in terms of θ. Assume that *P* keeps acting vertically downward as the crank turns.

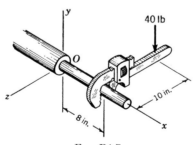

Fig. P4.7

4.7. A wrench is used to tighten a pipe by applying a 40-lb force as shown. Determine the moment of the force about each of the coordinate axes.

4.8. A single force F of unknown magnitude and direction acts at point A of the crank shown. Determine the moment M_x of F about the x axis, knowing that $M_y = -360$ lb-in. and $M_z = +730$ lb-in.

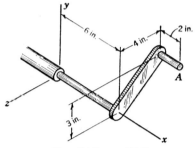

FIG. P4.8 AND P4.9

4.9. The primary purpose of the crank shown is, of course, to produce a moment about the x axis. Show that a single force acting at A and having a moment M_x different from zero about the x axis must also have a moment different from zero about at least one of the other coordinate axes.

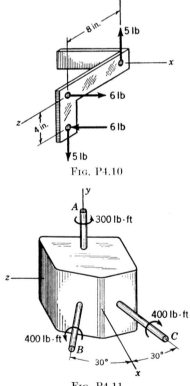

FIG. P4.10

FIG. P4.11

4.10. A bracket is acted upon by two couples as shown. (*a*) Determine the components of a single equivalent couple. (*b*) Check the result obtained by adding the moments of the individual forces about the coordinate axes.

4.11. Three shafts are connected to a gearbox as shown. Shaft *A* is vertical and is subjected to a 300-lb-ft couple. Shafts *B* and *C* are horizontal and subjected to 400-lb-ft couples. Represent the resultant couple exerted on the gearbox by component couples directed along the coordinate axes.

4.12. Solve Prob. 4.11 assuming that the sense of the couple applied to shaft *B* is reversed.

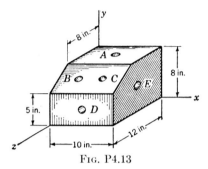

Fig. P4.13

4.13. An automatic drilling machine drills five holes simultaneously in a machined block as shown. Each drill exerts a 100-lb-in. clockwise couple on the block. Determine the *x*, *y*, and *z* components of the single couple equivalent to the five applied couples.

4.3. Resolution of a Given Force into a Force at *O* and a Couple.

Consider a force *F* applied at the corner *A* of a rectangular box. Since a force may always be resolved into components parallel to the coordinate

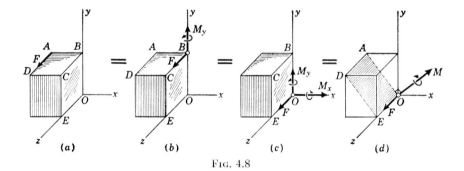

Fig. 4.8

axes, we shall assume that *F* is parallel to one of the axes, say, the *z* axis (Fig. 4.8*a*).

Operating in plane *ABCD* according to the rules established in Chap. 3, we replace the given force by a force-couple system at *B*. The force, of magnitude F, is parallel to the z axis; the couple, of moment equal to the moment M_y of F (in its original position) about the y axis, is contained in plane $ABCD$ and may therefore be represented by a vector directed along the y axis (Fig. 4.8b).   Operating now in plane $BCEO$, we move the couple vector to O and replace the force F acting at B by a force-couple system at O; the new couple, of moment equal to the moment M_x of F (acting at B or at A) about the x axis, may be represented by a vector directed along the x axis (Fig. 4.8c).   We conclude therefore that *the force F acting at A may be moved to O, provided that couple vectors are added along the coordinate axes; the magnitude of each couple vector must equal the moment of F (in its original position) about the corresponding axis.*   Since, in the case considered, F has zero moment about the z axis, there is no couple vector along that axis.

The couple vectors may be replaced by their resultant.   In the case considered, the resultant of M_x and M_y is a couple vector M lying in the xy plane (Fig. 4.8d).   Thus, *the couple vector M is perpendicular to the force F.*   Note that the vector M represents a couple acting in plane $ADEO$ and could have been obtained more directly by moving the force from A to O within that plane.   While the representation given in Fig. 4.8d is more compact than that given in Fig. 4.8c, the representation of Fig. 4.8c is usually preferred since it shows more clearly the action of the original force on the rigid body.

4.4.   Reduction of a System of Forces to One Force and One Couple. Consider a system of forces F_1, F_2, F_3, etc., acting on a rigid body (Fig. 4.9a).   We first resolve each force into rectangular components; according to Sec. 4.3, these components may be replaced by equivalent forces and

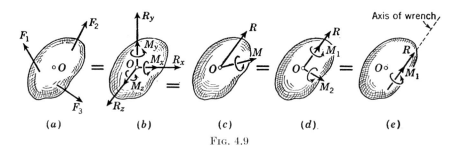

(a)   (b)   (c)   (d)   (e)

Fig. 4.9

couples at O.   Adding all x, y, and z components, we obtain, respectively, the forces R_x, R_y, and R_z, directed along the coordinate axes; similarly, adding all moments about the x, y, and z axes, we obtain, respectively, the couple vectors M_x, M_y, and M_z (Fig. 4.9b).   It is advisable to arrange the computations in tabular form as shown in Sample Probs. 4.3 and 4.4. The forces and couple vectors obtained are together equivalent to the given system; they give a clear representation of the action exerted by that system on the rigid body. Note that different couple vectors would be obtained if a different origin O were chosen.

We shall observe that, to be equivalent, two given systems of forces should reduce to the same forces and couple vectors at O. The sums of their x, y, and z components and the sums of their moments about the x, y, and z axes should therefore be, respectively, equal.

If desired, the three forces R_x, R_y, R_z of Fig. 4.9b may be replaced by their resultant R; similarly, the couple vectors M_x, M_y, M_z may be replaced by a single couple vector M (Fig. 4.9c). The magnitude and direction of the force R and of the couple vector M may be obtained by the method of Sec. 2.9. Denoting by θ_x, θ_y, θ_z and ϕ_x, ϕ_y, ϕ_z the angles formed, respectively, by R and M with the coordinate axes, we write

$$R = \sqrt{R_x^2 + R_y^2 + R_z^2} \qquad\qquad M = \sqrt{M_x^2 + M_y^2 + M_z^2} \qquad (4.2)$$

$$\frac{\cos \theta_x}{R_x} = \frac{\cos \theta_y}{R_y} = \frac{\cos \theta_z}{R_z} = \frac{1}{R} \qquad \frac{\cos \phi_x}{M_x} = \frac{\cos \phi_y}{M_y} = \frac{\cos \phi_z}{M_z} = \frac{1}{M} \qquad (4.3)$$

An important difference between the reduction of a system of coplanar forces and the reduction of a system of space forces should be noted. It was shown in Sec. 3.10 that the force-couple system obtained by reducing a system of coplanar forces may be further reduced to a single force. In the case of a system of space forces, this will generally not be possible. A force-couple system may be reduced to a single force only if the force and the couple act in the same plane, i.e., if the force and the couple vector are mutually perpendicular (see Sec. 4.3).

If, as is generally the case, the force and couple vector are not at a right angle, the couple vector may be replaced by two other couple vectors obtained by resolving M into a component M_1 along R and a component M_2 in a direction perpendicular to R (Fig. 4.9d). The couple vector M_2 and the force R may then be replaced by a single force R acting along a new line of action; the original system of forces reduces to R and to a couple of moment M_1 acting in a plane perpendicular to R (Fig. 4.9e). This particular force-couple combination is called a *wrench*. The force R and the couple of moment M_1 tend to move the rigid body along the line of action of R and, at the same time, tend to rotate it about that line. The line of action of R is known as the *axis of the wrench*.

Thus, it is seen that, while the action of a system of coplanar forces may always be represented by that of a single force (or of a single couple), it is generally necessary to use a wrench, i.e., the combination of a force and a couple, to represent the action of space forces. An important exception to this rule is the case of a system of parallel forces; such a system may be reduced to a single force (see Sample Prob. 4.4).

SAMPLE PROBLEM 4.3

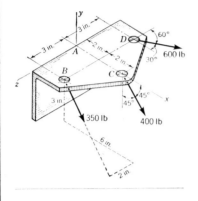

Three cables are attached to a bracket as shown. Replace the forces exerted by the cables by three forces at A and three couples directed along the coordinate axes.

Solution. Because of the many computations involved, this problem is most efficiently solved in tabular fashion. First the components of the forces are computed and entered in the table. These components are also plotted on the three projection planes, and their moments are determined about each axis and entered in the table. The components and moments are then added.

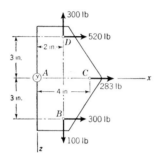

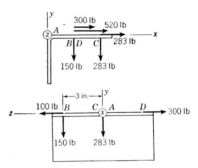

Force	F_x, lb	F_y, lb	F_z, lb	$M_x +\circlearrowleft$, lb-in.	$M_y +\circlearrowleft$, lb-in.	$M_z +\circlearrowleft$, lb-in.
B	$+300$	-150	$+100$	$+450$	$+\ \ 900$ $-\ \ 200$	$-\ \ 300$
C	$+283$	-283	0	0	0	$-1,132$
D	$+520$	0	-300	0	$+\ \ 600$ $-1,560$	0
	$R_x =$ $+1,103$	$R_y =$ -433	$R_z =$ -200	$M_x =$ $+450$	$M_y =$ -260	$M_z =$ $-1,432$

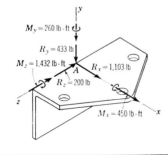

The given system may thus be replaced by three forces R_x, R_y, R_z and by three couple vectors of moments M_x, M_y, M_z as shown. The three forces could be replaced by a single force R of components R_x, R_y, and R_z and the three couple vectors by a single couple vector M of components M_x, M_y, and M_z.

116

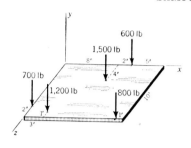

A 10- by 15-ft slab supports five columns which exert on the slab the forces indicated. Determine the magnitude and point of application of the single force equivalent to the given forces.

Solution. The x and z components of the given forces and their moments about the y axis are obviously zero. Therefore only the y components and the moments M_x and M_z are entered in the table.

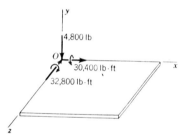

$F_y + \uparrow$, lb	$M_x + \rangle$, lb-ft	$M_z + \rangle$, lb-ft
$-$ 600	0	$-$ 6,000
$-$ 700	+ 5,600	0
$-$ 800	+ 8,000	$-$11,200
$-1,200$	+10,800	$-$ 3,600
$-1,500$	+ 6,000	$-$12,000
$R_y = -4,800$	$M_x = +30,400$	$M_z = -32,800$

From the table, it is seen that the given system of forces may be replaced by a 4,800-lb force acting at O and two couples represented by couple vectors located along the x and z axes.

The two couple vectors are perpendicular to the force and thus may be eliminated by moving the force to a new point of application. The coordinates of this point are

$$x = \frac{32{,}800 \text{ lb-ft}}{4{,}800 \text{ lb}} = 6.83 \text{ ft}$$

$$z = \frac{30{,}400 \text{ lb-ft}}{4{,}800 \text{ lb}} = 6.33 \text{ ft}$$

A 4,800-lb downward vertical force acting at this point will have the required moments about the x and z axes and will be equivalent to the five given forces.

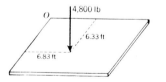

PROBLEMS

4.14. A 15-kip load is applied eccentrically on a column. Determine the components of the force and couple at G which are equivalent to the 15-kip load.

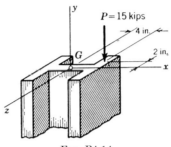

Fig. P4.14

4.15. A 2,000-lb force is applied on the outside face of the short leg of a rolled angle section as shown. Determine the components of the force and couple at G which are equivalent to the 2,000-lb load.

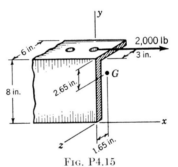

Fig. P4.15

4.16. Determine the magnitude and direction of the force and couple at O equivalent to the force $P = 50$ lb of Prob. 4.5 when $\theta = 60°$.

4.17. Determine the magnitude and direction of the force and couple at O equivalent to the 40-lb force of Prob. 4.7.

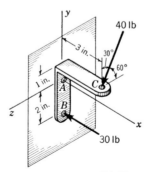

Fig. P4.18 and P4.19

4.18. Determine the components of the force and couple at A equivalent to the two forces shown in the figure.   The 30-lb force is perpendicular to the wall, and the 40-lb force is parallel to the wall.

4.19. Determine the components of the force and couple at B equivalent to the two forces shown.

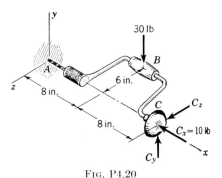

Fig. P4.20

4.20. In drilling a hole in a wall, a man applies a vertical 30-lb force at B on the brace and bit, while pushing at C with a 10-lb force to hold the bit against the wall. The brace is in the horizontal xz plane.   (a) Determine the other components of the total force which should be exerted at C if the bit is not to be bent about the y and z axes (i.e., if the system of forces applied on the brace is to have zero moment about both the y and z axes).   (b) Reduce the system of forces applied on the brace to an equivalent force and couple at A.

4.21. A small sign is welded to a vertical post.   The sign weighs 15 lb.   Wind blowing on the front face of the sign exerts forces equivalent to a 30-lb force acting at the center of the sign in a direction perpendicular to the sign.   Determine the components of a force and couple at O equivalent to the given forces.

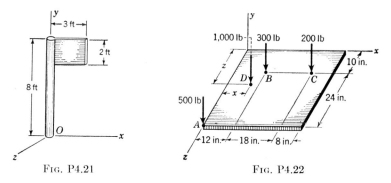

Fig. P4.21   Fig. P4.22

4.22. Four vertical loads act on a plate as shown.   Determine the coordinates of the point of application D of the 1,000-lb load so that the resultant of the four forces will pass through the center of the plate.

4.23. A horizontal plate in the shape of an equilateral triangle of side a supports equal vertical loads W at two vertices and a load $2W$ at the third vertex.   Determine the point of application of the resultant of the three forces.

4.24. Five loads are suspended from a rack as shown.   Determine the magnitude and the line of action of the resultant of the five weights.

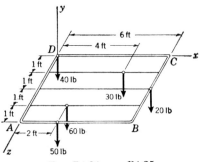

FIG. P4.24 AND P4.25

4.25. Determine the magnitude and point of application of the smallest additional load P which can be suspended from the rack if the resultant of the six loads is to pass through the center of the rack.

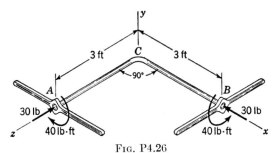

FIG. P4.26

4.26. Two men are threading the ends of a bent pipe simultaneously. Each man applies a 40-lb-ft couple and a force of 30 lb directed along the axis of the section he is threading. The thread at A is to be right-handed, and that at B is to be left-handed. (*a*) Replace the given system of forces by a force at C and a couple. (*b*) Show that the given system may be reduced to a single force, and determine the line of action of the force.

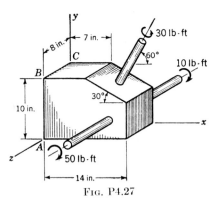

FIG. P4.27

4.27. The center of gravity of a 50-lb gearbox is located in the mid-plane of the box 6 in. from the rear face ABC. Three shafts exert the torques shown. (*a*) Replace the weight of the box and the given torques by a force at the origin and couples.

(b) Show that the system obtained may be reduced to a wrench, and determine the axis of the wrench.

EQUILIBRIUM OF RIGID BODIES

4.5. Equilibrium of a Rigid Body in Space. As was indicated in Sec. 3.12, *a rigid body is said to be in equilibrium when the external forces acting on it form a system of forces equivalent to zero.* In the case of space forces, a system of forces is equivalent to zero when the three forces and three couple vectors shown in Fig. 4.9b are all zero. The necessary and sufficient conditions for the equilibrium of a rigid body in space may thus be expressed analytically by writing the six equations

$$\Sigma F_x = 0 \qquad \Sigma F_y = 0 \qquad \Sigma F_z = 0 \qquad (4.4)$$
$$\Sigma M_x = 0 \qquad \Sigma M_y = 0 \qquad \Sigma M_z = 0 \qquad (4.5)$$

Equations (4.4) express the fact that the components of the external forces in the x, y, and z directions are balanced; Eqs. (4.5) express the fact that the moments of the external forces about the x, y, and z axes are balanced. The system of the external forces, therefore, will impart no motion of translation or rotation to the rigid body considered.

After a free-body diagram has been drawn, showing all the external forces acting on the body, the equations of equilibrium (4.4) and (4.5) may be solved for no more than *six unknowns*. These unknowns generally represent reactions at supports and connections. In practice, it will be found convenient to solve the moment equations (4.5) first, choosing axes which either intersect or are parallel to the lines of action of several unknown forces or force components. In this way, equations containing only two unknowns, possibly one, will be obtained. Once these unknowns have been determined, their values are carried into Eqs. (4.4) in order to reduce the number of unknowns in these equations.

While the six equations of equilibrium cannot be augmented by additional equations, any of them may be replaced by another equation. Thus, moment equations, written with respect to lines other than the axes of coordinates, may sometimes be substituted advantageously for one or several of Eqs. (4.4) and (4.5).

4.6. Reactions at Supports and Connections. The number of unknowns associated with reactions at supports and connections may vary from one to six in problems involving the equilibrium of a rigid body in space. Various types of supports and connections are shown in Fig. 4.10 with the corresponding reactions. A simple way of determining the type of reaction corresponding to a given support or connection and the number of unknowns involved is to find which of the six fundamental motions (translation in x, y, and z directions, rotation about the x, y, and z axes) are allowed and which motions are prevented.

Ball supports, smooth surfaces, and cables, for example, prevent trans-

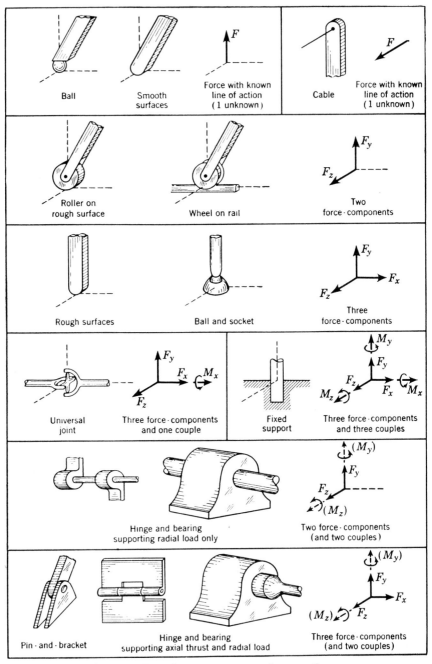

FIG. 4.10. Reactions at supports and connections.

lation in one direction only and thus exert a single force of known line of action; they each involve one unknown, namely, the magnitude of the reaction. Rollers on rough surfaces and wheels on rails prevent translation in two directions; the corresponding reactions consist of two unknown force components. Rough surfaces in direct contact and ball-and-socket supports prevent translation in three directions; these supports involve three unknown force components.

Some supports and connections may prevent rotation as well as translation; the corresponding reactions include, then, couples as well as forces. The reaction at a fixed support, for example, which prevents any motion (rotation as well as translation), consists of three unknown forces and three unknown couples. A universal joint, which is designed to allow rotation about two axes, will exert a reaction consisting of three unknown force components and one unknown couple.

Other supports and connections are primarily intended to prevent translation; their design, however, is such that they also prevent some rotations. The corresponding reactions consist essentially of force components but may also include couples. One group of supports of this type includes hinges and bearings designed to support radial loads only (for example, journal bearings, roller bearings). The corresponding reactions consist of two force components but may also include two couples. Another group includes pin-and-bracket supports, hinges, and bearings designed to support an axial thrust as well as a radial load (for example, ball bearings). The corresponding reactions consist of three force components but may include two couples. However, these supports will not exert any appreciable couples under normal conditions of use. Therefore, only force components should be included in their analysis, unless it is found that couples are necessary to maintain the equilibrium of the rigid body, or unless the support is known to have been specifically designed to exert a couple.

If the reactions involve more than six unknowns, there are more unknowns than equations and some of the reactions are *statically indeterminate* (see Sample Prob. 4.7). If the reactions involve less than six unknowns, there are more equations than unknowns and some of the equations of equilibrium cannot be satisfied under general loading conditions; the rigid body is said to be *unstable*. Under the particular loading conditions corresponding to a given problem, however, the extra equations often reduce to trivial identities such as $0 = 0$ and may be disregarded; although theoretically unstable, the rigid body remains in equilibrium (see Sample Probs. 4.5 and 4.6). Even with six or more unknowns, some equations of equilibrium sometimes will not be satisfied. This may occur when the supports are such that the reactions are forces which must either be parallel or intersect the same line; the rigid body is then *geometrically unstable*.

SAMPLE PROBLEM 4.5

A ladder used to reach high shelves in a storeroom is supported by two flanged wheels A and B mounted on a rail and by an unflanged wheel C resting against a rail fixed to the wall. A man stands on the ladder and leans to the right. The line of action of the 240-lb combined weight of the man and ladder intersects the floor at point D. Determine the components of the reactions at A, B, and C.

Solution. A free-body diagram of the ladder is drawn; there are five unknown reaction components, two at each flanged wheel and one at the unflanged wheel. The ladder is therefore not rigidly supported; it is free to roll along the rails. It is, however, in equilibrium under the given vertical load since the equation $\Sigma F_x = 0$ is satisfied. Three projections of the ladder are drawn, and the following equilibrium equations are written:

Equilibrium Equations

$+\rangle$ $\Sigma M_x = 0$:

$$-(240\text{ lb})(2\text{ ft}) + C(10\text{ ft}) = 0$$

$$C = +48\text{ lb}$$

Using the projections on the xy plane, we write

$+\rangle$ $\Sigma M_A = 0$:

$$-(240\text{ lb})(3\text{ ft}) + B_y(4\text{ ft}) = 0$$

$$B_y = +180\text{ lb}$$

$+\rangle$ $\Sigma M_B = 0$:

$$+(240\text{ lb})(1\text{ ft}) - A_y(4\text{ ft}) = 0$$

$$A_y = +60\text{ lb}$$

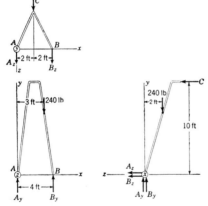

Using the projections on the xz plane and the computed value of C, we write

$+\rangle$ $\Sigma M_A = 0$: $\quad -(48\text{ lb})(2\text{ ft}) - B_z(4\text{ ft}) = 0 \quad$ **$B_z = -24\text{ lb}$**

$+\rangle$ $\Sigma M_B = 0$: $\quad +(48\text{ lb})(2\text{ ft}) + A_z(4\text{ ft}) = 0 \quad$ **$A_z = -24\text{ lb}$**

Check. We may check the results by verifying that equilibrium equations not used in the solution are satisfied, for example,

$$\Sigma F_y = A_y + B_y - 240\text{ lb} = 60\text{ lb} + 180\text{ lb} - 240\text{ lb} = 0$$

$$\Sigma F_z = A_z + B_z + C = -24\text{ lb} - 24\text{ lb} + 48\text{ lb} = 0$$

SAMPLE PROBLEM 4.6

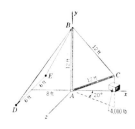

The derrick shown supports a 4,000-lb load. It is held by a ball and socket at A and by two cables attached at points D and E. In the position shown, the derrick stands in a vertical plane forming an angle of 20° with the xy plane. Determine the tension in each cable and the components of the reaction at A.

Solution. A free-body diagram of the derrick is drawn. Since the directions of the forces exerted at B by the cables are known, these forces involve one unknown each, namely, the magnitudes T_{BD} and T_{BE}. The reaction at A is a force of unknown direction and is represented by three unknown components A_x, A_y, and A_z. Since there are only five unknowns, the derrick is unstable. It may rotate freely about the y axis; it is, however, in equilibrium under the given loading since the equation $\Sigma M_y = 0$ is satisfied.

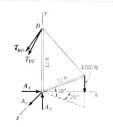

Recalling that force and distance components are proportional, the components of the forces exerted by the cables are expressed in terms of T_{BD} and T_{BE}. On the other hand, the distances a and b are obtained as follows:

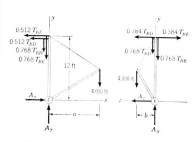

$$a = (12 \text{ ft}) \cos 30° \cos 20° = 9.77 \text{ ft}$$
$$b = (12 \text{ ft}) \cos 30° \sin 20° = 3.55 \text{ ft}$$

Equilibrium Equations. Using the projections shown, we write

$+\circlearrowright \; \Sigma M_x = 0: \quad 0.384 T_{BD}(12 \text{ ft}) + (4,000 \text{ lb})(3.55 \text{ ft}) - 0.384 T_{BE}(12 \text{ ft}) = 0$
$+\circlearrowright \; \Sigma M_z = 0: \quad 0.512 T_{BD}(12 \text{ ft}) + 0.512 T_{BE}(12 \text{ ft}) - (4,000 \text{ lb})(9.77 \text{ ft}) = 0$

Solving these two equations simultaneously, we obtain

$$T_{BD} = \mathbf{1,640 \text{ lb}} \qquad T_{BE} = \mathbf{4,720 \text{ lb}}$$

Using the computed magnitudes of T_{BD} and T_{BE}, we write

$\Sigma F_x = 0: \quad A_x - 0.512 T_{BD} - 0.512 T_{BE} = 0$
$\qquad\qquad A_x - 0.512(1,640 \text{ lb}) - 0.512(4,720 \text{ lb}) = 0 \qquad A_x = \mathbf{+3,260 \text{ lb}}$
$\Sigma F_y = 0: \quad A_y - 0.768 T_{BD} - 0.768 T_{BE} - 4,000 \text{ lb} = 0$
$\qquad\qquad A_y - 0.768(1,640 \text{ lb}) - 0.768(4,720 \text{ lb}) - 4,000 \text{ lb} = 0$
$$A_y = \mathbf{+8,880 \text{ lb}}$$
$\Sigma F_z = 0: \quad A_z + 0.384 T_{BD} - 0.384 T_{BE} = 0$
$\qquad\qquad A_z + 0.384(1,640 \text{ lb}) - 0.384(4,720 \text{ lb}) = 0 \qquad A_z = \mathbf{+1,183 \text{ lb}}$

Remark. Alternate solutions are normally available for three-dimensional problems. For example, we might have initially written $\Sigma M_{DE} = 0$ and solved for A_y and then obtained A_x and A_z by writing $\Sigma M = 0$ with respect to lines through point B. The equations $\Sigma F_x = 0$ and $\Sigma F_y = 0$ would then yield T_{BD} and T_{BE}.

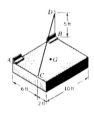

A 500-lb marquee, 8 by 10 ft, is held in a horizontal position by two horizontal hinges at A and B and by a cable CD attached to a point D located 5 ft directly above B. Determine the tension in the cable and the components of the reactions at the hinges.

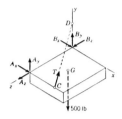

Solution. A free-body diagram of the marquee is drawn. The reactions involve seven unknowns, namely, the force T exerted by the cable and three unknown components at each hinge. Since we cannot write more than six independent equations, the problem is indeterminate and cannot be solved completely by the methods of statics.

Projections are drawn on each of the three coordinate planes, showing the weight, the unknown components at each hinge, and the components of the force exerted by the cable expressed in terms of T.

Equilibrium Equations. Using the projections shown, we write

$+\!\!\gamma\ \ \Sigma M_{AC} = 0$: $B_y(10\text{ ft}) - (500\text{ lb})(5\text{ ft}) = 0$ $B_y = +250$ lb

$+\!\!\gamma\ \ \Sigma M_y = 0$: $A_x(10\text{ ft}) = 0$ $A_x = 0$

$+\!\!\gamma\ \ \Sigma M_z = 0$: $0.394T(6\text{ ft}) - (500\text{ lb})(4\text{ ft}) = 0$ $T = +846$ lb

The values obtained for A_x, B_y, and T are carried into the following equilibrium equations:

$\Sigma F_x = 0$: $A_x + B_x - 0.473T = 0$ $0 + B_x - 0.473(846\text{ lb}) = 0$ $B_x = +400$ lb

$$\Sigma F_y = 0: \quad A_y + B_y + 0.394T - 500\text{ lb} = 0$$
$$A_y + 250\text{ lb} + 0.394(846\text{ lb}) - 500\text{ lb} = 0$$
$$A_y = -83.3\text{ lb}$$

$$\Sigma F_z = 0: \quad A_z + B_z - 0.788T = 0$$
$$A_z + B_z - 0.788(846\text{ lb}) = 0 \qquad A_z + B_z = 667\text{ lb}$$

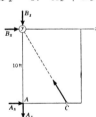

Components of T
$T_x = -0.473T$
$T_y = +0.394T$
$T_z = -0.788T$

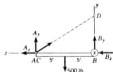

The z components of the reactions at the hinges cannot be determined separately; only their sum is known. Other equations of equilibrium may be written; such equations, however, are not independent of the six equations used above, and they cannot be used to determine A_z and B_z. If the hinge at B were modified so that it could not exert any axial thrust, we would then obtain $B_z = 0$ and

$$A_z = +667\text{ lb}$$

PROBLEMS

4.28. A 20-ft smokestack weighing 500 lb is held by three guy wires as shown. Determine the tension in each wire, knowing that the reaction at O is a 900-lb vertical force.

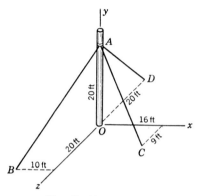

Fig. P4.28 and P4.29

4.29. A 20-ft smokestack weighing 500 lb is held by three guy wires. Knowing that the tension in wire AB is 450 lb and that the reaction at O is vertical, determine the tension in each of the other two wires and the reaction at O.

4.30. A surveying instrument weighing 15 lb is mounted on a tripod. The legs of the tripod are equally spaced and form an angle of 20° with the vertical. Find the reaction of the ground on each leg, neglecting the weight of the tripod and assuming (a) that the tripod is rigid and the ground is smooth, (b) that the screws connecting the legs to the instrument mount are loose but that the ground is sufficiently rough to keep the legs from sliding.

Fig. P4.30

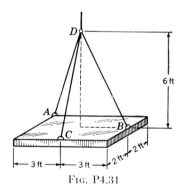

Fig. P4.31

4.31. A 4- by 6-ft plate weighing 900 lb is lifted by three cables which are joined at point D directly above the center of the plate. Determine the tension in each cable.

4.32. A 10-ft boom supports a 3,000-lb load as shown. The boom is held by a ball and socket at A and by two cables. Determine the tension in each cable and the reaction at A, neglecting the weight of the boom.

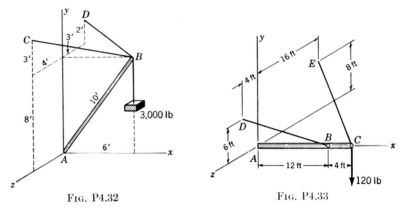

FIG. P4.32   FIG. P4.33

4.33. A uniform pole weighs 30 lb and supports a 120-lb load. It is held by a ball and socket at A and by two cables as shown. Determine the tension in each cable and the reaction at A.

4.34. Solve Prob. 4.33 assuming that the 120-lb load is attached at point B instead of point C.

4.35. The derrick is held at A by a ball-and-socket support and at B by two guy wires. Find the tension in each wire and the components of the reaction at A.

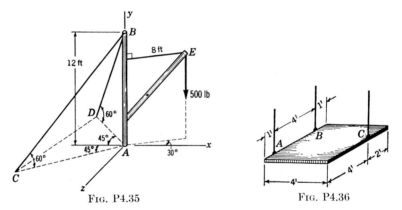

FIG. P4.35   FIG. P4.36

4.36. The rectangular plate shown weighs 60 lb and is supported by three wires. Determine the tension in each wire.

4.37. Determine the point where a 90-lb load should be attached to the plate of Prob. 4.36 if the tension is to be 50 lb in each of the three wires. The weight of the plate is 60 lb.

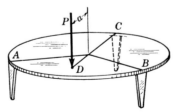

FIG. P4.38

4.38. The table shown weighs 40 lb and has a diameter of 4 ft.   It is supported by three legs equally spaced around the edge.   A vertical load $P = 100$ lb is applied to the top of the table at D.   Determine the maximum value of a if the table is not to tip over.   Show, on a sketch, the area of the table over which P can act without tipping the table.

4.39. The rack of Prob. 4.24 is supported by three vertical wires attached at corners A, B, and D, respectively.   For the loads shown, determine the tension in each wire.

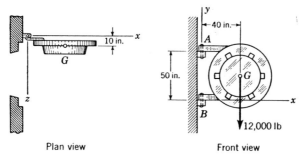

Plan view   Front view

Fig. P4.40

4.40. The door of a bank vault weighs 12,000 lb and is supported by two hinges as shown.   Find the components of the reactions at both hinges.

4.41. A 40-lb door is made self-closing by attaching to it a 30-lb weight by means of a cable CE.   The door is opened by a force P applied at point D, 3 ft above the floor, in a direction perpendicular to the door.   Determine the magnitude of P required to hold the door open and the components of the reactions at A and B when $\theta = 90°$.   It is assumed that the hinge at A does not exert any axial thrust.

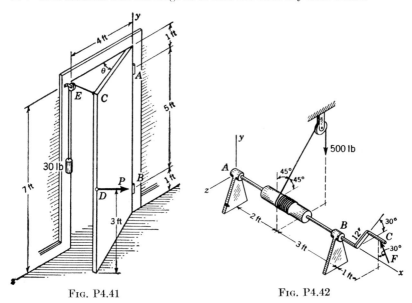

Fig. P4.41   Fig. P4.42

4.42. A windlass is used to lift a 500-lb load.   The rope winds on a drum of radius 3 in., and the bearing at A does not exert any axial thrust.   Determine (a) the force

F which should be applied to the handle C (in a direction perpendicular to the plane ABC) and (b) the components of the reactions at the bearings A and B.

4.43. Solve Prob. 4.42 assuming the force F is applied vertically to the handle C.

4.44. A 3- by 5-ft screen window weighs 15 lb and is held by hinges at A and B. In the position shown, it is held away from the side of the house by a 2-ft stick CD. Assuming that the hinge at A does not exert any axial thrust, determine the force exerted by the stick and the reactions at A and B.

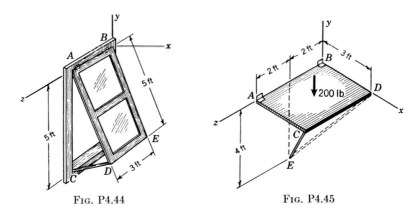

FIG. P4.44   FIG. P4.45

4.45. The horizontal platform $ABCD$ weighs 50 lb and supports a 200-lb load at its center. The platform is normally held in position by hinges at A and B and by braces CE and DE. If brace DE is removed, determine the reactions at the hinges and the force exerted by the remaining brace CE.

4.46. Solve Prob. 4.45 assuming that the 200-lb load is placed at corner D.

4.47. Same as Prob. 4.45 assuming that brace DE and hinge A are removed.

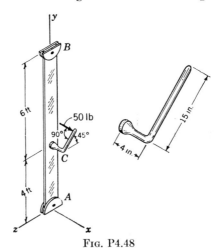

FIG. P4.48

4.48. A socket wrench is used to tighten a nut on a light, vertical column. A force of 50 lb is applied to the end of the handle as shown. Determine the components of the additional reactions produced at connections A and B.

4.49. Determine the reactions at support O for the crank of Prob. 4.5 when $\theta = 60°$.

4.50. A machinist seat is supported by an arm bent 90° which may be swung out of the way when so desired. (*a*) Determine the components of the force and couple representing the reaction at hinge *H* when a 160-lb man uses the seat. (*b*) Assuming that the couple is formed by two horizontal forces acting at two points *A* and *B*, determine the magnitude of the forces forming the couple and the exact location of *A* and *B*.

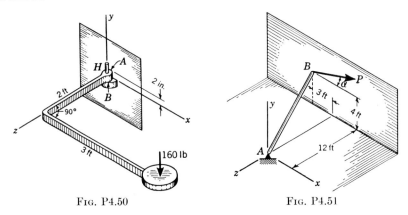

FIG. P4.50   FIG. P4.51

4.51. A slender rod *AB* weighing 30 lb is attached at *A* by a ball and socket and leans against a smooth wall; it is held in the position shown by a force *P* which lies in the plane of the wall. If $\alpha = 0$, determine the magnitude of *P* and the reaction at *A*.

***4.52.** In Prob. 4.51, the force *P* must lie in the plane of the wall. Determine the magnitude and direction of the minimum force *P* which will maintain the rod in equilibrium.

5. Distributed Forces:
Centroids and Centers of Gravity

AREAS AND LINES

5.1. Center of Gravity of a Two-dimensional Body. We have assumed so far that the attraction exerted by the earth on a rigid body could be represented by a single force W. This force, called the weight of the body, was to be applied at the *center of gravity* of the body (Sec. 3.1). Actually, the earth exerts a force on each of the particles forming the

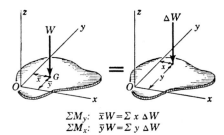

$$\Sigma M_y: \quad \bar{x}W = \Sigma\, x\, \Delta W$$
$$\Sigma M_x: \quad \bar{y}W = \Sigma\, y\, \Delta W$$

FIG. 5.1. Center of gravity of a plate.

body. The action of the earth on a rigid body should thus be represented by a large number of small forces distributed over the entire body. We shall see in this chapter, however, that all these small forces may be replaced by a single equivalent force W. We shall also learn to determine the center of gravity, i.e., the point of application of the resultant W, for various shapes of bodies.

Let us first consider a flat horizontal plate (Fig. 5.1). We may divide the plate into n small elements. The coordinates of the first element are denoted by x_1 and y_1, those of the second element by x_2 and y_2, etc. The forces exerted by the earth on the elements of plate will be denoted, respectively, by $\Delta W_1, \Delta W_2, \ldots, \Delta W_n$. These forces or weights are directed toward the center of the earth; however, for all practical purposes they may be assumed parallel. Their resultant is therefore a single force in the same direction. The magnitude W of this force is obtained by

132

adding the elementary weights,

$$\Sigma F_z: \qquad\qquad W = \Delta W_1 + \Delta W_2 + \cdots + \Delta W_n \qquad\qquad (5.1)$$

To obtain the coordinates $\bar{x}$ and $\bar{y}$ of the point G where the resultant W should be applied, we write that the moments of W about the y and x axes are equal to the sum of the corresponding moments of the elementary weights,

$$\Sigma M_y: \qquad \bar{x}W = x_1\,\Delta W_1 + x_2\,\Delta W_2 + \cdots + x_n\,\Delta W_n$$
$$\Sigma M_x: \qquad \bar{y}W = y_1\,\Delta W_1 + y_2\,\Delta W_2 + \cdots + y_n\,\Delta W_n \qquad (5.2)$$

If we now increase the number of elements into which the plate is divided and simultaneously decrease the size of each element, we obtain at the limit the following expressions:

$$W = \int dW \qquad \bar{x}W = \int x\,dW \qquad \bar{y}W = \int y\,dW \qquad (5.3)$$

These equations define the weight W and the coordinates $\bar{x}$ and $\bar{y}$ of the center of gravity G of a flat plate.   The same equations may be derived

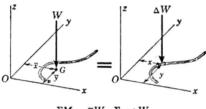

$$\Sigma M_y: \quad \bar{x}W = \Sigma x\,\Delta W$$
$$\Sigma M_x: \quad \bar{y}W = \Sigma y\,\Delta W$$

Fig. 5.2. Center of gravity of a wire.

for a wire lying in the xy plane (Fig. 5.2).   We shall observe, in the latter case, that the center of gravity G will generally not be located on the wire.

5.2. Centroids of Areas and Lines.   In the case of a homogeneous plate of uniform thickness, the weight ΔW of an element of plate may be expressed as

$$\Delta W = \gamma t\,\Delta A$$

where γ = specific weight (weight per unit volume) of material
  t = thickness of plate
  ΔA = area of element

If γ is expressed in lb/ft³, t in feet, and ΔA in square feet, we check that ΔW is expressed in pounds.   Similarly, we may write the weight W of the entire plate in the form

$$W = \gamma t A$$

where A is the total area of the plate.

Substituting for ΔW and W in the moment equations (5.2) and dividing throughout by γt, we write

$$\Sigma M_y: \qquad \bar{x}A = x_1\,\Delta A_1 + x_2\,\Delta A_2 + \cdots + x_n\,\Delta A_n$$
$$\Sigma M_x: \qquad \bar{y}A = y_1\,\Delta A_1 + y_2\,\Delta A_2 + \cdots + y_n\,\Delta A_n \qquad (5.4)$$

If we increase the number of elements into which the area A is divided and simultaneously decrease the size of each element, we obtain at the limit

$$\bar{x}A = \int x\,dA \qquad \bar{y}A = \int y\,dA \qquad \textbf{(5.5)}$$

These formulas define the coordinates $\bar{x}$ and $\bar{y}$ of the center of gravity of a homogeneous plate. The point of coordinates $\bar{x}$ and $\bar{y}$ is also known as the *centroid C of the area* A of the plate (Fig. 5.3). If the plate is not homogeneous, the formulas cannot be used to determine the center of gravity of the plate; they still define, however, the centroid of the area.

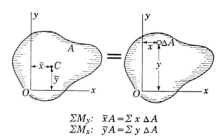

$$\Sigma M_y: \quad \bar{x}A = \Sigma\,x\,\Delta A$$
$$\Sigma M_x: \quad \bar{y}A = \Sigma\,y\,\Delta A$$

FIG. 5.3. Centroid of an area.

The integral $\int x\,dA$ is defined as the *first moment of the area A with respect to the y axis*. Similarly, the integral $\int y\,dA$ is defined as the *first moment of A with respect to the x axis*. It is seen from formulas (5.5) that, if the centroid of an area is located on a coordinate axis, the first moment of the area with respect to that axis is zero.

In the case of a homogeneous wire of uniform cross section, the weight ΔW of an element of wire may be expressed as

$$\Delta W = \gamma a\,\Delta L$$

where γ = specific weight of material
a = cross-sectional area of wire
ΔL = length of element

The center of gravity of the wire then coincides with the *centroid C of the line L* defining the shape of the wire (Fig. 5.4). The coordinates $\bar{x}$ and $\bar{y}$ of the centroid of the line L are obtained from the formulas

$$\bar{x}L = \int x\,dL \qquad \bar{y}L = \int y\,dL \qquad \textbf{(5.6)}$$

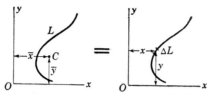

$$\Sigma M_y: \quad \bar{x}L = \Sigma\, x\, \Delta L$$
$$\Sigma M_x: \quad \bar{y}L = \Sigma\, y\, \Delta L$$

Fig. 5.4. Centroid of a line.

An area A is said to be *symmetrical about an axis BB'* if to every point P of the area corresponds a point P' of the same area such that the line PP' is perpendicular to BB' and is divided into two equal parts by that axis (Fig. 5.5). A line L is said to be symmetrical about BB' if it satisfies similar conditions. When an area A or a line L possesses an axis of symmetry BB', the centroid of the area or line must be located on that axis. If the axis of symmetry is chosen as the y axis, the coordinate $\bar{x}$ of the centroid is found to be zero, since to every product $x\, dA$ or $x\, dL$ appearing in the first integral in formulas (5.5) or (5.6) will correspond a product of equal magnitude but of opposite sign. It follows that, if an area or line possesses two axes of symmetry, the centroid of the area or line is

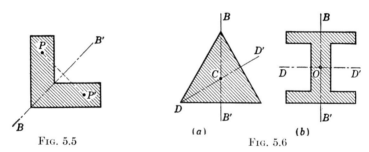

Fig. 5.5.   (a)   (b)   Fig. 5.6

located at the intersection of the two axes of symmetry (Fig. 5.6). This property enables us to determine immediately the centroid of areas such as circles, ellipses, squares, rectangles, equilateral triangles, or any other symmetrical figures, as well as the centroid of lines in the shape of the circumference of a circle, the perimeter of a square, etc.

Fig. 5.7

An area is said to be *symmetrical about a center O* if to every point P of the area corresponds a point P' of the same area such that the line PP' is divided into two equal parts by O (Fig. 5.7). A line L is said to be symmetrical about O if it satisfies similar conditions. A reasoning similar to that used above would show that, when an area A or line L possesses a center of symmetry O, the point O must be the centroid of the area or

Shape		$\bar{x}$	$\bar{y}$	Area
Triangular area	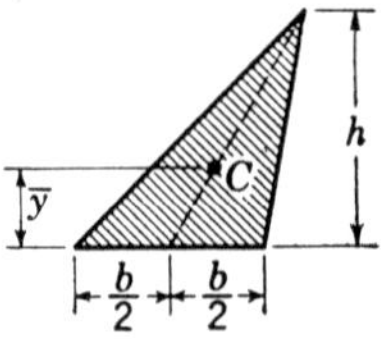		$\dfrac{h}{3}$	$\dfrac{bh}{2}$
Quarter-circular area	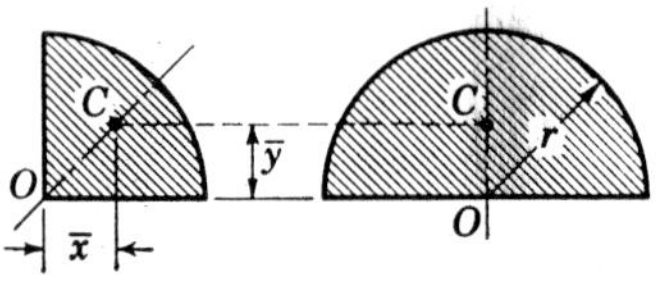	$\dfrac{4r}{3\pi}$	$\dfrac{4r}{3\pi}$	$\dfrac{\pi r^2}{4}$
Semicircular area		0	$\dfrac{4r}{3\pi}$	$\dfrac{\pi r^2}{2}$
Quarter-elliptical area	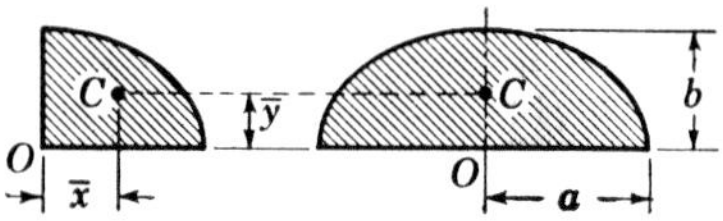	$\dfrac{4a}{3\pi}$	$\dfrac{4b}{3\pi}$	$\dfrac{\pi ab}{4}$
Semielliptical area		0	$\dfrac{4b}{3\pi}$	$\dfrac{\pi ab}{2}$
Semiparabolic area	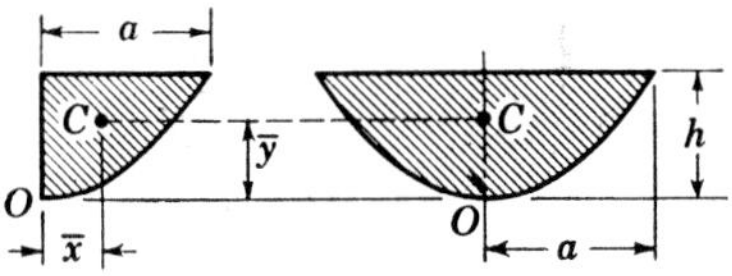	$\dfrac{3a}{8}$	$\dfrac{3h}{5}$	$\dfrac{2ah}{3}$
Parabolic area		0	$\dfrac{3h}{5}$	$\dfrac{4ah}{3}$
Parabolic spandrel	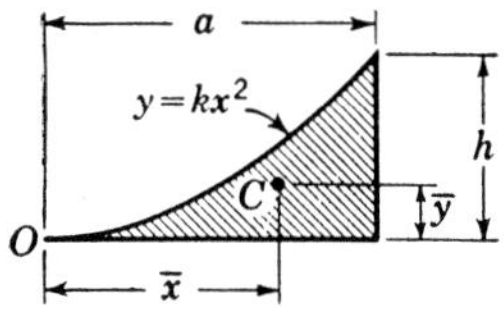	$\dfrac{3a}{4}$	$\dfrac{3h}{10}$	$\dfrac{ah}{3}$
General spandrel	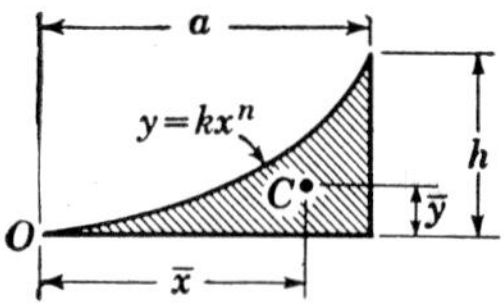	$\dfrac{n+1}{n+2}a$	$\dfrac{n+1}{4n+2}h$	$\dfrac{ah}{n+1}$
Circular sector	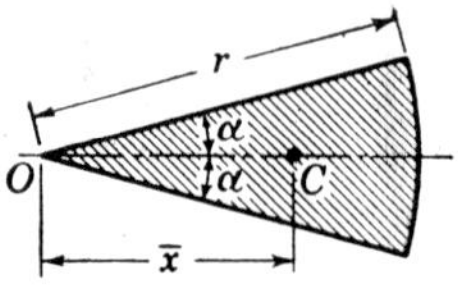	$\dfrac{2r\sin\alpha}{3\alpha}$	0	αr^2

Fig. 5.8A. Centroids of common shapes of areas.

line.   It should be noted that a figure possessing a center of symmetry does not necessarily possess an axis of symmetry (Fig. 5.7).   On the other hand, a figure possessing two axes of symmetry does not necessarily possess a center of symmetry (Fig. 5.6a).

Shape		$\bar{x}$	$\bar{y}$	Length
Quarter-circular arc	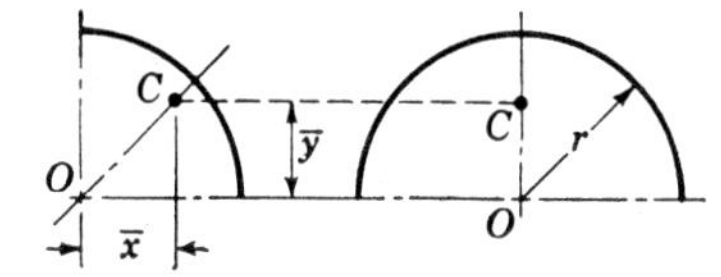	$\dfrac{2r}{\pi}$	$\dfrac{2r}{\pi}$	$\dfrac{\pi r}{2}$
Semicircular arc		0	$\dfrac{2r}{\pi}$	πr
Arc of circle	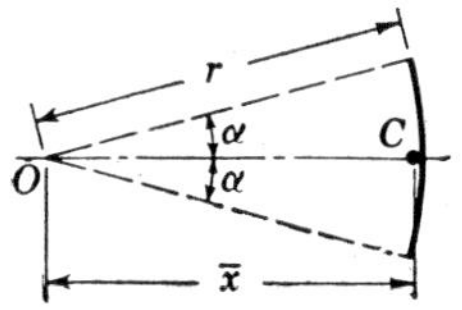	$\dfrac{r \sin \alpha}{\alpha}$	0	$2\alpha r$

FIG. 5.8B. Centroids of common shapes of lines.

Centroids of unsymmetrical areas and lines and of areas and lines possessing only one axis of symmetry will be determined by the methods of Secs. 5.4 and 5.5.   Centroids of common shapes of areas and lines are shown in Fig. 5.8A and B.   The formulas defining these centroids will be derived in the Sample Problems and Problems following Secs. 5.4 and 5.5.

5.3. Composite Plates and Wires.   In many instances, a flat plate may be divided into rectangles, triangles, or other common shapes shown in Fig. 5.8A.   The abscissa $\bar{X}$ of its center of gravity G may be determined from the abscissas $\bar{x}_1, \bar{x}_2, \ldots$ of the centers of gravity of the various parts by expressing that the moment of the weight of the whole plate

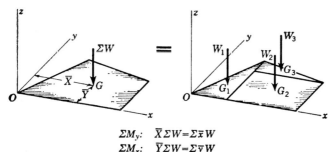

$$\Sigma M_y: \quad \bar{X}\Sigma W = \Sigma \bar{x} W$$
$$\Sigma M_x: \quad \bar{Y}\Sigma W = \Sigma \bar{y} W$$

FIG. 5.9. Center of gravity of a composite plate.

about the y axis is equal to the sum of the moments of the weights of the various parts about the same axis (Fig. 5.9).   The ordinate $\bar{Y}$ of the center of gravity of the plate is found in a similar way by equating moments about the x axis.

$$\Sigma M_y: \quad \bar{X}(W_1 + W_2 + \cdots + W_n) = \bar{x}_1 W_1 + \bar{x}_2 W_2 + \cdots + \bar{x}_n W_n$$
$$\Sigma M_x: \quad \bar{Y}(W_1 + W_2 + \cdots + W_n) = \bar{y}_1 W_1 + \bar{y}_2 W_2 + \cdots + \bar{y}_n W_n$$
$$\text{(5.7)}$$

If the plate is homogeneous and of uniform thickness, the center of gravity coincides with the centroid C of its area. The abscissa $\bar{X}$ of the centroid of the area may then be determined by expressing that the first moment of the composite area with respect to the y axis is equal to the sum of the

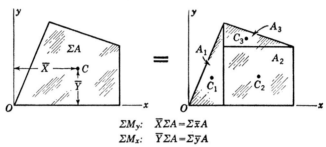

$$\Sigma M_y: \quad \bar{X}\Sigma A = \Sigma \bar{x}A$$
$$\Sigma M_x: \quad \bar{Y}\Sigma A = \Sigma \bar{y}A$$

FIG. 5.10. Centroid of a composite area.

first moments of the elementary areas with respect to the same axis (Fig. 5.10). The ordinate $\bar{Y}$ of the centroid is found in a similar way by equating first moments of areas with respect to the x axis.

$$\Sigma M_y: \quad \bar{X}(A_1 + A_2 + \cdots + A_n) = \bar{x}_1 A_1 + \bar{x}_2 A_2 + \cdots + \bar{x}_n A_n$$
$$\Sigma M_x: \quad \bar{Y}(A_1 + A_2 + \cdots + A_n) = \bar{y}_1 A_1 + \bar{y}_2 A_2 + \cdots + \bar{y}_n A_n \quad \text{(5.8)}$$

Care should be taken to record the moment of each area with the appropriate sign. First moments of areas, just like moments of forces, may be positive or negative. For example, an area whose centroid is located to the left of the y axis will have a negative first moment with respect to that axis. Also, the area of a hole should be recorded with a negative sign (Fig. 5.11).

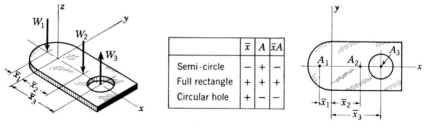

	$\bar{x}$	A	$\bar{x}A$
Semi-circle	−	+	−
Full rectangle	+	+	+
Circular hole	+	−	−

FIG. 5.11

Similarly, it is possible in many cases to determine the center of gravity of a composite wire or the centroid of a composite line by dividing the wire or line into simpler elements (Sample Prob. 5.3).

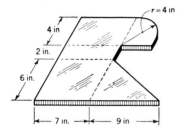

Determine the center of gravity of the thin homogeneous plate shown.

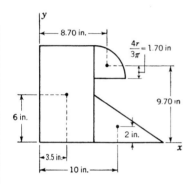

Solution. Since the plate is homogeneous, we may locate the center of gravity by determining the centroid of the area of the plate. The area is divided into its component parts: a rectangle, a triangle, and a quarter circle. Coordinate axes are chosen with the origin at the lower left corner of the plate. The centroid of each component part is indicated in the figure, and $\bar{x}$ and $\bar{y}$ are computed for each component. The moments of the component areas with respect to the coordinate axes are determined in the following table:

Component	A	$\bar{x}$	$\bar{y}$	$\bar{x}A$	$\bar{y}A$
Rectangle..........	84	3.5	6.0	294	504
Triangle............	27	10.0	2.0	270	54
Quarter circle.......	12.56	8.7	9.7	109.2	121.8
	$\Sigma A =$ 123.6	....	...	$\Sigma \bar{x}A =$ 673.2	$\Sigma \bar{y}A =$ 679.8

Substituting the values obtained from the table into the equations defining the centroid of a composite area, we obtain

$$\bar{X}\Sigma A = \Sigma \bar{x}A \quad \bar{X}(123.6) = 673.2 \quad \bar{X} = \textbf{5.45 in.}$$

$$\bar{Y}\Sigma A = \Sigma \bar{y}A \quad \bar{Y}(123.6) = 679.8 \quad \bar{Y} = \textbf{5.50 in.}$$

The above values of $\bar{X}$ and $\bar{Y}$ define the centroid of the area and also the center of gravity of the plate. The center of gravity, of course, is actually located halfway between the upper and lower faces of the plate.

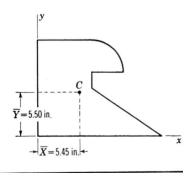

SAMPLE PROBLEM 5.2

Determine the centroid of the area shown.

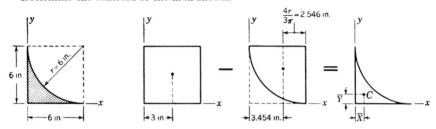

Solution. Since the area is symmetrical with respect to a line drawn at 45° through the origin, the centroid must be located on this line; therefore, $\bar{X} = \bar{Y}$. The given area may be obtained by subtracting a quarter circle from a square. The centroid of the quarter circle is obtained from Fig. 5.8,A and the following table is constructed:

Component	A	$\bar{x}$	$\bar{x}A$
Square..........	36.00	3.00	108.00
Quarter circle...	−28.27	3.454	−97.64
	$\Sigma A =$ 7.73	.....	$\Sigma \bar{x}A =$ 10.36

Since we are subtracting numbers of about the same magnitude, accuracy greater than standard is required in the table in order to obtain standard accuracy (0.2 per cent) in the result.

$\bar{X}\Sigma A = \Sigma \bar{x}A:$ $\bar{X}(7.73) = 10.36$

$\bar{X} = \bar{Y} = \mathbf{1.34\ in.}$

SAMPLE PROBLEM 5.3

The figure shown is made of a thin homogeneous wire. Determine the dimension b such that the center of gravity will be located at point G.

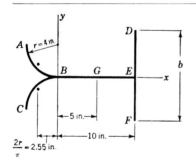

Segment	L	$\bar{x}$	$\bar{x}L$
ABC	12.56	−2.55	−32.0
BGE	10.00	5.00	50.0
DEF	b	10.00	$10b$
	$\Sigma L =$ 22.56 + b	......	$\Sigma \bar{x}L =$ 18 + 10b

Solution. Since the figure is formed of homogeneous wire, its center of gravity may be located by determining the centroid of the corresponding line. The origin is arbitrarily placed at point B, and the line is divided into three segments ABC, BGE, and DEF.

Since the value of $\bar{X}$ is known to be 5 in., the value of b is determined as follows:

$\bar{X}\Sigma L = \Sigma \bar{x}L:$ $5(22.56 + b) = 18 + 10b$

$b = \mathbf{18.96\ in.}$

PROBLEMS

5.1 through 5.12. Locate the centroid of the plane area shown.

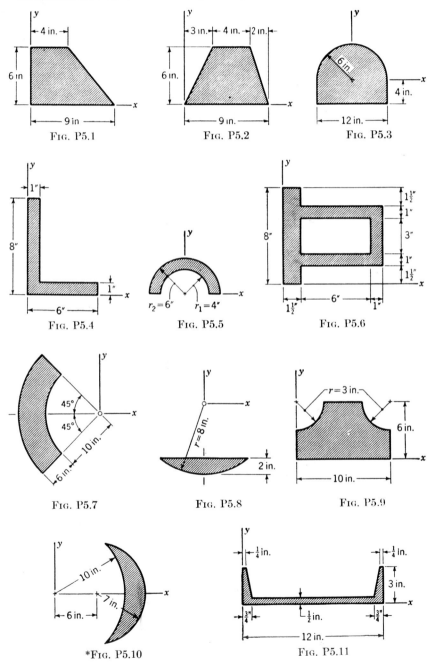

FIG. P5.1

FIG. P5.2

FIG. P5.3

FIG. P5.4

FIG. P5.5

FIG. P5.6

FIG. P5.7

FIG. P5.8

FIG. P5.9

*FIG. P5.10

FIG. P5.11

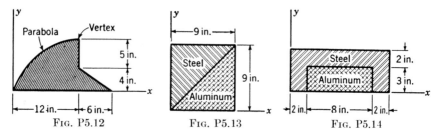

FIG. P5.12   FIG. P5.13   FIG. P5.14

5.13 and 5.14. Locate the center of gravity of each of the thin plates shown. Each plate is of uniform thickness. (Specific weight of steel = 490 lb/ft³; of aluminum = 170 lb/ft³.)

5.15 and 5.16. A thin homogeneous wire is bent into the figure shown. Locate the center of gravity of the figure.

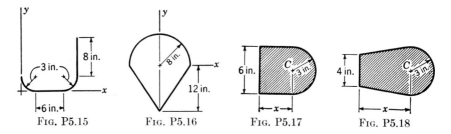

FIG. P5.15   FIG. P5.16   FIG. P5.17   FIG. P5.18

5.17 and 5.18. Determine the unknown dimension x so that the centroid of the area is located at point C.

5.19. One-inch-diameter holes have been drilled in the 20-in.-diameter plate at A and B as shown. Where should a two-inch-diameter hole be drilled so that the center of gravity of the plate will be at the geometric center O?

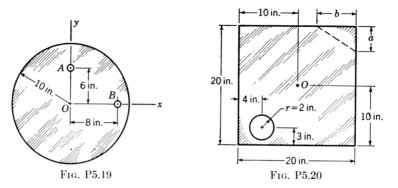

FIG. P5.19   FIG. P5.20

*5.20. A 4-in.-diameter hole has been cut in the square plate shown. Determine the dimensions a and b such that the center of gravity will be located at O after the corner of the plate has been cut off.

*5.21. Locate the centroid C in Prob. 5.5 in terms of r_1 and r_2, and show that, as r_1 approaches r_2, the location of C approaches that for a semicircular arc of radius $\frac{1}{2}(r_1 + r_2)$.

5.4. Determination of Centroids by Integration.   The centroid of an area bounded by analytical curves (i.e., curves defined by algebraic equations) is usually determined by computing the integrals in formulas (5.5) of Sec. 5.2.

$$\bar{x}A = \int x\, dA \qquad \bar{y}A = \int y\, dA \tag{5.5}$$

If the element of area dA is chosen equal to a small square of sides dx and dy, the determination of each of these integrals requires a *double integration* in x and y.   A double integration is also necessary if polar coordinates are used and if dA is chosen equal to a small square of sides dr and $r\, d\theta$.

In most cases, however, it is possible to determine the coordinates of the centroid of an area by performing a single integration.   This is

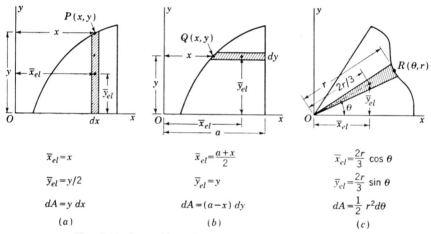

$\bar{x}_{el} = x$	$\bar{x}_{el} = \dfrac{a+x}{2}$	$\bar{x}_{el} = \dfrac{2r}{3}\cos\theta$
$\bar{y}_{el} = y/2$	$\bar{y}_{el} = y$	$\bar{y}_{el} = \dfrac{2r}{3}\sin\theta$
$dA = y\, dx$	$dA = (a-x)\, dy$	$dA = \dfrac{1}{2}r^2 d\theta$
(a)	(b)	(c)

FIG. 5.12. Centroids and areas of differential elements.

achieved by choosing for dA a thin rectangle or strip or a thin sector or pie-shaped element (Fig. 5.12).   The coordinates of the centroid of the area under consideration are then obtained by expressing that the first moment of the entire area with respect to each of the coordinate axes is equal to the sum (or integral) of the corresponding moments of the elements of area.   Denoting by $\bar{x}_{el}$ and $\bar{y}_{el}$ the coordinates of the centroid of the element dA, we write

$$\Sigma M_y: \qquad \bar{x}A = \int \bar{x}_{el}\, dA$$
$$\Sigma M_x: \qquad \bar{y}A = \int \bar{y}_{el}\, dA \tag{5.9}$$

If the area itself is not already known, it may also be computed from these elements.

The coordinates $\bar{x}_{el}$ and $\bar{y}_{el}$ of the centroid of the element of area should be expressed in terms of the coordinates of a point located on the curve bounding the area under consideration. Also, the element of area dA should be expressed in terms of the coordinates of the point and their differentials. This has been done in Fig. 5.12 for three common types of elements; the pie-shaped element of part c should be used when the equation of the curve bounding the area is given in polar coordinates. The appropriate expressions should be substituted in formulas (5.9), and the equation of the curve should be used to express one of the coordinates in terms of the other. The integration is thus reduced to a single integration which may be performed according to the usual rules of calculus.

The centroid of a line defined by an algebraic equation may be determined by computing the integrals in formulas (5.6) of Sec. 5.2.

$$\bar{x}L = \int x \, dL \qquad \bar{y}L = \int y \, dL \qquad (5.6)$$

The element dL should be replaced by one of the following expressions, depending upon the type of equation used to define the line (these expressions may be derived by using the Pythagorean theorem).

$$dL = \sqrt{1 + \left(\frac{dy}{dx}\right)^2} \, dx \qquad dL = \sqrt{1 + \left(\frac{dx}{dy}\right)^2} \, dy \qquad dL = \sqrt{r^2 + \left(\frac{dr}{d\theta}\right)^2} \, d\theta$$

The equation of the line is then used to express one of the coordinates in terms of the other, and the integration may be performed by the methods of calculus.

5.5. Theorems of Pappus-Guldinus. These theorems, which were first formulated by the Greek geometer Pappus during the third century A.D. and later restated by the Swiss mathematician Guldinus, or Guldin (1577–1643), deal with surfaces and bodies of revolution.

A *surface of revolution* is a surface which may be generated by rotating a plane curve about a fixed axis. For example (Fig. 5.13), the surface of a sphere may be obtained by rotating a semicircular arc ABC about the

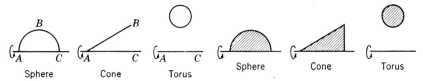

FIG. 5.13. Generating a surface of revolution.   FIG. 5.14. Generating a body of revolution.

diameter AC; the surface of a cone by rotating a straight line AB about an axis AC; the surface of a torus or ring by rotating the circumference of a circle about a nonintersecting axis. A *body of revolution* is a body which may be generated by rotating a plane area about a fixed axis. A solid sphere may be obtained by rotating a semicircular area, a cone by rotating a triangular area, and a solid torus by rotating a full circular area (Fig. 5.14).

THEOREM I.   *The area of a surface of revolution is equal to the length of the generating curve times the distance traveled by the centroid of the curve while the surface is being generated.*

Proof.   Consider an element dL of the line L (Fig. 5.15) which is revolved about the x axis.   The area dA generated by the element dL is equal to $2\pi y\, dL$.   Thus, the entire area generated by L is $A = \int 2\pi y\, dL$. But we saw in Sec. 5.2 that the integral $\int y\, dL$ is equal to $\bar{y}L$.   We have therefore

$$A = 2\pi\bar{y}L \tag{5.10}$$

where $2\pi\bar{y}$ is the distance traveled by the centroid of L.   It should be noted that the generating curve should not cross the axis about which it is rotated; if it did, the two sections on either side of the axis would generate areas of opposite signs and the theorem would not apply.

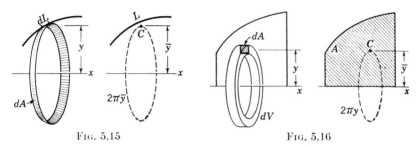

FIG. 5.15   FIG. 5.16

THEOREM II.   *The volume of a body of revolution is equal to the generating area times the distance traveled by the centroid of the area while the body is being generated.*

Proof.   Consider an element dA of the area A which is revolved about the x axis (Fig. 5.16).   The volume dV generated by the element dA is equal to $2\pi y\, dA$.   Thus, the entire volume generated by A is $V = \int 2\pi y\, dA$.   But since the integral $\int y\, dA$ is equal to $\bar{y}A$ (Sec. 5.2), we have

$$V = 2\pi\bar{y}A \tag{5.11}$$

where $2\pi\bar{y}$ is the distance traveled by the centroid of A.   Again, it should be noted that the theorem does not apply if the axis of rotation intersects the generating area.

The theorems of Pappus-Guldinus offer a simple way for computing the area of surfaces of revolution and the volume of bodies of revolution. They may also be used conversely to determine the centroid of a plane curve when the area of the surface generated by the curve is known or to determine the centroid of a plane area when the volume of the body generated by the area is known (see Sample Prob. 5.8).

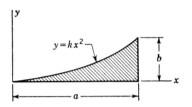

Determine by direct integration the centroid of the parabolic spandrel shown.

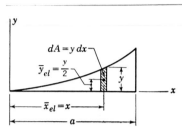

Solution. The value of k is determined by substituting $x = a$ and $y = b$ in the given equation.

$$y = kx^2 \qquad b = ka^2 \qquad k = \frac{b}{a^2}$$

The equation of the curve is thus

$$y = \frac{b}{a^2} x^2 \qquad \text{or} \qquad x = \frac{a}{b^{\frac{1}{2}}} y^{\frac{1}{2}}$$

Vertical Differential Element. We choose the differential element shown and find the total area of the figure.

$$A = \int dA = \int y \, dx = \int_0^a \frac{b}{a^2} x^2 \, dx = \left[\frac{b}{a^2} \frac{x^3}{3} \right]_0^a = \frac{ab}{3}$$

The moment of the differential element with respect to the y axis is $\bar{x}_{el} \, dA$; hence, the moment of the entire area with respect to this axis is

$$\int \bar{x}_{el} \, dA = \int xy \, dx = \int_0^a x \left(\frac{b}{a^2} x^2 \right) dx = \left[\frac{b}{a^2} \frac{x^4}{4} \right]_0^a = \frac{a^2 b}{4}$$

Thus,

$$\bar{x} A = \int \bar{x}_{el} \, dA \qquad \bar{x} \frac{ab}{3} = \frac{a^2 b}{4} \qquad \bar{x} = \tfrac{3}{4} a$$

Likewise, the moment of the differential element with respect to the x axis is $\bar{y}_{el} \, dA$, and the moment of the entire area is

$$\int \bar{y}_{el} \, dA = \int \frac{y}{2} y \, dx = \int_0^a \frac{1}{2} \left(\frac{b}{a^2} x^2 \right)^2 dx = \left[\frac{b^2}{2a^4} \frac{x^5}{5} \right]_0^a = \frac{ab^2}{10}$$

Thus,

$$\bar{y} A = \int \bar{y}_{el} \, dA \qquad \bar{y} \frac{ab}{3} = \frac{ab^2}{10} \qquad \bar{y} = \tfrac{3}{10} b$$

Horizontal Differential Element. The same result may be obtained by considering the horizontal element shown. The moments of the area are

$$\int \bar{x}_{el} \, dA = \int \frac{a + x}{2} (a - x) \, dy = \int_0^b \frac{a^2 - x^2}{2} \, dy = \frac{1}{2} \int_0^b \left(a^2 - \frac{a^2}{b} y \right) dy = \frac{a^2 b}{4}$$

$$\int \bar{y}_{el} \, dA = \int y(a - x) \, dy$$

$$= \int y \left(a - \frac{a}{b^{\frac{1}{2}}} y^{\frac{1}{2}} \right) dy$$

$$= \int_0^b \left(ay - \frac{a}{b^{\frac{1}{2}}} y^{\frac{3}{2}} \right) dy = \frac{ab^2}{10}$$

These moments are again substituted in the equations defining the centroid of the area to obtain $\bar{x}$ and $\bar{y}$.

SAMPLE PROBLEM 5.5

Determine the centroid of a quarter circle by direct integration.

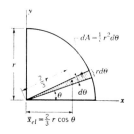

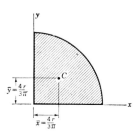

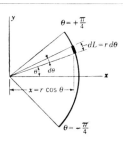

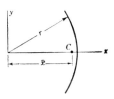

Solution. A differential element is chosen as shown, and the area of the quarter circle is determined.

$$A = \int dA = \int_0^{\pi/2} \tfrac{1}{2} r^2\, d\theta = \tfrac{1}{4}\pi r^2$$

The moment of the area with respect to the y axis is

$$\int_0^{\pi/2} \bar{x}_{el}\, dA = \int_0^{\pi/2} (\tfrac{2}{3} r \cos \theta)(\tfrac{1}{2} r^2\, d\theta)$$

$$= \tfrac{1}{3} r^3 \int_0^{\pi/2} \cos \theta\, d\theta = \tfrac{1}{3} r^3$$

Thus,

$$\bar{x}A = \int \bar{x}_{el}\, dA \qquad \bar{x}(\tfrac{1}{4}\pi r^2) = \tfrac{1}{3} r^3 \qquad \bar{x} = \frac{4r}{3\pi}$$

Since the area is symmetrical with respect to a 45° line drawn through the origin, we have

$$\bar{x} = \bar{y} = \frac{4r}{3\pi}$$

SAMPLE PROBLEM 5.6

Determine the centroid of the 90° circular arc shown.

Solution. The arc is symmetrical with respect to the x axis, and we note that $\bar{y} = 0$. Since the arc subtends an angle of $90° = \tfrac{1}{2}\pi$ radians, the length of arc is $L = \tfrac{1}{2}\pi r$. A differential element of arc is chosen as shown, and the moment of the entire arc with respect to the y axis is determined.

$$\int x\, dL = \int_{-\pi/4}^{\pi/4} (r \cos \theta)(r\, d\theta)$$

$$= r^2 \int_{-\pi/4}^{\pi/4} \cos \theta\, d\theta = \sqrt{2}\, r^2$$

Thus,

$$\bar{x}L = \int x\, dL \qquad \bar{x}(\tfrac{1}{2}\pi r) = \sqrt{2}\, r^2$$

$$\bar{x} = \frac{2\sqrt{2}}{\pi} r$$

147

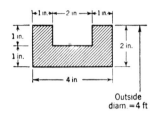

The outside diameter of a steel flywheel is 4 ft, and the cross section of the rim is as shown. Determine the weight of the rim. Specific weight of steel = 490 lb/ft³.

Solution. The volume of the rim may be found by applying Theorem II of Pappus-Guldinus, which states that the volume equals the product of the given cross-sectional area and of the distance traveled by its centroid in one complete revolution. However, the volume may be more easily obtained by considering the cross section as a 4- by 2-in. rectangle minus a 2- by 1-in. rectangle as shown. The volume of the rim is then equal to the difference of the volumes generated by rotating the rectangles about the x axis.

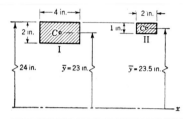

Component	Area	$\bar{y}$	Distance traveled by C	Volume
I	8 in.²	23.0 in.	$2\pi(23.0$ in.$) = 144.5$ in.	(8 in.²)(144.5 in.) = 1,156 in.³
II	−2 in.²	23.5 in.	$2\pi(23.5$ in.$) = 147.6$ in.	(−2 in.²)(147.6 in.) = −295 in.³
				Volume of rim = 861 in.³

Since the specific weight of steel is 490 lb/ft³, the weight of the rim is

$$W = \gamma V = \frac{490 \text{ lb/ft}^3}{1{,}728 \text{ in.}^3/\text{ft}^3} (861 \text{ in.}^3) \qquad W = \mathbf{244 \text{ lb}}$$

Using the theorems of Pappus-Guldinus, determine (a) the centroid of a semicircular area, (b) the centroid of a semicircular arc. We recall that the volume of a sphere is $\frac{4}{3}\pi r^3$ and that its surface area is $4\pi r^2$.

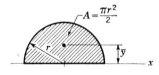

Solution. The volume of a sphere is equal to the product of the area of a semicircle and of the distance traveled by the centroid of the semicircle in one revolution about the x axis.

$$V = 2\pi\bar{y}A \qquad \tfrac{4}{3}\pi r^3 = 2\pi\bar{y}(\tfrac{1}{2}\pi r^2) \qquad \bar{y} = \frac{4r}{3\pi}$$

Likewise, the area of a sphere is equal to the product of the length of the generating semicircle and of the distance traveled by its centroid in one revolution.

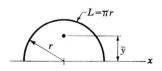

$$A = 2\pi\bar{y}L \qquad 4\pi r^2 = 2\pi\bar{y}(\pi r) \qquad \bar{y} = \frac{2r}{\pi}$$

PROBLEMS

5.22 through 5.26. Determine by direct integration the centroid of the area shown.

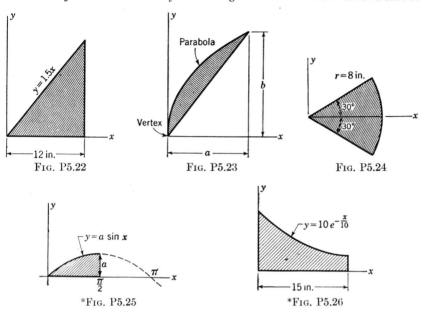

Fig. P5.22   Fig. P5.23   Fig. P5.24

*Fig. P5.25   *Fig. P5.26

5.27 through 5.33. Derive by direct integration the expressions for $\bar{x}$ and $\bar{y}$ given in Fig. 5.8 for:

5.27. A semicircular area.

5.28. A quarter-elliptical area.

5.29. A circular sector.

5.30. A semiparabolic area.

5.31. A parabolic spandrel.

5.32. A general spandrel ($y = kx^n$).

5.33. An arc of circle.

5.34. Determine the volume and the total area of a right circular cone of height h and base radius r.

5.35. Determine the surface area and the volume of the torus obtained by rotating the circle shown about the line AA'.

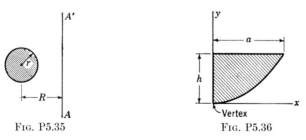

Fig. P5.35   Fig. P5.36

5.36. Determine the volume of the paraboloid of revolution obtained by rotating the parabola shown about the y axis.

5.37. The inside diameter of a spherical tank is 8 ft. What volume of liquid is required to fill the tank to a depth of 2 ft?

5.38. In Prob. 5.37, find the area of the inside surface which is below the level of the liquid.

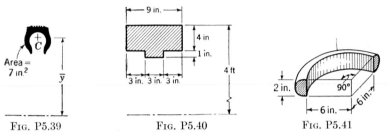

FIG. P5.39   FIG. P5.40   FIG. P5.41

5.39. An automobile tire weighs 24 lb and has a cross-sectional area of 7 in.² The specific weight of the rubber used is 80 lb/ft³; determine the location of the centroid of the cross-sectional area.

5.40. The cross section of a steel flywheel rim is shown. Determine the weight of the rim. (Specific weight of steel = 490 lb/ft³.)

5.41. Determine the volume and total surface area of the portion of ring shown. The cross section of the ring is a semicircle.

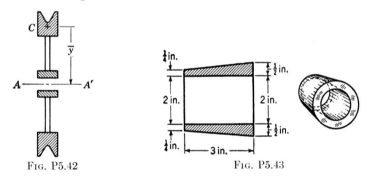

FIG. P5.42   FIG. P5.43

5.42. The rim of a steel V-belt pulley weighs 8.6 lb, and the area of the cross section of the rim is 0.81 in.² Determine the distance from the axle AA' to the centroid of the cross-sectional area of the rim. (Specific weight of steel = 490 lb/ft³.)

5.43. Determine the volume of the conical taper shown.

*5.6. **Distributed Loads on Beams.*** The concept of centroid of an area may be used to solve other problems, besides those dealing with the weight of flat plates. Consider, for example, a beam supporting a *distributed load;* this load may consist of the weight of materials supported directly or indirectly by the beam, or it may be caused by wind or hydrostatic pressure. The distributed load may be represented by plotting the load w supported per unit length (Fig. 5.17). The force exerted on an element of beam of length dx is thus $dW = w\,dx$, and the total load supported by the beam is

$$W = \int_0^L w\,dx$$

But the product $w\,dx$ is equal to the element of area dA shown in Fig. 5.17; the load W is thus equal to the total area A under the load curve,

$$W = \int dA = A$$

The point P of the beam where the resultant W should be applied is obtained by expressing that the moment of W about point O is equal to the sum of the moments of the elementary forces $w\,dx$ about O (Fig. 5.18)

$$(OP)W = \int_0^L xw\,dx$$

or since $w\,dx = dA$ and $W = A$,

$$(OP)A = \int_0^L x\,dA \tag{5.12}$$

Since the integral represents the first moment with respect to the w axis of the area under the load curve (Fig. 5.18), it may be replaced by the

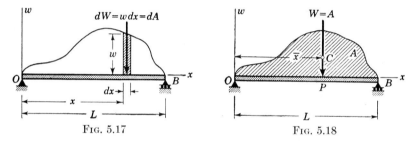

FIG. 5.17   FIG. 5.18

product $\bar{x}A$. We have therefore $OP = \bar{x}$, where $\bar{x}$ is the distance from the w axis to the centroid C of the area A (this is *not* the centroid of the beam).

A distributed load on a beam may thus be replaced by a concentrated load; the magnitude of this single load is equal to the area under the load curve, and its line of action passes through the centroid of that area. It should be noted, however, that the concentrated load is equivalent to the given loading only as far as external forces are concerned. It may be used to determine reactions but should not be used to compute internal forces and deflections.

*5.7. Forces on Submerged Surfaces. Another example of the use of first moments and centroids of areas is obtained by considering the forces exerted on a *rectangular surface* submerged in a liquid. Consider the rectangular plate shown in Fig. 5.19; it has a length L, and its width, perpendicular to the plane of the figure, is assumed equal to unity. Since the gage pressure in a liquid is $p = \gamma h$, where γ is the specific weight of the liquid and h the vertical distance from the free surface, the pressure on the plate varies linearly with the distance x. The width of the plate being taken equal to unity, the pressure p is equal to the force w per unit length used in Sec. 5.6. The results obtained in that section may thus be used here, and we find that the magnitude of the resultant R of the forces exerted on one face of the plate is equal to the area under the pressure curve; we also find that the line of action of R passes through the centroid C of that area.

Noting that the area under the pressure curve is equal to $p_E L$, where p_E is the pressure at the center E of the plate and L the length (or area) of the plate, we find that the resultant R may be obtained by multiplying the area of the plate by the pressure at the center E of the plate. The resultant R, however, *should not* be applied at E; as indicated above, its line of action passes through the centroid C of the area under the pressure curve. The point of application P of the resultant R is known as the *center of pressure*.

We shall consider next the forces exerted by a liquid on a curved surface of constant width (Fig. 5.20a). Since the determination of the

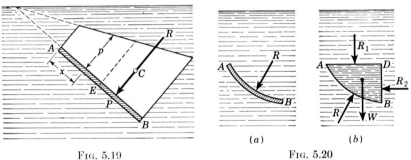

FIG. 5.19   (a)   (b)

FIG. 5.20

resultant R of these forces by direct integration would not be easy, we shall consider the free body obtained by detaching the volume of liquid ABD bounded by the curved surface AB and by the two plane surfaces AD and DB shown in Fig. 5.20b. The forces acting on the free body ABD consist of the weight W of the volume of liquid detached, the resultant R_1 of the forces exerted on AD, the resultant R_2 of the forces exerted on BD, and the resultant of the forces exerted *by the curved surface on the liquid*. This last resultant is equal and opposite to the resultant R of the forces exerted *by the liquid on the curved surface*. All the forces shown in Fig. 5.20b may be determined by standard methods; after their values have been found, R will be obtained by solving the equations of equilibrium for the free body of Fig. 5.20b.

The methods outlined in this section may be used to determine the resultant of the hydrostatic forces exerted on the surface of dams or on rectangular gates and vanes. Resultants of forces on submerged surfaces of variable width should be determined by the methods of Chap. 9.

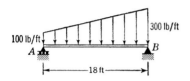

SAMPLE PROBLEM 5.9

A beam supports a distributed load as shown. (*a*) Determine the equivalent concentrated load. (*b*) Determine the reactions at the supports.

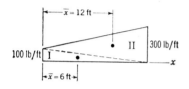

a. Equivalent Concentrated Load. The magnitude of the resultant of the load is equal to the area under the load curve, and the line of action of the resultant passes through the centroid of the same area. We divide the area under the load curve into two triangles and construct the following table:

Component	A	$\bar{x}$	$\bar{x}A$
Triangle I......	900	6	5,400
Triangle II.....	2,700	12	32,400
	$\Sigma A =$ 3,600	...	$\Sigma\bar{x}A =$ 37,800

Thus,

$$\bar{X}\Sigma A = \Sigma\bar{x}A \qquad \bar{X}(3,600) = 37,800$$
$$\bar{X} = 10.5 \text{ ft}$$

The equivalent concentrated load is **3,600 lb**, and its line of action is located **10.5 ft to the right of A.**

b. Reactions. The reaction at A is vertical and is denoted by A; the reaction at B is represented by its components B_x and B_y. The given load may be considered as the sum of two triangular loads as shown. The resultant of each triangular load is equal to the area of the triangle and acts at its centroid. We write the following equilibrium equations for the free body shown:

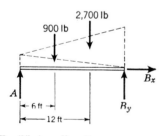

Equilibrium Equations

$\xrightarrow{+}\ \Sigma F_x = 0:$ $\qquad\qquad\qquad B_x = 0$

$+\!\!\downarrow\ \Sigma M_A = 0:$ $\quad (900 \text{ lb})(6 \text{ ft}) + (2,700 \text{ lb})(12 \text{ ft}) - B_y(18 \text{ ft}) = 0$ $\quad B_y = 2,100 \text{ lb}\uparrow$

$+\!\!\downarrow\ \Sigma M_B = 0:$ $\quad -(900 \text{ lb})(12 \text{ ft}) - (2,700 \text{ lb})(6 \text{ ft}) + A(18 \text{ ft}) = 0$ $\quad A = 1,500 \text{ lb}\uparrow$

Alternate Solution. The given distributed load may be replaced by its resultant, which was found in part *a*. The reactions may be determined by writing the equilibrium equations $\Sigma F_x = 0$, $\Sigma M_A = 0$, and $\Sigma M_B = 0$. We again obtain

$$B_x = 0 \qquad B_y = 2,100 \text{ lb}\uparrow \qquad A = 1,500 \text{ lb}\uparrow$$

153

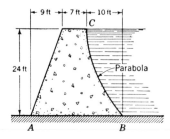

The cross section of a concrete dam is as shown. Consider a section of the dam 1 ft thick, and determine (a) the resultant of the reaction forces exerted by the ground on the base of the dam AB, (b) the resultant of the pressure forces exerted by the water on the face BC of the dam. Specific weight of concrete = 150 lb/ft³; of water = 62.4 lb/ft³.

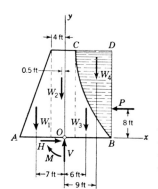

a. *Ground Reaction.* As a free body, we choose a section, 1 ft thick, of the dam and water as shown. The reaction forces exerted by the ground on the base AB are represented by an equivalent force-couple system at the center O of the base. Other forces acting on the free body are the weight of the dam, represented by the weights of its components W_1, W_2, and W_3, the weight of the water W_4, and the resultant P of the pressure forces exerted on section BD by the water to the right of section BD.

$$W_1 = \tfrac{1}{2}(9)(24)(150) = 16,200 \text{ lb}$$
$$W_2 = (7)(24)(150) = 25,200 \text{ lb}$$
$$W_3 = \tfrac{1}{3}(10)(24)(150) = 12,000 \text{ lb}$$
$$W_4 = \tfrac{2}{3}(10)(24)(62.4) = 9,980 \text{ lb}$$
$$P = \tfrac{1}{2}(24)^2(62.4) = 17,970 \text{ lb}$$

Equilibrium Equations. After calculating the magnitude of each force, we write

$\xrightarrow{+} \Sigma F_x = 0$: $\qquad H - 17,970 \text{ lb} = 0 \qquad H = \mathbf{17,970\ lb} \rightarrow$

$+\uparrow \Sigma F_y = 0$: $\quad +V - 16,200 \text{ lb} - 25,200 \text{ lb} - 12,000 \text{ lb} - 9,980 \text{ lb} = 0$

$$V = \mathbf{63,400\ lb} \uparrow$$

$+\downarrow \Sigma M_O = 0$: $\quad -(16,200 \text{ lb})(7 \text{ ft}) - (25,200 \text{ lb})(0.5 \text{ ft}) + (12,000 \text{ lb})(6 \text{ ft})$
$$+(9,980 \text{ lb})(9 \text{ ft}) - (17,970 \text{ lb})(8 \text{ ft}) + M = 0$$

$$M = \mathbf{108,000\ lb\text{-}ft} \downarrow$$

We may replace the force-couple system obtained by a single force acting at a distance d to the left of O, where

$$d = \frac{108,000 \text{ lb-ft}}{63,400 \text{ lb}} = 1.70 \text{ ft}$$

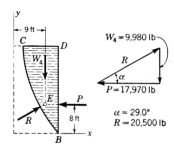

b. *Resultant of Water Forces.* The parabolic section of water BCD is chosen as a free body. The forces involved are the resultant R of the forces exerted by the dam on the water, the weight W_4, and the force P. Since these forces must be concurrent, R passes through the point of intersection E of W_4 and P. A force triangle is drawn from which R and α are determined. The resultant R of the forces exerted by the water on the face BC is equal and opposite:

$$R = \mathbf{20,500\ lb} \ \nwarrow\ \mathbf{29.0°}$$

PROBLEMS

5.44 and 5.45. Determine the magnitude and location of the resultant of the distributed load shown. Also calculate the reactions at A and B.

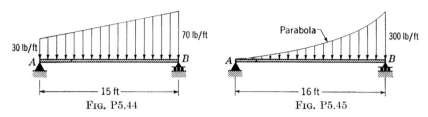

FIG. P5.44   FIG. P5.45

5.46 through 5.49. Determine the reactions at the beam supports for the given loading condition.

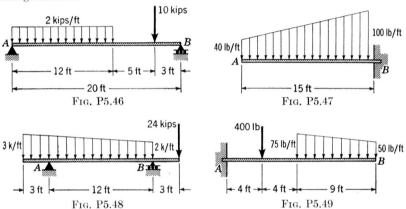

FIG. P5.46   FIG. P5.47

FIG. P5.48   FIG. P5.49

In the following problems, use 62.4 lb/ft^3 for the specific weight of fresh water:

5.50. A 4- by 4-ft gate is placed in a wall below water level as shown. (a) Determine the magnitude and location of the resultant of the forces exerted by the water on the gate. (b) If the gate is hinged at A, determine the minimum force which must be applied at B to hold the gate closed.

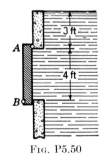

FIG. P5.50

5.51. Determine the magnitude and location of the resultant of the forces exerted by the water on portions AB and BC, respectively, of the dam shown. Consider a section of the dam 1 ft thick.

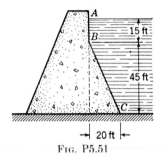

FIG. P5.51

5.52. An automatic valve consists of a square plate, 6 by 6 in., and is pivoted about a horizontal axis through A located $h = 2.5$ in. above the lower edge. Determine the depth of water d at which the valve will open.

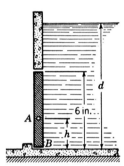

FIG. P5.52 AND P5.53

5.53. If the valve shown is to open when the depth of water is $d = 12$ in., determine the distance h from the bottom of the valve to the pivot A.

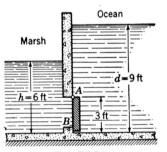

FIG. P5.54

5.54. A fresh-water marsh is drained to the ocean through an automatic tide gate which is 4 ft wide and 3 ft high. The gate is held by hinges located along its top edge at A and bears on a sill at B. At a given time, the water level in the marsh is $h = 6$ ft and in the ocean $d = 9$ ft. Determine the force exerted by the sill on the gate at B and the hinge reaction at A. (Specific weight of salt water $= 64$ lb/ft³.)

5.55. The automatic tide gate described in Prob. 5.54 is used to drain a fresh-water marsh into the ocean. If the water level in the marsh is $h = 6$ ft, determine the ocean level d for which the gate will open. (*Hint.* Reaction at the sill must be zero.)

In the following problems assume the specific weight of concrete equal to 150 lb/ft³:

5.56. Determine the minimum width x of the rectangular concrete dam so that the dam will not overturn about point A.

5.57. Solve Prob. 5.56 assuming that leakage occurs under the dam, causing an upward pressure on the bottom face AB which varies linearly from zero at A to the full hydrostatic pressure at B.

5.58. Concrete is a material which is weak in tension. In order to eliminate tension, the line of action of the resultant of the hydrostatic forces and of the weight of the dam must pass through the middle third of the base. Determine the minimum width x for which no tension will occur in the rectangular concrete dam shown.

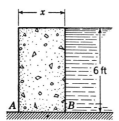

Fig. P5.56 and P5.58

5.59. Determine the minimum width x of the crest of the dam shown so that the dam will not overturn about A.

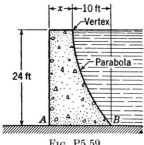

Fig. P5.59

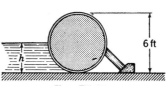

Fig. P5.60

5.60. A cylindrical drum, 10 ft long, is used as a temporary dam. Determine the resultant (magnitude and line of action) of the water pressure if $h = 3$ ft.

5.61. Solve Prob. 5.60 when $h = 6$ ft.

VOLUMES

5.8. Center of Gravity of a Three-dimensional Body. Centroid of a Volume.

The *center of gravity G* of a three-dimensional body is obtained by dividing the body into small elements and expressing that the weight W of the body attached at G is equivalent to the system of distributed forces representing the weights of the small elements. This has been done in Fig. 5.21 for two positions of the body. In part a of the figure, the y axis is vertical; in part b, the body and the axes have been rotated so that the z axis is vertical. Three independent equations are obtained, which may be used to determine the coordinates $\bar{x}$, $\bar{y}$, and $\bar{z}$ of the center of gravity G. Written in terms of infinitesimal elements of weight dW, these equations are

$$\bar{x}W = \int x \, dW \qquad \bar{y}W = \int y \, dW \qquad \bar{z}W = \int z \, dW \qquad (5.13)$$

If the body is made of a homogeneous material of specific weight γ, the weight dW may be expressed in terms of the volume dV of the element and the total weight W in terms of the total volume V.

$$dW = \gamma \, dV \qquad W = \gamma V$$

After substitution, formulas (5.13) become

$$\bar{x}V = \int x \, dV \qquad \bar{y}V = \int y \, dV \qquad \bar{z}V = \int z \, dV \qquad (5.14)$$

The point of coordinates $\bar{x}$, $\bar{y}$, $\bar{z}$ is also known as the *centroid C of the volume V* of the body. If the body is not homogeneous, formulas (5.14)

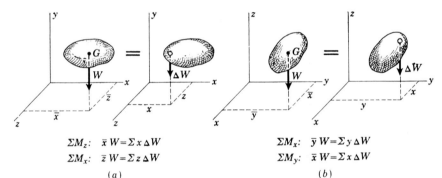

$$\Sigma M_z: \quad \bar{x}\,W = \Sigma x \,\Delta W$$
$$\Sigma M_x: \quad \bar{z}\,W = \Sigma z \,\Delta W$$
$$(a)$$

$$\Sigma M_x: \quad \bar{y}\,W = \Sigma y \,\Delta W$$
$$\Sigma M_y: \quad \bar{x}\,W = \Sigma x \,\Delta W$$
$$(b)$$

Fig. 5.21. Center of gravity of a three-dimensional body.

cannot be used to determine the center of gravity of the body; they still define, however, the centroid of the volume.

The integral $\int x \, dV$ is defined as the *first moment of the volume with respect to the yz plane*. Similarly, the integrals $\int y \, dV$ and $\int z \, dV$ are defined as the first moment of the volume with respect to the zx plane and the xy plane, respectively. It is seen from formulas (5.14) that, if the centroid of a volume is located in a coordinate plane, the first moment of the volume with respect to that plane is zero.

A volume is said to be symmetrical with respect to a given plane if to every point P of the volume corresponds a point P' of the same volume, such that the line PP' is perpendicular to the given plane and divided into two equal parts by that plane. The plane is said to be a *plane of symmetry* for the given volume. When a volume V possesses a plane of symmetry, the centroid of the volume must be located in that plane. When a volume possesses two planes of symmetry, the centroid of the volume must be located on the line of intersection of the two planes.

Shape		$\bar{x}$	Volume
Hemisphere	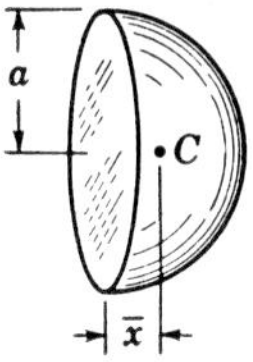	$\dfrac{3a}{8}$	$\frac{2}{3}\pi a^3$
Semiellipsoid of revolution	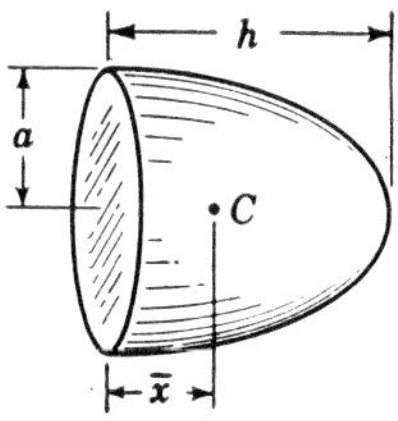	$\dfrac{3h}{8}$	$\frac{2}{3}\pi a^2 h$
Paraboloid of revolution	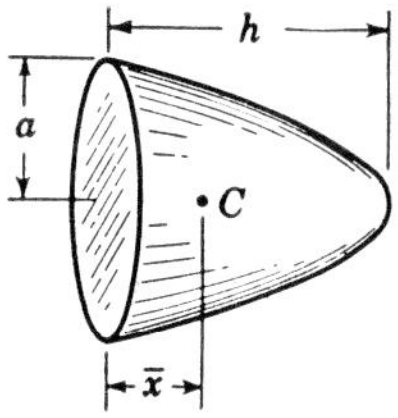	$\dfrac{h}{3}$	$\frac{1}{2}\pi a^2 h$
Cone	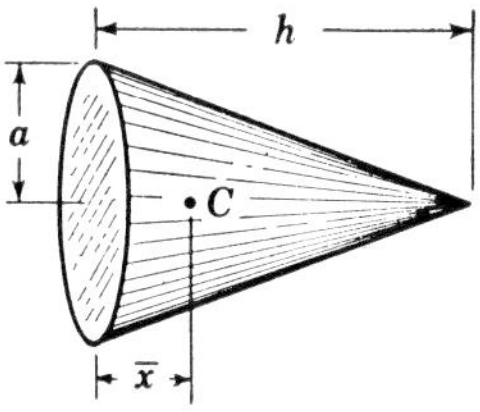	$\dfrac{h}{4}$	$\frac{1}{3}\pi a^2 h$
Pyramid	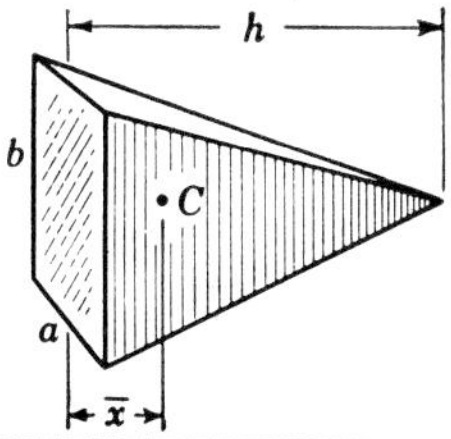	$\dfrac{h}{4}$	$\frac{1}{3}abh$

FIG. 5.22. Centroids of common shapes of volumes.

Finally, when a volume possesses three planes of symmetry which intersect in a well-defined point (i.e., not along a common line), the point of intersection of the three planes must coincide with the centroid of the volume. This property enables us to determine immediately the centroid of the volume of spheres, ellipsoids, cubes, rectangular parallelepipeds, etc.

Centroids of unsymmetrical volumes or of volumes possessing only one or two planes of symmetry should be determined by integration (Sec. 5.10). Centroids of common shapes of volumes are shown in Fig. 5.22. It should be observed that the centroid of a volume of revolution in general *does not coincide* with the centroid of its cross section. Thus, the centroid of a hemisphere is different from that of a semicircular area, and the centroid of a cone is different from that of a triangle.

5.9. Composite Bodies. If a body can be divided into several of the common shapes shown in Fig. 5.22, the coordinates $\bar{X}$, $\bar{Y}$, $\bar{Z}$ of its center of gravity G may be obtained by expressing that the moment of the total weight is equal to the sum of the moments of the weights of the various component parts. Moments should be taken about three axes for two positions of the body (see Fig. 5.21). The equations obtained are

$$\bar{X}\Sigma W = \Sigma\bar{x}W \qquad \bar{Y}\Sigma W = \Sigma\bar{y}W \qquad \bar{Z}\Sigma W = \Sigma\bar{z}W \qquad (5.15)$$

If the body is made of a homogeneous material, its center of gravity coincides with the centroid of its volume and the following equations may be used:

$$\bar{X}\Sigma V = \Sigma\bar{x}V \qquad \bar{Y}\Sigma V = \Sigma\bar{y}V \qquad \bar{Z}\Sigma V = \Sigma\bar{z}V \qquad (5.16)$$

5.10. Determination of Centroids of Volumes by Integration. The centroid of a volume bounded by analytical surfaces may be determined by computing the integrals given in Sec. 5.8.

$$\bar{x}V = \int x\,dV \qquad \bar{y}V = \int y\,dV \qquad \bar{z}V = \int z\,dV \qquad (5.17)$$

If the element of volume dV is chosen equal to a small cube of sides dx, dy, and dz, the determination of each of these integrals requires a *triple integration* in x, y, and z. However, it is possible to determine the coordinates of the centroid of most volumes by *double integration* if dV is chosen equal to the volume of a thin filament as shown in Fig. 5.23. The coordinates of the centroid of the volume are then obtained by writing

$$\bar{x}V = \int\bar{x}_{el}\,dV \qquad \bar{y}V = \int\bar{y}_{el}\,dV \qquad \bar{z}V = \int\bar{z}_{el}\,dV \qquad (5.18)$$

and substituting for the volume dV and the coordinates $\bar{x}_{el}$, $\bar{y}_{el}$, $\bar{z}_{el}$ the expressions given in Fig. 5.23. Using the equation of the surface to express z in terms of x and y, the integration is reduced to a double integration in x and y.

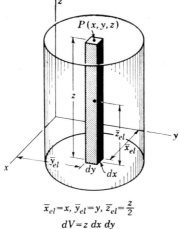

$$\bar{x}_{el}=x, \ \bar{y}_{el}=y, \ \bar{z}_{el}=\frac{z}{2}$$
$$dV=z \, dx \, dy$$

FIG. 5.23. Determination of the centroid of a volume by double integration.

If the volume under consideration possesses *two planes of symmetry*, its centroid must be located on their line of intersection. Choosing the x axis along this line, we have

$$\bar{y} = \bar{z} = 0$$

and the only coordinate to determine is $\bar{x}$. This will be done most conveniently by dividing the given volume into thin slabs parallel to the

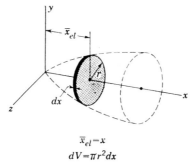

$$\bar{x}_{el}=x$$
$$dV=\pi r^2 dx$$

FIG. 5.24. Determination of the centroid of a body of revolution.

yz plane. In the particular case of a body of revolution, these slabs are circular, and the value of their volume dV is given in Fig. 5.24. Substituting for $\bar{x}_{el}$ and dV into the equation

$$\bar{x}V = \int \bar{x}_{el} \, dV \tag{5.19}$$

and expressing the radius r of the slab in terms of x, we may determine $\bar{x}$ by a single integration.

SAMPLE PROBLEM 5.11

Determine the center of gravity of the homogeneous body shown.

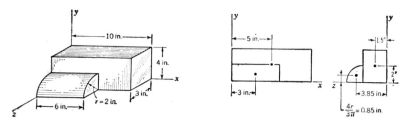

Solution. Since the body is homogeneous, its center of gravity coincides with its centroid. The body is made of a rectangular parallelepiped and a quarter cylinder, whose centroids are shown. The total volume and the moment of the volume with respect to each coordinate plane are determined from the table.

Component	V	$\bar{x}$	$\bar{y}$	$\bar{z}$	$\bar{x}V$	$\bar{y}V$	$\bar{z}V$
Parallelepiped..	120.0	5	2	1.5	600	240	180
Quarter cylinder	18.85	3	0.85	3.85	56.5	16.0	72.6
	$\Sigma V =$ 138.8	.	. . . . .	. . . . .	$\Sigma\bar{x}V =$ 656.5	$\Sigma\bar{y}V =$ 256.0	$\Sigma\bar{z}V =$ 252.6

$\bar{X}\Sigma V = \Sigma\bar{x}V$ $\bar{X} = $ **4.73 in.**

$\bar{Y}\Sigma V = \Sigma\bar{y}V$ $\bar{Y} = $ **1.84 in.**

$\bar{Z}\Sigma V = \Sigma\bar{z}V$ $\bar{Z} = $ **1.82 in.**

SAMPLE PROBLEM 5.12

Determine the center of gravity of the homogeneous body of revolution shown.

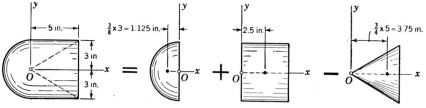

Solution. Because of symmetry, the center of gravity lies on the x axis. The body is seen to consist of a hemisphere, plus a cylinder, minus a cone, as shown above.

Component	Volume		$\bar{x}$	$\bar{x}V$
Hemisphere........	$\dfrac{1}{2}\dfrac{4\pi}{3}(3)^3 =$	56.5	-1.125	-63.6
Cylinder..........	$\pi(3)^2(5) =$	141.4	$+2.50$	$+353.5$
Cone.............	$\dfrac{\pi}{3}(3)^2(5) =$	-47.1	$+3.75$	-176.6
	$\Sigma V =$	150.8	....	$\Sigma\bar{x}V =$ $+113.3$

$\bar{X}\Sigma V = \Sigma\bar{x}V$

$\bar{X}(150.8) = 113.3$

$\bar{X} = $ **0.75 in.**

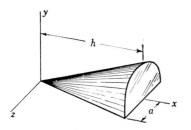

Determine the location of the centroid of the half right circular cone shown.

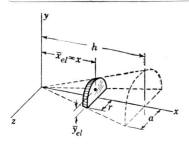

Solution. Since the xy plane is a plane of symmetry, the centroid lies in this plane and $\bar{z} = 0$. A slab of thickness dx is chosen as a differential element. The volume of this element is

$$dV = \tfrac{1}{2}\pi r^2\, dx$$

The coordinates $\bar{x}_{el}$ and $\bar{y}_{el}$ of the centroid of the element are obtained from Fig. 5.8 (semicircular area).

$$\bar{x}_{el} = x \qquad \bar{y}_{el} = \frac{4r}{3\pi}$$

We observe that x and r are proportional and write

$$\frac{r}{x} = \frac{a}{h} \qquad r = \frac{a}{h}x$$

The volume of the body is

$$V = \int dV = \int_0^h \tfrac{1}{2}\pi r^2\, dx = \int_0^h \tfrac{1}{2}\pi \left(\frac{a}{h}x\right)^2 dx = \tfrac{1}{2}\pi \left(\frac{a}{h}\right)^2 \int_0^h x^2\, dx = \frac{\pi a^2 h}{6}$$

The moment of the differential element with respect to the yz plane is $\bar{x}_{el}\, dV$; and the total moment of the body with respect to this plane is

$$\int \bar{x}_{el}\, dV = \int_0^h x(\tfrac{1}{2}\pi r^2)\, dx = \int_0^h x(\tfrac{1}{2}\pi)\left(\frac{a}{h}x\right)^2 dx = \tfrac{1}{2}\pi \left(\frac{a}{h}\right)^2 \int_0^h x^3\, dx = \frac{\pi a^2 h^2}{8}$$

Thus,

$$\bar{x}V = \int \bar{x}_{el}\, dV \qquad \bar{x}\,\frac{\pi a^2 h}{6} = \frac{\pi a^2 h^2}{8} \qquad \bar{x} = \tfrac{3}{4}h$$

Likewise, the moment of the differential element with respect to the xz plane is $\bar{y}_{el}\, dV$; and the total moment is

$$\int \bar{y}_{el}\, dV = \int_0^h \frac{4r}{3\pi}(\tfrac{1}{2}\pi r^2)\, dx = \frac{2}{3}\int_0^h \left(\frac{a}{h}x\right)^3 dx = \frac{a^3 h}{6}$$

Thus,

$$\bar{y}V = \int \bar{y}_{el}\, dV \qquad \bar{y}\,\frac{\pi a^2 h}{6} = \frac{a^3 h}{6} \qquad \bar{y} = \frac{a}{\pi}$$

PROBLEMS

5.62. A hemisphere and a cylinder are placed together as shown. Determine the ratio h/r such that the centroid of the composite body is located in the plane between the hemisphere and the cylinder.

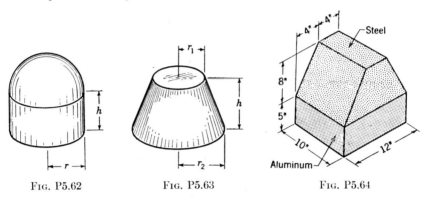

FIG. P5.62   FIG. P5.63   FIG. P5.64

5.63. Locate the centroid of the frustum of a right circular cone when $r_1 = 5$ in., $r_2 = 7.5$ in., and $h = 8$ in.

5.64. The upper portion of the body shown is made of steel and the lower portion of aluminum. Locate the center of gravity of the composite body. (Specific weights: steel = 490 lb/ft³; aluminum = 170 lb/ft³.)

5.65. A 1-in.-diameter hole is drilled 5 in. into the end of a taper as shown. Locate the center of gravity of the taper.

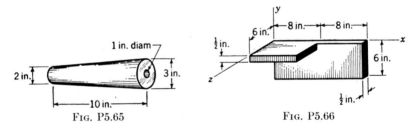

FIG. P5.65   FIG. P5.66

5.66. A portion of one leg of a 6- by 6- by $\frac{1}{2}$-in. angle is cut off. Determine the coordinates of the center of gravity of the remaining portion of the angle.

5.67. A block of steel was originally 5 by 6 by 18 in. A 2-in.-diameter hole was drilled through the block at A, and a quarter-cylindrical piece was cut from one end as shown. Determine the coordinates of the center of gravity of the remaining portion of the block.

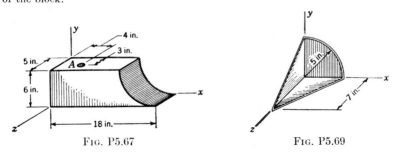

FIG. P5.67   FIG. P5.69

5.68. The side and base of a cylindrical drum are made of sheet metal of the same gage (thickness). If r is the radius and h is the height of the drum, locate the center of gravity of the drum when empty and without a cover.

5.69. Three thin plates are joined at right angles to each other as shown. One plate is in the shape of a quarter circle, and two are triangular. Locate the center of gravity of the composite body. All the plates are of uniform thickness and are made of the same material.

5.70. Locate the center of gravity of a thin hemispherical shell of radius r and thickness t. (*Hint.* Consider the shell as formed by removing a hemisphere of radius r from a hemisphere of radius $r + t$; neglect, then, the terms containing t^2 and t^3, and keep those terms containing t.)

5.71 through 5.74. Derive by direct integration the expression for $\bar{x}$ given in Fig. 5.22 for:

5.71. A hemisphere.

5.72. A circular cone.

5.73. A semiellipsoid of revolution.

5.74. A paraboloid of revolution.

*5.75. A spherical tank is 8 ft in diameter and is filled with water to a depth of 2 ft. Determine by direct integration the center of gravity of the water in the tank.

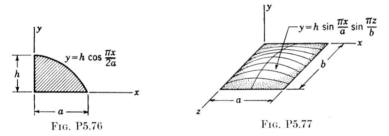

FIG. P5.76   FIG. P5.77

*5.76. Locate the centroid of the volume generated by revolving the portion shown of the cosine curve about the y axis. (*Hint.* Use as an element of volume a thin cylindrical shell of radius r and thickness dr.)

*5.77. Determine by direct integration the location of the centroid of the volume between the xz plane and the portion shown of the surface $y = h \sin (\pi x/a) \sin (\pi z/b)$.

*5.78. A circular cylinder of radius a is cut by an oblique plane as shown. Determine by direct integration the location of the centroid.

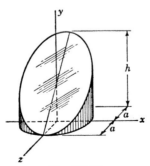

FIG. P5.78

*5.79. Locate the centroid of the frustum of the right circular cone of Prob. 5.63 expressing the result in terms of r_1, r_2, and h.

6. Analysis of Structures

6.1. Internal Forces. Newton's Third Law. The problems considered in the preceding chapters concerned the equilibrium of a single rigid body, and all forces involved were external to the rigid body. We shall now consider problems dealing with the equilibrium of structures made of several connected parts. These problems call not only for the determination of the external forces acting on the structure but also for the determination of the forces which hold together the various parts of the structure. From the point of view of the structure as a whole, these forces are *internal forces*.

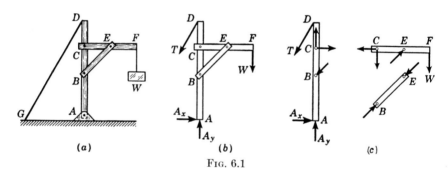

(a) (b) (c)

Fɪɢ. 6.1

Consider, for example, the crane shown in Fig. 6.1*a*, which carries a load W. The crane consists of three beams AD, CF, and BE connected by smooth pins; it is supported by a smooth pin at A and by a cable DG. The free-body diagram of the crane has been drawn in Fig. 6.1*b*. The external forces are shown in the diagram and include the weight W, the two components of the reaction at A, and the force T exerted by the cable at D. The internal forces holding the various parts of the crane together do not appear in the diagram. If, however, the crane is dismembered and if a free-body diagram is drawn for each of its component parts, the forces holding the three beams together must also be represented, since these forces are external forces from the point of view of each component part (Fig. 6.1*c*).

It will be noted that the force exerted at B by member BE on member AD has been represented as equal and opposite to the force exerted at

166

the same point by member AD on member BE; similarly, the force exerted at E by BE on CF is shown equal and opposite to the force exerted by CF on BE; and the components of the force exerted at C by CF on AD are shown equal and opposite to the components of the force exerted by AD on CF. This is in conformity with Newton's third law, which states that *the forces of action and reaction between bodies in contact have the same magnitude, the same line of action, and opposite sense.* As pointed out in Chap. 1, this law is one of the six fundamental principles of elementary mechanics and is based on experimental evidence. Its application is essential to the solution of problems involving connected bodies.

TRUSSES

6.2. Definition of a Truss. The truss is one of the major types of engineering structures. It provides both a practical and an economical solution to many engineering situations, especially in the design of bridges

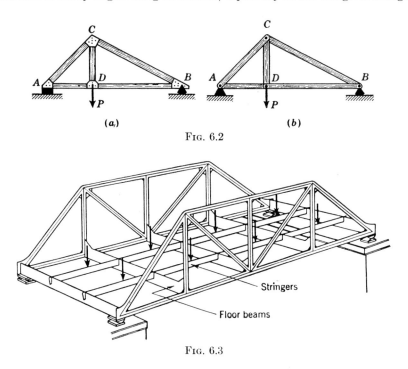

FIG. 6.2

FIG. 6.3

and buildings. A truss consists of straight members connected at joints; a typical truss is shown in Fig. 6.2a. Truss members are connected at their extremities only; thus no member is continuous through a joint. In Fig. 6.2a, for example, there is no member AB; there are instead two distinct members AD and DB. Actual structures are made of several trusses joined together to form a space framework. Each truss is designed to carry those loads which act in its plane and thus may be treated as a two-dimensional structure.

In general, the members of a truss are slender and can support little lateral load; all loads, therefore, must be applied to the various joints, and not to the members themselves. When a concentrated load is to

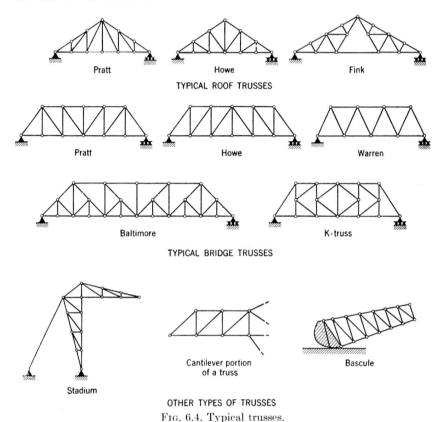

TYPICAL ROOF TRUSSES

TYPICAL BRIDGE TRUSSES

OTHER TYPES OF TRUSSES

Fig. 6.4. Typical trusses.

be applied between two joints, or when a distributed load is to be supported by the truss, as in the case of a bridge truss, a floor system must be provided which, through the use of stringers and floor beams, transmits the load to the joints (Fig. 6.3).

The weights of the members of the truss are also assumed to be applied to the joints, half of the weight of each member being applied to each of the two joints the member connects. Although the members are actually joined together by means of riveted and welded connections, it is customary to assume that the members are pinned together; therefore, the forces acting at each end of a member reduce to a single force and no couple. Thus, the only forces assumed to be applied to a truss member are a single force at each end of the member. Each member may then be treated as a two-force member, and the entire truss may be considered as a group of pins and two-force members (Fig. 6.2b). An individual member may be acted upon as shown in either of the two sketches of

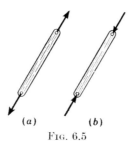

(a)　　　(b)

FIG. 6.5

Fig. 6.5. In the first sketch, the forces tend to pull the member apart, and the member is in tension, while, in the second sketch, the forces tend to compress the member, and the member is in compression. Several typical trusses are shown in Fig. 6.4.

6.3. Simple Trusses. Consider the truss of Fig. 6.6a, which is made of four members connected by pins at A, B, C, and D. If a load is applied at B, the truss will deform and take the shape indicated by the dashed line. On the other hand, the truss of Fig. 6.6b, which is made of three members connected by pins at A, B, and C, will deform only slightly under a load applied at B. The only possible deformation for this truss

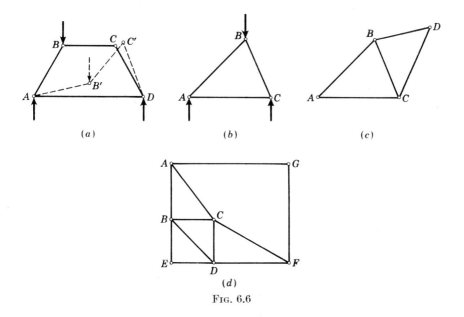

(a)　　　　(b)　　　　(c)

(d)

FIG. 6.6

is one involving small changes in the length of its members. The truss
of Fig. 6.6*b* is said to be a *rigid truss*, the term rigid being used here to
indicate that the truss *will not collapse.*

As shown in Fig. 6.6*c*, a larger rigid truss may be obtained by adding
two members BD and CD to the basic triangular truss of Fig. 6.6*b*. This
procedure may be repeated as many times as desired, and the resulting
truss will be rigid if, each time we add two new members, we attach them
to separate existing joints and connect them together at a new joint.†
A truss which may be constructed in this manner is called a *simple truss.*

It should be noted that a simple truss is not necessarily made only of
triangles. The truss of Fig. 6.6*d*, for example, is a simple truss which
was constructed from triangle ABC by adding successively the joints D,
E, F, and G. On the other hand, rigid trusses are not always simple
trusses, even when they appear to be made of triangles. The Fink and
Baltimore trusses shown in Fig. 6.4, for instance, are not simple trusses,
since they cannot be constructed from a single triangle in the manner
described above. All the other trusses shown in Fig. 6.4 are simple
trusses, as may be easily checked. (For the K truss, start with one of the
central triangles.)

Returning to the basic triangular truss of Fig. 6.6*b*, we note that this
truss has three members and three joints. The truss of Fig. 6.6*c* has two
more members and one more joint, i.e., altogether five members and four
joints. Observing that every time two new members are added, the
number of joints is increased by one, we find that in a simple truss the
total number of members is $m = 2n - 3$, where n is the total number of
joints.

6.4. Analysis of Trusses by the Method of Joints. We saw in Sec. 6.2
that a truss may be considered as a group of pins and two-force members.
The truss of Fig. 6.2, whose free-body diagram is shown in Fig. 6.7*a*,
may thus be dismembered, and a free-body diagram can be drawn for
each pin and each member (Fig. 6.7*b*). Each member is acted upon by
two forces, one at each end; these forces have the same magnitude, the
same line of action, and opposite sense (Sec. 3.16). Besides, Newton's
third law indicates that the forces of action and reaction between a member and a pin are equal and opposite. Therefore, the forces exerted by
a member on the two pins it connects must be directed along the member
and be equal and opposite. It may also be seen that the total number
of unknown internal forces is equal to the number m of members forming
the truss.

Since the entire truss is in equilibrium, each pin must be in equilibrium.
The fact that a pin is in equilibrium may be expressed by drawing its
free-body diagram and writing two equilibrium equations (Sec. 2.6). If
the truss contains n pins, there will be therefore $2n$ equations available,

---

† The three joints must not be in a straight line.

which may be solved for $2n$ unknowns. In the case of a simple truss, we have $m = 2n - 3$, that is, $2n = m + 3$, and the number of unknowns which may be determined from the free-body diagrams of the pins is thus $m + 3$. This means that all the internal forces, the two components of the reaction R_1, and the reaction R_2 may be found by considering the free-body diagrams of the pins.

The fact that the entire truss is a rigid body in equilibrium may be used to write three more equations involving the forces shown in the free-body diagram of Fig. 6.7a. Since they do not contain any new information, these equations are not independent from the equations associated with the free-body diagrams of the pins. Nevertheless, they may be used to determine immediately the components of the reactions at the supports. The arrangement of pins and members in a simple truss is such that it will then always be possible to find a joint involving only

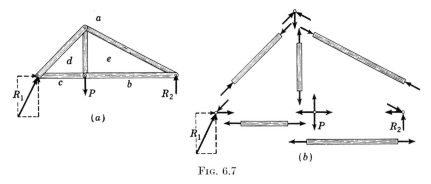

FIG. 6.7

two unknown forces. These forces may be determined by the methods of Sec. 2.8 and their values transferred to the adjacent joints and treated as known quantities at these joints. This procedure may be repeated until all unknown forces have been determined.

In order to expedite the analysis of trusses, it is desirable to establish a uniform method for denoting the various joints, members, loads, and forces. This is done by using Bow's notation, already introduced in Sec. 3.19. A lower-case letter is assigned to every region between loads and reactions, moving clockwise around the truss, and to every area inside the truss (Fig. 6.7a). Each joint, member, load, and force may then be denoted as follows:

1. *Joints.* A joint is specified by naming in clockwise order the letters corresponding to all the areas adjacent to the joint. For example, the joint at the left support (Fig. 6.7a) is joint *adc*, or joint *dca*, or joint *cad*. For convenience, however, joints will be denoted sometimes by a number.

2. *Members.* A member is specified by naming the letters of the two adjacent areas. For example, the vertical member above the load P is member *de* or member *ed*.

3. *Loads.* A load is specified by reading in *clockwise* order the letters of the two areas adjacent to the load. The name of the load is then recorded with capital letters. For example, at joint *debc*, the load P is called BC.

4. *Forces Exerted by Members on Pins.* As noted above, the forces exerted by a member on the two pins it connects must be directed along the member and be equal and opposite. In considering the action of the member on one of the two pins, we denote the force it exerts by reading the letters of the two areas adjacent to the member in *clockwise order* with respect to the joint. For example, the force exerted by member *ad* on pin *adc* is AD, while the force exerted by the same member on pin *aed* is DA. The common magnitude of the two forces exerted by a member on the pins it connects is usually referred to as the *force in the member* considered.

We shall now proceed to analyze the truss of Fig. 6.7 by considering successively the equilibrium of each pin, starting with a joint at which only two forces are unknown. In the truss considered, all pins are subjected to at least three unknown forces. Therefore, the reactions at the supports must first be determined by considering the entire truss as a free body and using the equations of equilibrium of a rigid body. We find in this way that R_1 is vertical and determine the magnitudes of R_1 and R_2. The number of unknown forces at joint *adc* is thus reduced to two; and these forces may be determined by considering the equilibrium of pin *adc*. The magnitude and sense of AD and DC are obtained from the corresponding force triangle (Fig. 6.8).

We may now proceed to joint *debc*, where only two forces, DE and EB, are still unknown. BC is the given load P and hence is known; CD is the force exerted on the pin by the member *cd* and, as indicated above, is equal and opposite to the force DC exerted by the same member on pin *adc*.

Next, joint *aed* is considered; its free-body diagram is shown in Fig. 6.8. It is noted that both ED and DA are known from the analysis of the preceding joints and that only AE is unknown. Since the equilibrium of each pin provides sufficient information to determine two unknowns, a check of our analysis is obtained at this joint. The force triangle is drawn, and the magnitude and sense of AE are determined. The check is obtained by verifying that the force AE and the member *ae* are parallel.

At joint *eab*, all the forces are known. Since the corresponding pin is in equilibrium, the force triangle must close and an additional check of the analysis is obtained.

From the free-body diagrams shown in Fig. 6.8, it is seen that some forces act away from a given joint and others toward it. If the force acts away from the joint, the corresponding member pulls on the pin and the member is in tension; if the force acts toward the joint, the corre-sponding member pushes on the pin and the member is in compression. For example, at joint adc, it is seen from the free-body diagram and the force triangle that force AD acts toward the joint; hence, member ad pushes on the pin and is in compression. If we consider joint aed, it

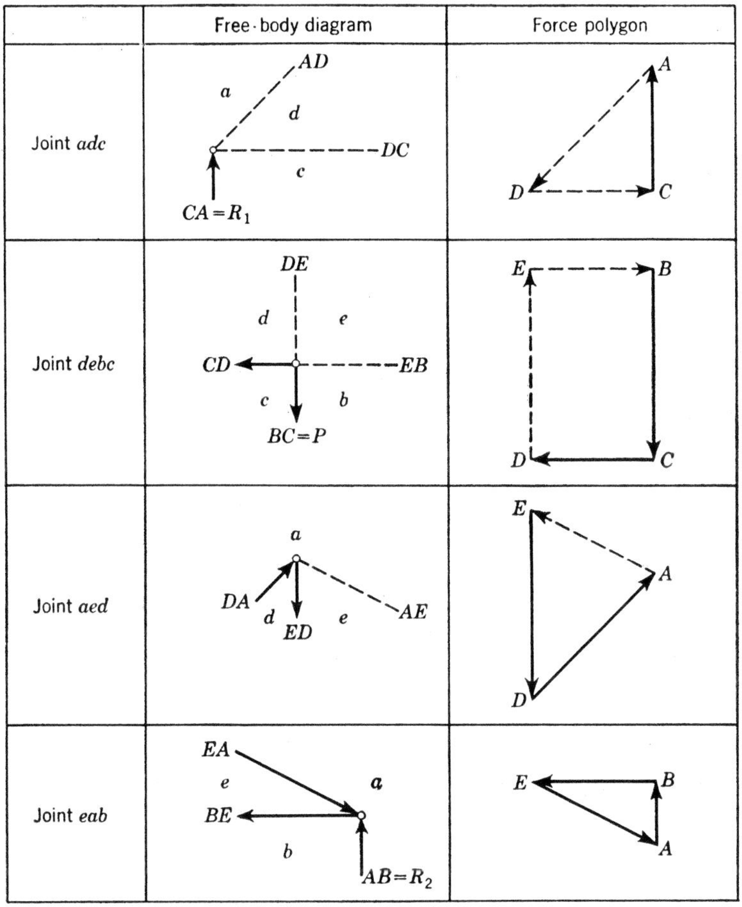

	Free-body diagram	Force polygon
Joint adc		
Joint $debc$		
Joint aed		
Joint eab		

Fig. 6.8

is seen that DA also acts toward the joint; hence, member ad is again found to push and thus to be in compression.

*6.5. Joints under Special Loading Conditions. Consider the joint shown in Fig. 6.9a, which connects four members lying in two intersecting straight lines. The free-body diagram of Fig. 6.9b shows that the pin is subjected to two pairs of directly opposite forces. The corresponding force polygon, therefore, must be a parallelogram (Fig. 6.9c), and *the forces in opposite members must be equal.*

Consider next the joint shown in Fig. 6.10a, which connects three members and supports a load P. Two of the members lie in the same line, and the load P acts along the third member. The free-body diagram of the pin and the corresponding force polygon again will be as shown in Fig. 6.9b and c. Thus, *the forces in the two opposite members must be equal, and the force in the other member must equal the load P*. A particular case of special interest is shown in Fig. 6.10b. Since, in this case, no external load is applied to the joint, we have $P = 0$ and the force in member *cd* is zero. Member *cd* is said to be a *zero-force member*.

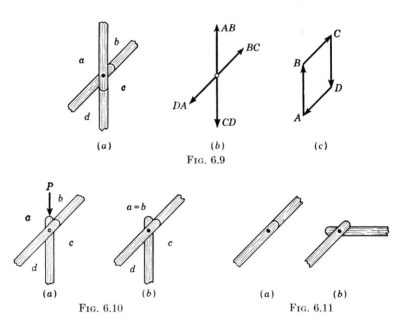

(a)   (b)   (c)

FIG. 6.9

(a)   (b)   (a)   (b)

FIG. 6.10   FIG. 6.11

Consider now a joint connecting two members only. From Sec. 2.6, we know that a particle which is acted upon by two forces will be in equilibrium if the two forces have same magnitude, same line of action, and opposite sense. In the case of the joint of Fig. 6.11a, which connects two members lying in the same line, the equilibrium of the pin requires therefore that *the forces in the two members be equal*. In the case of the joint of Fig. 6.11b, equilibrium is impossible unless the forces in both members are zero. Members connected as shown in Fig. 6.11b, therefore, must be *zero-force members*.

Spotting the joints which are under the special loading conditions listed above will expedite the analysis of a truss. Consider, for example, a Howe truss loaded as shown in Fig. 6.12. All the members represented by dashed lines will be recognized as zero-force members. Joint *3* connects three members, two of which lie in the same line, and is not subjected to any external load; member hi is thus a zero-force member. Applying the same reasoning to joint *11*, we find that member pq is also a zero-force member. But joint *10* is now in the same situation as joints *3* and *11*, and member po must be a zero-force member. The examination of joints *3*, *10*, and *11* also shows that the forces in members fh and if are equal, that the forces in members od and dq are equal, and that the forces in members ep and qe are equal. Furthermore, turning now our attention to joint *9*, where the 4-kip load and member no are collinear, we note that the force in member no is 4 kips (tension) and that the forces in members fn and pe are equal. Hence, the forces in members ep, eq, and fn are equal.

Students, however, should be warned against misusing the rules established in this section. For example, it would be wrong to assume that

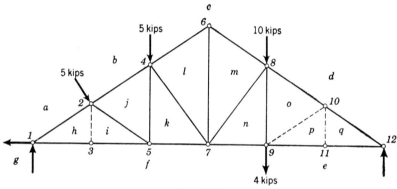

Fig. 6.12

the force in member kj is 5 kips or that the forces in members bj and ha are equal. The conditions discussed above do not apply to joints *2* and *4*. The forces in these members and in all remaining members should be found by carrying out the analysis of joints *1*, *2*, *4*, *5*, *6*, *7*, *8*, and *12* in the usual manner. Until they have become thoroughly familiar with the conditions of application of the rules established in this section, students would be well advised to draw the free-body diagrams of all pins and to write the corresponding equilibrium equations (or draw the corresponding force polygons), whether or not the joints considered fall into the categories listed above.

A final remark concerning zero-force members: These members are not useless. While they do not carry any load under the particular loading conditions shown, the zero-force members of Fig. 6.12 will probably carry loads if the loading conditions are changed. Besides, even in the case considered, these members are needed to support the weight of the truss and to maintain the truss in the desired shape.

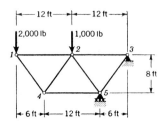

Using the method of joints, determine the force in each member of the truss shown.

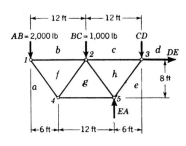

Solution. A free-body diagram of the entire truss is drawn; external forces acting on this free body consist of the applied loads and the reactions. The truss is then lettered, using Bow's notation. The applied loads are thus $AB = 2,000$ lb and $BC = 1,000$ lb; the reactions are CD, DE, and EA.

Equilibrium of Entire Truss

$+\!\!\curvearrowleft \Sigma M_3 = 0$: $(EA)(6\text{ ft}) - (2,000\text{ lb})(24\text{ ft}) - (1,000\text{ lb})(12\text{ ft}) = 0$

$$EA = 10,000\text{ lb} \uparrow$$

$\xrightarrow{+} \Sigma F_x = 0$: $DE = 0$

$+\!\uparrow \Sigma F_y = 0$: $-2,000\text{ lb} - 1,000\text{ lb} + 10,000\text{ lb} - CD = 0$ $CD = 7,000\text{ lb} \downarrow$

Joint 1. This joint is subjected to only two unknown forces, namely, the forces exerted by members bf and fa. A force triangle is used to determine BF and FA. We note that member bf pulls on the joint and thus is in tension and that member fa pushes on the joint and thus is in compression.

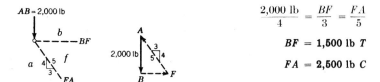

$$\frac{2,000\text{ lb}}{4} = \frac{BF}{3} = \frac{FA}{5}$$

$$BF = 1,500\text{ lb } T$$

$$FA = 2,500\text{ lb } C$$

Joint 4. Since the force exerted by member af has been determined, only two unknown forces are now involved at this joint. Again, a force triangle is used to determine the unknown forces in members fg and ga.

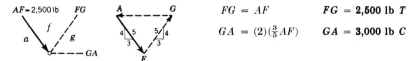

$FG = AF$ $FG = 2,500\text{ lb } T$

$GA = (2)(\tfrac{3}{5}AF)$ $GA = 3,000\text{ lb } C$

***Joint* 2.** Since more than three forces act at this joint, we determine the two unknown forces CH and HG by solving the equilibrium equations $\Sigma F_x = 0$ and $\Sigma F_y = 0$. We arbitrarily assume that both unknown forces act away from the joint, i.e., that the members are in tension. The positive value obtained for CH indicates that our assumption was correct; member ch is in tension. The negative value of HG indicates that our assumption was wrong; member hg is in compression.

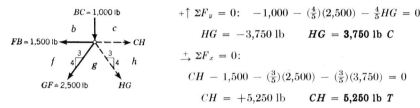

$+\uparrow \Sigma F_y = 0: \quad -1,000 - (\tfrac{4}{5})(2,500) - \tfrac{4}{5}HG = 0$

$HG = -3,750 \text{ lb} \qquad \boldsymbol{HG = 3,750 \text{ lb } C}$

$\xrightarrow{+} \Sigma F_x = 0:$

$CH - 1,500 - (\tfrac{3}{5})(2,500) - (\tfrac{3}{5})(3,750) = 0$

$CH = +5,250 \text{ lb} \qquad \boldsymbol{CH = 5,250 \text{ lb } T}$

***Joint* 5.** The unknown force HE is assumed to act away from the joint. Summing x components, we write

$\xrightarrow{+} \Sigma F_x = 0: \quad \tfrac{3}{5}HE + 3,000 + (\tfrac{3}{5})(3,750) = 0$

$HE = -8,750 \text{ lb} \qquad \boldsymbol{HE = 8,750 \text{ lb } C}$

Summing y components, we obtain a check of our computations:

$+\uparrow \Sigma F_y = 10,000 - (\tfrac{4}{5})(3,750) - (\tfrac{4}{5})(8,750)$

$= 10,000 - 3,000 - 7,000 = 0 \quad \text{(checks)}$

***Joint* 3.** Using the computed values of HC and EH, we may determine the reactions CD and DE by considering the equilibrium of this joint. Since these reactions have already been determined from the equilibrium of the entire truss, we will obtain two checks of our computations. We may also merely use the computed values of all forces acting on the joint (forces in members and reactions) and check that the joint is in equilibrium.

$\xrightarrow{+} \Sigma F_x = -5,250 + (\tfrac{3}{5})(8,750)$

$= -5,250 + 5,250 = 0 \quad \text{(checks)}$

$+\uparrow \Sigma F_y = -7,000 + (\tfrac{4}{5})(8,750)$

$= -7,000 + 7,000 = 0 \quad \text{(checks)}$

PROBLEMS

6.1 through 6.12. Using the method of joints, determine the force in each member of the truss shown. State whether each member is in tension or compression.

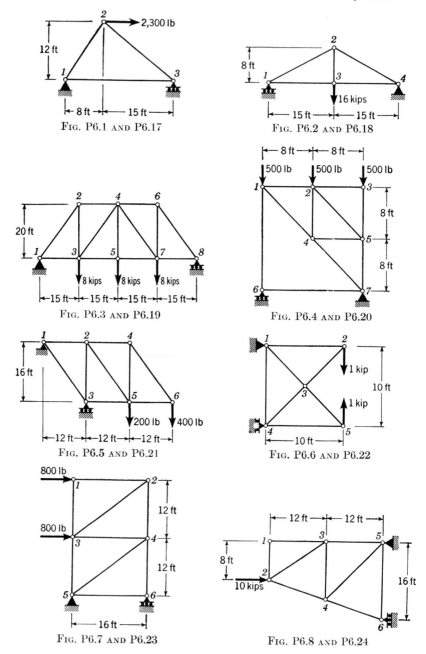

FIG. P6.1 AND P6.17

FIG. P6.2 AND P6.18

FIG. P6.3 AND P6.19

FIG. P6.4 AND P6.20

FIG. P6.5 AND P6.21

FIG. P6.6 AND P6.22

FIG. P6.7 AND P6.23

FIG. P6.8 AND P6.24

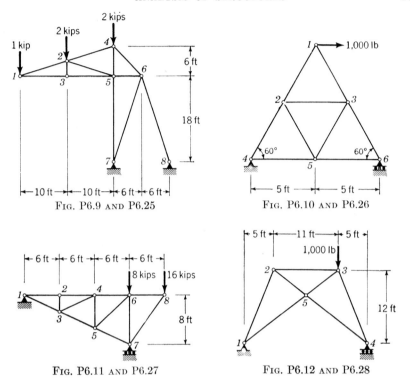

FIG. P6.9 AND P6.25

FIG. P6.10 AND P6.26

FIG. P6.11 AND P6.27

FIG. P6.12 AND P6.28

6.13 and 6.14. Determine the zero-force members in the truss shown for the given loading.

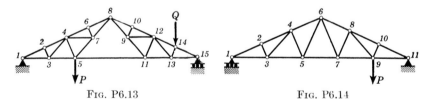

FIG. P6.13

FIG. P6.14

6.15. Indicate the zero-force members for the trusses and loadings considered in Probs. 6.4, 6.8, 6.9, and 6.11.

6.16. Indicate whether the trusses given in Probs. **6.10** through 6.14 are simple trusses.

6.6. Graphical Analysis of Trusses: Maxwell's Diagram.

The method of joints may be used as the basis for a graphical analysis of trusses. We shall develop this graphical analysis by considering the truss already discussed in Sec. 6.4. This truss is shown again in Fig. 6.13a, and a force polygon has been drawn to scale for each joint in Fig. 6.13b; the force in each member may now be measured from one of these force polygons. The number of lines which have to be drawn can be greatly reduced, however, if the various force polygons are superimposed. The resulting diagram is shown in Fig. 6.13c and is known as the *Maxwell diagram* of the truss.

In order to draw the Maxwell diagram directly, we shall proceed as follows:

1. A lower-case letter is assigned to every region outside the truss, moving clockwise around the truss, and also to every area inside the truss (Fig. 6.13a).

2. The reactions R_1 and R_2 are determined. This is done either by drawing the string polygon or by solving the equations of equilibrium

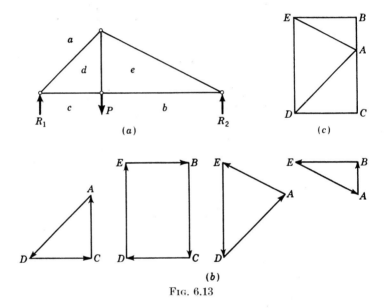

Fig. 6.13

for the entire truss. The force polygon for the entire truss is then drawn to scale (line $ABCA$ in Fig. 6.14a). If a joint can be found which is acted upon by only two forces, this step may be omitted or at least postponed.

3. A force polygon is then drawn for each joint by treating successively joints acted upon by only two unknown forces. All lines previously drawn may be used; thus, it is necessary to draw only two additional lines to complete each new force polygon. For example, starting at joint adc, we draw a line parallel to ad through point A and a line parallel to dc through point C; this determines point D and thus completes the force triangle ADC, which corresponds to joint adc (Fig. 6.14a). Considering next joint $debc$, we draw a line parallel to de through D and a

line parallel to *eb* through *B*; we obtain point *E* and thus complete the force polygon *DEBC*, which corresponds to joint *debc* (Fig. 6.14*b*). Next, we consider joint *aed* and draw a line parallel to *ae* through point *A* (Fig. 6.14*c*); we check that this line passes through the point *E* previously obtained. This completes the force triangle *AED* corresponding to joint *aed* and also completes the Maxwell diagram. At joint *eab*, all the forces are now known; we simply check that they form a closed triangle *EAB* (Fig. 6.14*d*).

4. The magnitude of the force in each member may now be measured on the Maxwell diagram. Thus, the magnitude of the force in member

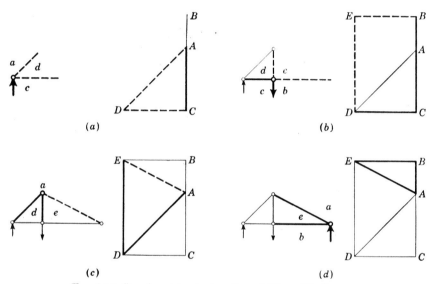

FIG. 6.14. Step-by-step construction of Maxwell's diagram.

ad is *AD*. To determine whether a member is in tension or in compression, we shall determine whether it pulls or pushes on either of the two joints it connects. For example, consider member *ad*, which connects joints *adc* and *aed*. (*a*) We select one of these two joints, say, *adc*. (*b*) We read the names of the areas adjacent to the member in clockwise order around the joint in Fig. 6.13*a*; we read *ad*. (*c*) The direction of the force exerted on the joint is found by reading the corresponding letters of the Maxwell diagram in the same order (Fig. 6.13*c*). Since force *AD* is directed down and to the left, member *ad* pushes on the joint and must be in compression. The same result may be found by considering joint *aed*. The member is now read *da* and the corresponding force *DA*. Since force *DA* is directed up and to the right, member *da* pushes on joint *aed* and is again found to be in compression.

SAMPLE PROBLEM 6.2

By drawing Maxwell's diagram determine the force in each member of the truss considered in Sample Prob. 6.1.

Solution. 1. The truss is drawn to scale; both the applied loads and the reactions are indicated. Using Bow's notation, a lower-case letter is assigned to each region outside the truss and to each individual area inside the truss.

2. By considering the entire truss as a free body, we compute the reactions (see Sample Prob. 6.1). The force polygon of the external forces is then drawn to scale in tip-to-tail fashion; points A, B, C, D, and E are thus located on the Maxwell diagram.

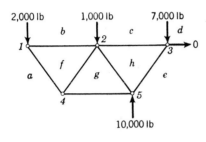

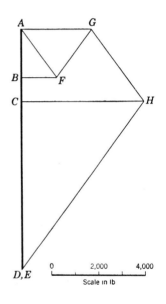

Member	Force
bf	1,500 lb T
fa	2,500 lb C
fg	2,500 lb T
ga	3,000 lb C
hg	3,750 lb C
ch	5,250 lb T
he	8,750 lb C

3. Considering joint *1*, we now locate point F by drawing lines BF and AF, which are parallel to members bf and fa, respectively. We next consider joint *4*, where there are now only two unknown forces and hence only one unknown point in the corresponding triangle of the Maxwell diagram. Lines FG and AG are drawn parallel to fg and ga, respectively; point G is located at the intersection of these lines. We next consider joint *2* and locate point H at the intersection of lines CH and GH which are drawn parallel to ch and hg, respectively. All the points of the Maxwell diagram have now been located. Since HE represents the force in member he, we may draw a line through point H parallel to member he; this line should pass through point E, which is already located. This provides a check on the accuracy of the drawing of the Maxwell diagram.

4. The magnitude and sense of the force in each member are determined from the Maxwell diagram; the magnitude is measured directly, and the sense is found as indicated in Sec. 6.6. The results are given in the table.

182

PROBLEMS

6.17 through 6.28. Determine the force in each member of the truss shown by drawing Maxwell's diagram. Indicate whether the member is in tension or compression. (These trusses are given on pages 178 and 179.)

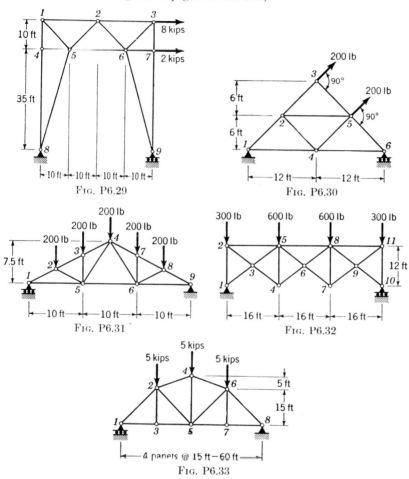

FIG. P6.29

FIG. P6.30

FIG. P6.31

FIG. P6.32

FIG. P6.33

6.29 through 6.33. Determine the force in each member of the truss shown by drawing Maxwell's diagram. Indicate whether the member is in tension or compression.

6.7. Analysis of Trusses by the Method of Sections. The method of joints and Maxwell's diagram are most effective when the forces in all the members of a truss are to be determined. If, however, the force in only one member or the forces in a very few members are desired, a third method, the method of sections, will prove more efficient.

Assume, for example, that we want to determine the force F_{BD} in member BD of the truss shown in Fig. 6.15a. To do this, we must determine the force with which member BD acts on either joint B or joint D. If we were to use the method of joints, we would choose either joint B or joint D as a free body. However, we may also choose as a free body a larger portion of the truss, composed of several joints and members, provided that the desired force F_{BD} is one of the external forces acting on that portion. If, in addition, the portion of the truss is chosen so that there is a total of only three unknown forces acting upon it, the desired force may be obtained by solving the equations of equilibrium for this portion of the truss. In practice, the portion of the truss to be utilized is obtained by *passing a section* through three members of the truss, one of which is the desired member, i.e., by drawing a line which divides the truss into two completely separate parts but does not intersect more than three members. Either of the two portions of the truss obtained after the intersected members have been removed may then be used as a free body.†

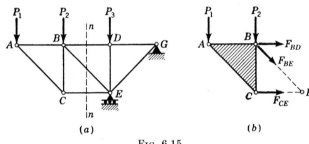

Fig. 6.15

In Fig. 6.15a, the section nn has been passed through members BD, BE, and CE, and the portion ABC of the truss is chosen as the free body (Fig. 6.15b). The forces acting on the free body are the loads P_1 and P_2 at points A and B and the three unknown forces F_{BD}, F_{BE}, and F_{CE}. Since it is not known whether the members removed were in tension or compression, the three forces have been arbitrarily drawn away from the free body as if the members were in tension.

The fact that the rigid body ABC is in equilibrium can be expressed by writing three equations which may be solved for the three unknown forces. If only the force F_{BD} is desired, we need write only one equation, provided that the equation does not contain the other unknowns. Thus the equation $\Sigma M_E = 0$ yields the value of F_{BD}. A positive sign in the answer will indicate that our original assumption regarding the sense of F_{BD} was correct and that member BD is in tension; a negative sign will indicate that our assumption was incorrect and that BD is in compression. On the other hand, if only force F_{CE} is desired, an equation which does

---

† In the analysis of certain trusses, sections are passed which intersect more than three members; the forces in some of the intersected members may be obtained, provided that the conditions of equilibrium of the free body used can be expressed by equations containing no more than three unknowns (see Probs. 6.44 and 6.45).

not include F_{BD} or F_{BE} should be written; the appropriate equation is $\Sigma M_B = 0$. Again a positive sign indicates a correct assumption, hence tension; and a negative sign indicates an incorrect assumption, hence compression.

If only the force F_{BE} is desired, the appropriate equation is $\Sigma F_y = 0$. Whether the member is in tension or compression is again determined from the sign of the answer.

When the force in only one member is calculated, no independent check of the computation is available. However, when all the unknown forces acting on the free body are calculated, the computations can be checked by writing an additional equation. For instance, if F_{BD}, F_{BE}, and F_{CE} are calculated as indicated above, the computation can be checked by verifying that $\Sigma F_x = 0$.

*6.8. Trusses Made of Several Simple Trusses. Consider two simple trusses ABC and DEF. If they are connected by three bars BD, BE,

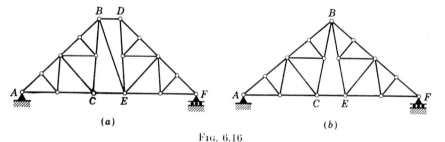

(a) (b)

Fig. 6.16

and CE as shown in Fig. 6.16a, they will form together a rigid truss $ABDF$. The trusses ABC and DEF can also be combined into a single rigid truss by joining joints B and D into a single joint B and by connecting joints C and E by a bar CE (Fig. 6.16b). The truss thus obtained is known as a Fink truss. It should be noted that the trusses of Fig. 6.16a and b are *not* simple trusses; they cannot be constructed from a triangular truss by adding successive pairs of members as prescribed in Sec. 6.3. They are rigid trusses, however, as we may check by comparing the systems of connections used to hold the simple trusses ABC and DEF together (three bars in Fig. 6.16a, one smooth pin and one bar in Fig. 6.16b) with the systems of supports discussed in Secs. 3.14 and 3.15. Trusses made of several simple trusses rigidly connected are known as compound trusses.

It may be checked that in a compound truss the number of members m and the number of joints n are still related by the formula $m = 2n - 3$. If a compound truss is supported by a smooth pin and a roller (involving three unknown reactions), the total number of unknowns is $m + 3$ and this number is therefore equal to the number $2n$ of equations obtained by expressing that the n pins are in equilibrium. Compound trusses supported by a smooth pin and a roller, or by an equivalent system

of supports, are *statically determinate and stable*. This means that all
unknown reactions and forces in members can be determined by the
methods of statics and that, all equilibrium equations being satisfied,

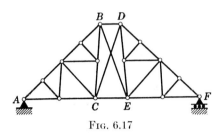

FIG. 6.17

the truss will not collapse. The
forces in the members, however,
cannot all be determined by the
method of joints, unless one is will-
ing to solve a large number of
simultaneous equations. In the
case of the compound truss of Fig.
6.16a, for example, it will be found
more expeditious to pass a section
through members BD, BE, and CE in order to determine the forces in
these members.

Suppose, now, that the simple trusses ABC and DEF are connected
by *four* bars BD, BE, CD, and CE (Fig. 6.17). The number of members
m is now larger than $2n - 3$; the truss obtained is *overrigid*, and one of
the four members BD, BE, CD, or CE is said to be *redundant*. If the
truss is supported by a smooth pin at A and a roller at F, the total number
of unknowns is $m + 3$. This number is now larger than the number $2n$
of available independent equations; the truss is *statically indeterminate*.

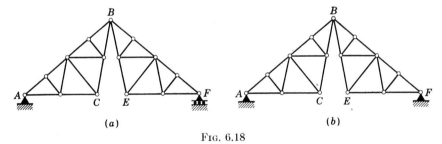

FIG. 6.18

Finally, we shall assume that the two simple trusses ABC and DEF are
joined by a smooth pin as shown in Fig. 6.18a. The number of members
m is smaller than $2n - 3$. If the truss is supported by a smooth pin at
A and a roller at F, the total number of unknowns is $m + 3$. This number is now smaller than the number $2n$ of equilibrium equations which
should be satisfied; the truss is *unstable* and will collapse under its own
weight. However, if two smooth pins are used to support it, the truss
will be *stable* and will not collapse (Fig. 6.18b). The truss is then still
considered as a rigid truss, although it really consists, not of one, but of
two distinct rigid parts. We note that the total number of unknowns
is now $m + 4$ and is thus equal to the number of equations. While
necessary, this condition, however, is not sufficient for the equilibrium of
a structure made of several rigid parts, as we shall see in Sec. 6.11.

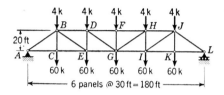

Determine the forces in members DE and HJ of the truss shown.

Solution. Considering the entire truss as a free body, we determine the reactions at A and L.

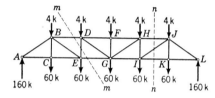

$A = 160$ kips ↑

$L = 160$ kips ↑

Force in Member HJ. Section nn is passed through the truss so that it intersects member HJ and only two additional members. After the intersected members have been removed, we choose the right-hand portion of the truss as a free body. Three unknown forces are involved; to eliminate the two forces passing through point I, we write

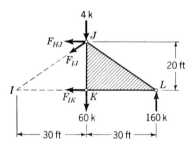

$+\curvearrowleft \Sigma M_I = 0$: $-(160 \text{ kips})(60 \text{ ft})$
$+ (60 \text{ kips})(30 \text{ ft}) + (4 \text{ kips})(30 \text{ ft})$
$- F_{HJ}(20 \text{ ft}) = 0$

$F_{HJ} = -384$ kips

The sense of F_{HJ} was chosen assuming member HJ to be in tension; the negative sign obtained indicates that the member is in compression.

$F_{HJ} = \textbf{384 kips } C$

Force in Member DE. Section mm is passed through the truss so that it intersects member DE and only two additional members. After the intersected members have been removed, the left-hand portion of the truss is chosen as a free body. Three unknown forces are again involved; since the equation $\Sigma F_y = 0$ involves only F_{DE} as an unknown, we write

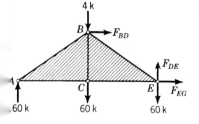

$+\uparrow \Sigma F_y = 0$: $+160 \text{ kips} - 60 \text{ kips} - 4 \text{ kips}$
$- 60 \text{ kips} + F_{DE} = 0$

$F_{DE} = -36$ kips

$F_{DE} = \textbf{36 kips } C$

SAMPLE PROBLEM 6.4

Determine the forces in members FH, GH, and GI of the roof truss shown.

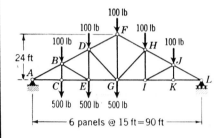

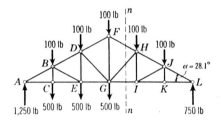

Solution. Section nn is passed through the truss as shown. The right-hand portion of the truss will be taken as a free body. Since the reaction at L acts on this free body, the value of L must be calculated separately, using the entire truss as a free body; the equation $\Sigma M_A = 0$ yields $L = 750$ lb.

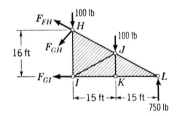

Force in Member GI. Using the portion HLI of the truss as a free body, the value of F_{GI} is obtained by writing

$$+\!\!\uparrow\ \Sigma M_H = 0: \quad -(750\ \text{lb})(30\ \text{ft})$$
$$+ (100\ \text{lb})(15\ \text{ft}) + F_{GI}(16\ \text{ft}) = 0$$

$$F_{GI} = +1{,}313\ \text{lb} \qquad F_{GI} = \textbf{1,313 lb } T$$

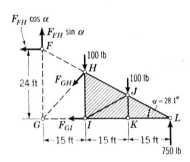

Force in Member FH. The value of F_{FH} is obtained from the equation $\Sigma M_G = 0$. We move F_{FH} along its line of action until it acts at point F, where it is resolved into its x and y components. The moment of F_{FH} with respect to point G is now equal to $F_{FH} \cos \alpha\ (24\ \text{ft})$.

$$+\!\!\uparrow\ \Sigma M_G = 0: \quad -(750\ \text{lb})(45\ \text{ft})$$
$$+ (100\ \text{lb})(30\ \text{ft}) + (100\ \text{lb})(15\ \text{ft})$$
$$- F_{FH} \cos \alpha (24\ \text{ft}) = 0$$

$$F_{FH} = -1{,}382\ \text{lb} \qquad F_{FH} = \textbf{1,382 lb } C$$

Force in Member GH. The value of F_{GH} is determined by first resolving the force into x and y components at point G and then solving the equation $\Sigma M_L = 0$.

$$+\!\!\uparrow\ \Sigma M_L = 0: \quad -(100\ \text{lb})(30\ \text{ft})$$
$$- (100\ \text{lb})(15\ \text{ft}) - F_{GH} \cos \beta (45\ \text{ft}) = 0$$

$$F_{GH} = -137.2\ \text{lb} \qquad F_{GH} = \textbf{137.2 lb } C$$

188

PROBLEMS

6.34. Determine the force in members *CE* and *BC* of the Howe truss shown.

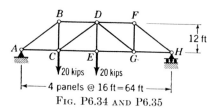

FIG. P6.34 AND P6.35

6.35. Determine the force in members *DG* and *EG* of the Howe truss shown.

6.36. Determine the force in members *DF* and *DE* of the Warren truss shown.

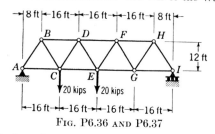

FIG. P6.36 AND P6.37

6.37. Determine the force in members *CD* and *CE* of the Warren truss shown.

6.38. Determine the force in members *DF*, *DE*, and *CE* of the truss shown.

6.39. Determine the force in members *BD*, *CD*, and *CE* of the truss shown.

6.40. Determine the force in member *CD* of the Fink roof truss shown.

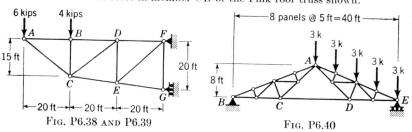

FIG. P6.38 AND P6.39

FIG. P6.40

6.41. Determine the force in members *FH*, *GH*, and *GI* of the stadium truss shown.

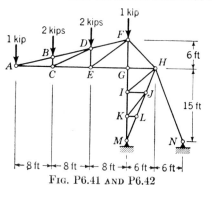

FIG. P6.41 AND P6.42

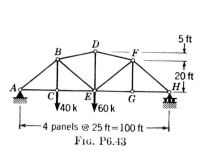

FIG. P6.43

6.42. Determine the force in members *DF*, *EF*, and *EG* of the stadium truss shown.

6.43. Determine the force in members *BD*, *BE*, and *CE* of the bridge truss shown.

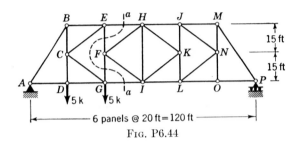

FIG. P6.44

6.44. Determine the force in member *EH* of the K truss shown. (*Hint.* Use section *aa.*)

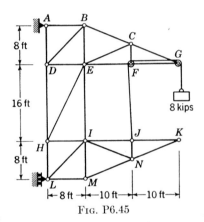

FIG. P6.45

6.45. An 8-kip load is supported by a cable which passes over small pulleys at *F* and *G*. The cable is attached to the truss at joint *J*. Determine the force in members *HE* and *HI*.

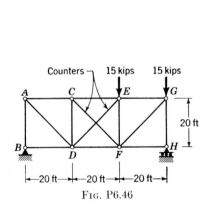

FIG. P6.46

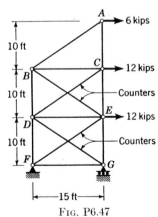

FIG. P6.47

6.46. The diagonal members in the center panel of the truss shown are very slender and can act only in tension; such members are known as *counters*. Determine the force in members *CE*, *DF* and in the counter which is acting under the given loading.

6.47. Determine the force in member *DE* and in the counters which are acting under the given loading (see Prob. 6.46 for the definition of a counter).

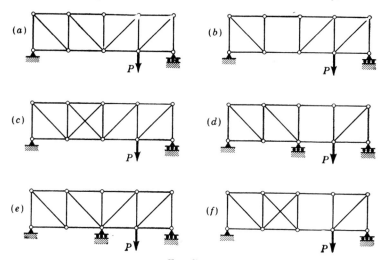

FIG. P6.48

6.48 and 6.49. Classify each of the given structures as stable or unstable; if stable, further classify the structure as determinate or indeterminate. (All members can act both in tension and in compression.)

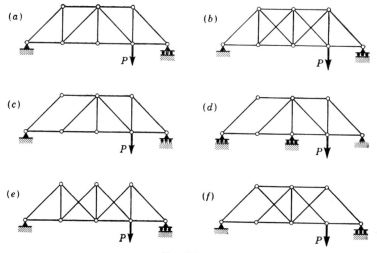

FIG. P6.49

FRAMES AND MACHINES

6.9. Structures Containing Multiforce Members. Under Trusses, we have considered structures consisting entirely of pins and of straight two-force members. The forces acting on the two-force members were known to be directed along the members themselves. We shall now consider structures in which at least one of the members is a *multiforce* member, i.e., a member acted upon by three or more forces. These forces will generally not be directed along the members on which they act; their direction is unknown, and they should be represented therefore by two unknown components.

Frames and machines are structures containing multiforce members. *Frames* are designed to support loads and are usually stationary, stable structures. *Machines* are designed to transmit and modify forces; they may or may not be stationary and will always contain moving parts.

6.10. Analysis of a Frame. As a first example of analysis of a frame, we shall consider again the crane described in Sec. 6.1, which carries a given load W (Fig. 6.19*a*). The free-body diagram of the entire frame

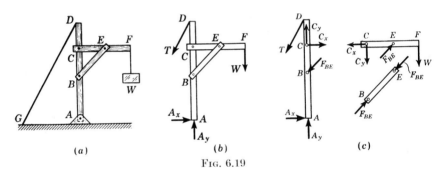

(a)   (b)   (c)

FIG. 6.19

is shown in Fig. 6.19*b*. This diagram may be used to determine the external forces acting on the frame. Summing moments about A, we first determine the tension T in the cable; summing x and y components, we then determine the components A_x and A_y of the reaction at the pin A.

In order to determine the internal forces holding the various parts of a frame together, we must dismember the frame and draw a free-body diagram for each of its component parts (Fig. 6.19*c*). First, the two-force members should be considered. In this frame, member BE is the only two-force member. The forces acting at each end of this member must have the same magnitude, the same line of action, and opposite sense (Sec. 3.16). They are therefore directed along BE. Their magnitude will be denoted by F_{BE} and their sense arbitrarily assumed as shown in Fig. 6.19*c*. The correctness of this assumption will be checked later by the sign of the numerical answer obtained.

Next, we consider the multiforce members, i.e., the members which are acted upon by three or more forces. According to Newton's third law, the force exerted at B by member BE on member AD must be equal and opposite to the force exerted by AD on BE. It must therefore be denoted by F_{BE} and directed as shown in Fig. 6.19c. Similarly, the force exerted at E by member BE on member CF must be denoted by F_{BE} and directed as shown. At C, two multiforce members are connected. Since neither the direction nor the magnitude of the forces acting at C is known, these forces will be represented by their x and y components. The components of the force acting on member AD will be denoted by C_x and C_y and arbitrarily directed to the right and upward. Since, according to Newton's third law, the forces exerted by member CF on AD and by member AD on CF are equal and opposite, the components of the force acting on member CF *must* be denoted by C_x and C_y and *must* be directed to the left and downward. The free-body diagrams of the multiforce members are completed by showing the external forces acting at A, D, and F.

The internal forces may now be determined by considering the free-body diagram of either of the two multiforce members. Choosing the free-body diagram of CF, for example, we write the equations $\Sigma M_C = 0$, $\Sigma M_E = 0$, and $\Sigma F_x = 0$, which yield the values of F_{BE}, C_y, and C_x, respectively. These values may be checked by verifying that member AD is also in equilibrium.

It should be noted that the free-body diagrams of the pins were not shown in Fig. 6.19c. This was because the pins were assumed to form an integral part of one of the two members they connected. This assumption can always be used to simplify the analysis of frames and machines. When a pin connects three or more members, however, or when a pin connects a support and two or more members, a clear decision must be made in choosing the member to which the pin will be assumed to belong. (If multiforce members are involved, the pin should be attached to one of these members.) The forces exerted on the pin by the other members or by the support should then be clearly identified. This is illustrated in Sample Prob. 6.7.

6.11. Frames Consisting of Two or More Rigid Parts. The crane analyzed in Sec. 6.10 was so constructed that it could keep the same shape without the help of its supports; it was therefore considered as a rigid body. Many frames, however, will collapse if detached from their supports; such frames cannot be considered as rigid bodies. Consider, for example, the frame shown in Fig. 6.20a, which consists of two members AC and CB carrying loads P and Q at their mid-points; the members are supported by pins at A and B and are connected by a pin at C. If detached from its supports, this frame will not maintain its shape; it should therefore be considered as made of *two distinct rigid parts* AC and CB.

The equations $\Sigma F_x = 0$, $\Sigma F_y = 0$, $\Sigma M = 0$ (about any given point) express the conditions for the *equilibrium of a rigid body* (Chap. 3); we should use them, therefore, in connection with the free-body diagrams of rigid bodies, namely, the free-body diagrams of members AC and CB (Fig. 6.20b). Since these members are multiforce members, and since pins are used at the supports and at the connection, the reactions at A and B and the forces at C will each be represented by two components. In accordance with Newton's third law, the components of the forces at C, exerted, respectively, by CB on AC and by AC on CB, will be denoted by the same symbols and represented by vectors having opposite senses.

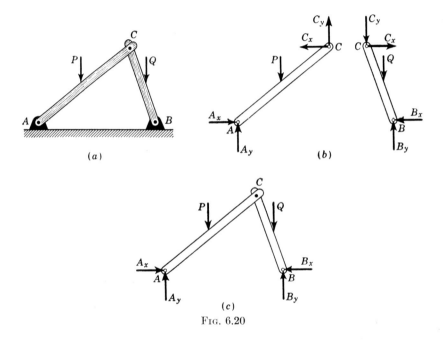

FIG. 6.20

We note that four unknown force components act on free body AC, while only three independent equations may be used to express that the body is in equilibrium; similarly, four unknowns, but only three equations, are associated with CB. However, only six different unknowns are involved in the analysis of the two members, and altogether six equations are available to express that the members are in equilibrium. Writing $\Sigma M_A = 0$ for free body AC and $\Sigma M_B = 0$ for CB, we obtain two simultaneous equations which may be solved for C_x and C_y. Writing, then, $\Sigma F_x = 0$ and $\Sigma F_y = 0$ for each of the two free bodies, we obtain successively A_x, A_y, B_x, and B_y.

We shall observe, now, that, since the equations of equilibrium $\Sigma F_x = 0$, $\Sigma F_y = 0$, $\Sigma M = 0$ (about any given point) are satisfied by the forces acting on free body AC, and since they are also satisfied by the forces acting on free body CB, they must be satisfied when the forces acting on the two free bodies are considered simultaneously. Since the internal forces at C cancel each other, we find that the equations of equilibrium must be satisfied by the external forces shown on the free-body diagram of the frame ACB itself (Fig. 6.20c), although the frame is not a rigid body. These equations may be used to determine some of the components of the reactions at A and B. We shall note, however, that *the reactions cannot be completely determined from the free-body diagram of the whole frame.* It is thus necessary to dismember the frame and to consider the free-body diagrams of its component parts (Fig. 6.20b), even when we are interested only in finding external reactions. This may be explained by the fact that the equilibrium equations obtained for free body ACB are *necessary conditions* for the equilibrium of a nonrigid structure, *but not sufficient conditions.*

The method of solution outlined in the second paragraph of this section involved simultaneous equations. We shall now discuss a more expeditious method, which utilizes the free body ACB as well as the free bodies AC and CB. Writing $\Sigma M_A = 0$ and $\Sigma M_B = 0$ for free body ACB, we obtain B_y and A_y. Writing $\Sigma M_C = 0$, $\Sigma F_x = 0$, and $\Sigma F_y = 0$ for free body AC, we obtain successively A_x, C_x, and C_y. Finally, writing $\Sigma F_x = 0$ for ACB, we obtain B_x.

We noted above that the analysis of the frame of Fig. 6.20 involves six unknown force components and six independent equilibrium equations (the equilibrium equations for the whole frame were obtained from the original six equations and, therefore, are not independent). Moreover, we checked that all unknowns could be actually determined and that all equations could be satisfied. The frame considered is *statically determinate and stable.* In general, to determine whether a structure is statically determinate and stable, we should draw a free-body diagram for each of its component parts and count the reactions and internal forces involved. We should also determine the number of independent equilibrium equations (excluding equations expressing the equilibrium of the whole structure or of groups of component parts already analyzed). If there are more unknowns than equations, the structure is *statically indeterminate.* If there are fewer unknowns than equations, the structure is *unstable.* If there are as many unknowns as equations, and if all unknowns may be determined and all equations satisfied under general loading conditions, the structure is *statically determinate and stable;* if, however, all unknowns cannot be determined and all equations cannot be satisfied, the structure is *geometrically unstable.*

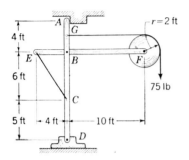

In the small frame shown, members EBF and $ABCD$ are connected by a pin at B and by the cable EC. A 75-lb load is supported by a second cable which passes over a pulley at F and is attached to the vertical member at G. Determine the tension in cable EC and the components of the pin reaction at B.

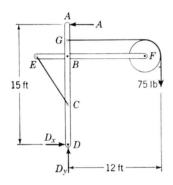

Entire Frame. The external reactions on the frame involve three unknowns; these reactions are determined by taking the entire frame as a free body.

$+\uparrow \Sigma F_y = 0$: $D_y - 75 \text{ lb} = 0$

$$D_y = \textbf{75 lb} \uparrow$$

$+\curvearrowleft \Sigma M_D = 0$: $(75 \text{ lb})(12 \text{ ft}) - A(15 \text{ ft}) = 0$

$$A = \textbf{60 lb} \leftarrow$$

$\xrightarrow{+} \Sigma F_x = 0$: $-60 \text{ lb} + D_x = 0$

$$D_x = \textbf{60 lb} \rightarrow$$

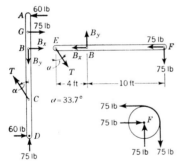

Members. The frame is dismembered; since only two members are connected at B, the components of the unknown forces acting on EBF and $ABCD$ at B are, respectively, equal and opposite. The forces exerted at E and C by the cable EC are equal and opposite, and their direction is known. From the free-body diagram of the pulley, it is seen that the force exerted at F by the pulley on member EBF may be resolved into two 75-lb components as shown. The cable also exerts a 75-lb force on $ABCD$ at point G.

Member EBF. Using the free body EBF, we write

$+\curvearrowleft \Sigma M_E = 0$: $(75 \text{ lb})(14 \text{ ft}) - B_y(4 \text{ ft}) = 0$ $B_y = \textbf{+263 lb}$

$+\curvearrowleft \Sigma M_B = 0$: $-T \cos \alpha(4 \text{ ft}) + (75 \text{ lb})(10 \text{ ft}) = 0$ $T = \textbf{+225 lb}$

$\xrightarrow{+} \Sigma F_x = 0$: $+T \sin \alpha - B_x - 75 \text{ lb} = 0$ $B_x = \textbf{+50.0 lb}$

Since the values obtained are positive, the forces are directed as shown on the diagram.

Member ABCD (Check). The computations are checked by considering the free body $ABCD$. For example,

$\xrightarrow{+} \Sigma F_x = -60 \text{ lb} + 75 \text{ lb} + B_x - T \sin \alpha + 60 \text{ lb}$

$\qquad = -60 \text{ lb} + 75 \text{ lb} + 50 \text{ lb} - (225 \text{ lb}) \sin 33.7° + 60 \text{ lb} = 0$ (checks)

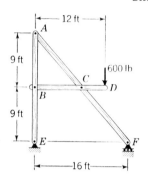

Determine the components of the forces acting on each member of the frame shown.

Entire Frame. Since the external reactions involve only three unknowns, we compute the reactions by considering the free-body diagram of the entire frame (see diagram below).

$+\circlearrowleft \Sigma M_E = 0:$ $\quad (600 \text{ lb})(12 \text{ ft}) - F(16 \text{ ft}) = 0$

$$F = +450 \text{ lb} \qquad \mathbf{F = 450 \text{ lb} \uparrow}$$

$+\uparrow \Sigma F_y = 0:$ $\quad -600 \text{ lb} + 450 \text{ lb} + E_y = 0$

$$E_y = +150 \text{ lb} \qquad \mathbf{E_y = 150 \text{ lb} \uparrow}$$

$\xrightarrow{+} \Sigma F_x = 0:$ $\qquad \mathbf{E_x = 0}$

The frame is now dismembered; since only two members are connected at each joint, equal and opposite components are shown on each member at each joint.

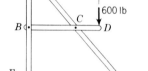

Member BCD

$+\circlearrowleft \Sigma M_B = 0:$ $\quad +(600 \text{ lb})(12 \text{ ft}) - C_y(8 \text{ ft}) = 0$

$$C_y = +900 \text{ lb}$$

$+\circlearrowleft \Sigma M_C = 0:$ $\quad +(600 \text{ lb})(4 \text{ ft}) - B_y(8 \text{ ft}) = 0$

$$B_y = +300 \text{ lb}$$

$\xrightarrow{+} \Sigma F_x = 0:$ $\quad -B_x + C_x = 0$

We note that neither B_x nor C_x can be obtained by considering only member BCD.

Member ABE

$+\circlearrowleft \Sigma M_A = 0:$ $\quad -B_x(9 \text{ ft}) = 0 \qquad \mathbf{B_x = 0}$

$\xrightarrow{+} \Sigma F_x = 0:$ $\quad +B_x - A_x = 0 \qquad \mathbf{A_x = 0}$

$+\uparrow \Sigma F_y = 0:$ $\quad -A_y + B_y + 150 \text{ lb} = 0$
$-A_y + 300 \text{ lb} + 150 \text{ lb} = 0 \qquad \mathbf{A_y = +450 \text{ lb}}$

Member BCD. Returning now to member BCD, we write

$\xrightarrow{+} \Sigma F_x = 0:$ $\quad -B_x + C_x = 0 \qquad 0 + C_x = 0$
$$\mathbf{C_x = 0}$$

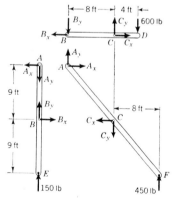

Member ACF (Check). All unknown components have now been found; the results may be checked by verifying that member ACF is in equilibrium.

$+\circlearrowleft \Sigma M_C = -(450 \text{ lb})(8 \text{ ft}) + A_y(8 \text{ ft}) + A_x(9 \text{ ft})$

$= -(450 \text{ lb})(8 \text{ ft}) + (450 \text{ lb})(8 \text{ ft}) + 0 = 0 \qquad \text{(checks)}$

Determine the forces acting on each member of the frame shown.

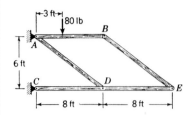

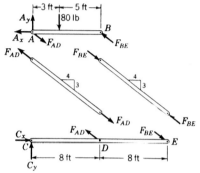

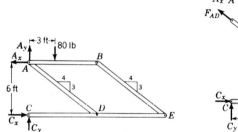

Entire Frame. The entire frame is chosen as a free body; although the reactions involve four unknowns, A_x and C_x may be determined by writing

$+\!\!\downarrow \Sigma M_A = 0$: $(80 \text{ lb})(3 \text{ ft}) - C_x(6 \text{ ft}) = 0$ $C_x = +40 \text{ lb}$ $C_x = 40 \text{ lb} \rightarrow$

$\xrightarrow{+} \Sigma F_x = 0$: $-A_x + C_x = 0$ $A_x = +40 \text{ lb}$ $A_x = 40 \text{ lb} \leftarrow$

The equations of equilibrium of the entire frame are not sufficient to determine A_y and C_y. The equilibrium of the various members must now be considered in order to proceed with the solution. In dismembering the frame, we have assumed that the pin at A is attached to member AB, and we have noted that both AD and BE are two-force members. The free-body diagrams of the various members are now considered separately.

Member AB

$+\!\!\downarrow \Sigma M_A = 0$: $(80 \text{ lb})(3 \text{ ft}) - \frac{3}{5}F_{BE}(8 \text{ ft}) = 0$ $F_{BE} = +50 \text{ lb}$

Member CDE. Since the force F_{BE} has been determined, we may compute F_{AD} by writing

$+\!\!\downarrow \Sigma M_C = 0$: $-\frac{3}{5}F_{AD}(8 \text{ ft}) + \frac{3}{5}F_{BE}(16 \text{ ft}) = 0$ $F_{AD} = +100 \text{ lb}$

Using $F_{AD} = +100 \text{ lb}$, we now determine C_y by writing

$+\!\!\uparrow \Sigma F_y = 0$: $C_y + \frac{3}{5}F_{AD} - \frac{3}{5}F_{BE} = 0$ $C_y = -30 \text{ lb}$ $C_y = 30 \text{ lb} \downarrow$

Entire Frame. Since C_y has been determined, we may return to the free-body diagram of the entire frame and write

$+\!\!\uparrow \Sigma F_y = 0$: $C_y + A_y - 80 \text{ lb} = 0$ $A_y = +110 \text{ lb}$ $A_y = 110 \text{ lb} \uparrow$

Member AB (Check). We may check our computations by verifying that the equation $\Sigma F_y = 0$ is satisfied by the forces acting on member AB.

$+\!\!\uparrow \Sigma F_y = A_y - \frac{3}{5}F_{AD} + \frac{3}{5}F_{BE} - 80 \text{ lb} = 110 \text{ lb} - 60 \text{ lb} + 30 \text{ lb} - 80 \text{ lb} = 0$ (checks)

PROBLEMS

6.50. A 160-lb man stands on a 6-ft stepladder so that half his weight is carried by the legs shown. The two legs shown are connected by a hinge at B and by a folding link DE. Neglecting the weight of the ladder and assuming the floor to be smooth, determine the components of the force exerted at B on leg AB and the tension in the link DE.

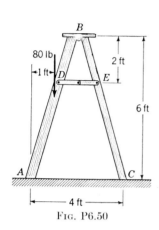

Fig. P6.50

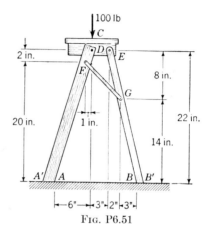

Fig. P6.51

6.51. A 200-lb man stands at C on the step stool shown. Half the man's weight is carried by the legs shown. Determine the components of the force exerted at E on leg BE, assuming that the bottom of the legs is not quite parallel to the floor and that bearing occurs only at points A and B. Neglect the weight of the stool, and assume the floor to be smooth.

6.52. Determine the components of the forces exerted at B and C on the horizontal member of the hanger shown. Take $a = 6$ in., $b = 8$ in., and $L = 10$ in.

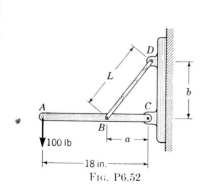

Fig. P6.52

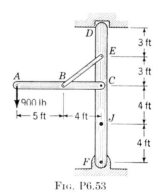

Fig. P6.53

6.53. Determine the components of all forces exerted on the vertical member DF of the crane shown.

6.54. A pipe weighs 20 lb/ft and is supported every 30 ft by a small frame; a typical frame is shown. Determine the components of the reactions and the components of the force exerted at B on member AB.

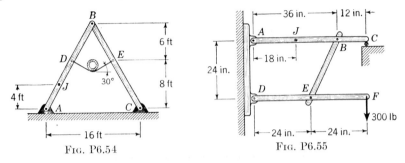

FIG. P6.54　　　　　FIG. P6.55

6.55. Determine the components of all forces acting on the two horizontal members of the frame shown.

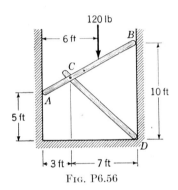

FIG. P6.56

6.56. A 120-lb load is supported by two members AB and CD connected by a pin at C and placed between two smooth walls as shown. Determine the components of all forces exerted on member AB.

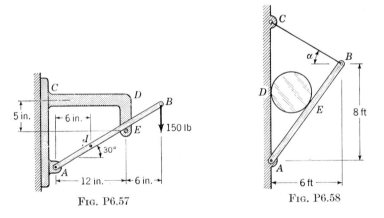

FIG. P6.57　　　　　FIG. P6.58

6.57. In the bracket shown, member AB is hinged at A and supported by a smooth pin attached to member CDE. Determine the force exerted on the pin E and the reactions at A and C.

6.58. A 3-ft-diameter 500-lb cylinder is supported as shown. Assuming that $\alpha = 30°$, determine all forces acting on member AB. The cylinder is assumed to be frictionless.

6.59. Determine the angle α at which the cable in Prob. 6.58 must be attached so that the reaction at A has no vertical component.

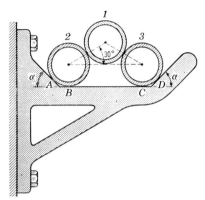

Fig. P6.60

6.60. Three equal lengths of 6-in. pipe weighing 50 lb each are placed on two racks so that each rack supports half the weight of the pipes. Neglecting friction at all surfaces, determine the reactions exerted at A and B by the rack shown on pipe 2 when $\alpha = 45°$.

6.61. Determine the smallest value of the angle α for which equilibrium is possible in Prob. 6.60.

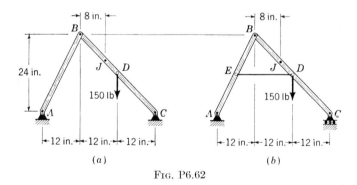

(a)   (b)

Fig. P6.62

6.62. Determine the reactions for each of the frames shown. Also determine the force exerted at B on member BC in each frame.

6.63. Determine the components of all forces acting on member BC of the A frame shown.

6.64. Determine the reactions at E and F and the force exerted on pin C for the frame shown.

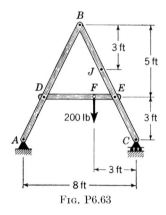

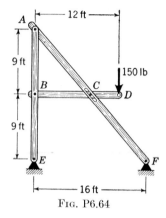

Fig. P6.63   Fig. P6.64

6.65. Determine the reactions at E and F and the force exerted on pin C for the frame of Prob. 6.64, assuming now that pin C is attached to member ACF and may slide in a horizontal slot in member BD.

6.66. Two loads P and Q may be attached to the three-hinged arch shown. If $P = 10$ kips and $Q = 0$, determine the reactions and the force exerted at B on segment AB.

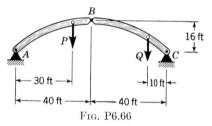

Fig. P6.66

6.67. Same as Prob. 6.66 assuming $P = 10$ kips and $Q = 15$ kips.

6.68 and 6.69. Determine the reactions at the supports for each of the trusses shown. Indicate whether the truss is stable or unstable. The height of each truss is 20 ft; the length of each panel is 20 ft; and $P = 4$ kips.

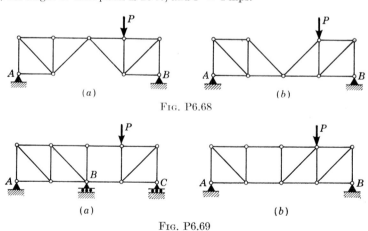

(a)   (b)

Fig. P6.68

(a)   (b)

Fig. P6.69

6.70 and 6.71. Determine the reactions at the supports for the beam shown.

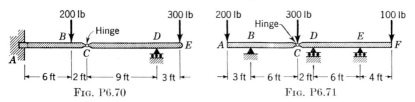

FIG. P6.70   FIG. P6.71

6.72. Determine the components of the reactions at A and E for the frame shown, knowing that each pulley is 2 ft in diameter.

6.73. A cable passes around two pulleys and exerts on member BC a couple of moment $Td = 1,600$ lb-ft. Determine the reactions and the forces exerted at C and E on the horizontal member.

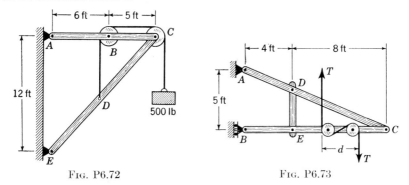

FIG. P6.72   FIG. P6.73

6.74. A weight $W = 800$ lb may be supported by a small frame in each of the three ways shown. The diameter of the pulley is 1 ft. For each case, determine the force components and the couple representing the reaction at A and also the force exerted at D on the vertical member.

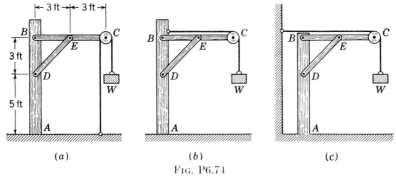

(a)   (b)   (c)

FIG. P6.74

6.75. (a) Show that, when a frame supports a pulley at A, an equivalent loading of the frame and of each of its component parts may be obtained by removing the pulley and applying at A two forces equal and parallel to the forces of tension in the cable. (b) Further show that if one end of the cable is attached to the frame at a point B, a force equal to the tension should also be applied at B.

6.76. Determine (a) the components of all forces acting on member ACE, (b) the force in member AD.

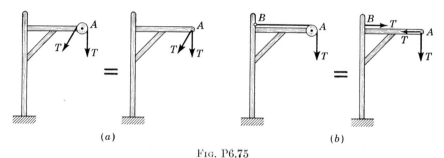

(a)   (b)

Fig. P6.75

*6.77. Show that the force in member AD is the same for any position of the vertical 100-lb load on member AB. (*Hint.* Choose a as a parameter, and determine the force in AD in terms of a.)

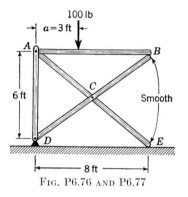

Fig. P6.76 and P6.77

*6.78. In the folding chair shown, members $ABEH$ and CFK are parallel. Determine the components of all forces acting on member $ABEH$ when a 160-lb man sits

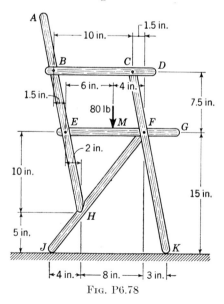

Fig. P6.78

in the chair. It may be assumed that half the man's weight is carried by each side of the chair and is applied at point M.

*6.79. In the hanger shown in Prob. 6.52, the length of member BD is to be $L = 10$ in. Determine the dimensions a and b so that the tension in BD will be as small as possible.

6.12. Machines. Machines are structures designed to transmit and modify forces. Whether they are simple tools or include complicated mechanisms, their main purpose is to transform *input forces* into *output forces*. Consider, for example, a pair of cutting pliers used to cut a wire (Fig. 6.21a). If we apply two equal and opposite input forces P on their handles, they will exert output forces Q on the wire (Fig. 6.21b).

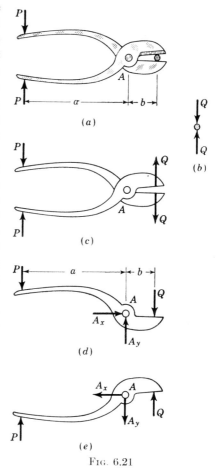

FIG. 6.21

To determine the output forces Q when the input forces P are known (or, conversely, to determine the forces P when the forces Q are known), we draw a free-body diagram of the pliers *alone*, showing the input forces P and the *reactions* to the output forces Q that the wire exerts on the pliers (Fig. 6.21c). However, since a pair of pliers form a nonrigid structure, we must use one of the component parts as a free body in order to determine the unknown forces. Considering Fig. 6.21d, for example, and taking moments about A, we obtain the relation $Pa = Qb$, which defines Q in terms of P or P in terms of Q. The same free-body diagram may be used to determine the components of the internal force at A; we find $A_x = 0$ and $A_y = P + Q$.

In the case of more complicated machines, it generally will be necessary to use several free-body diagrams and, possibly, to solve simultaneous equations involving various internal forces. The free bodies should be chosen to include the input forces and the reactions to the output forces, and the total number of unknown force components involved should not exceed the number of available independent equations. While it is advisable to check whether the problem is determinate before attempting to solve it, there is no point in discussing the stability of a machine. A machine includes moving parts and thus must be unstable.

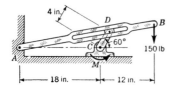

Determine the magnitude of the couple M which must be applied to the crank CD to hold the mechanism in equilibrium. The block at D is pinned to the crank CD and is free to slide in a slot cut in member AB.

Solution. For the given position of the crank, we compute the following:

$$a = (4 \text{ in.}) \sin 60° = 3.46 \text{ in.}$$

$$b = (4 \text{ in.}) \cos 60° = 2.00 \text{ in.}$$

$$\tan \alpha = \frac{3.46}{20} \qquad \alpha = 9.8°$$

$$\sin \alpha = \frac{3.46}{c} \qquad c = 20.3 \text{ in.}$$

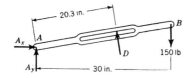

The mechanism is now dismembered; since the block at D slides freely along the slot, the internal force at D must be perpendicular to member AB.

Member AB

$+\!\!\downarrow \Sigma M_A = 0$:
$$(150 \text{ lb})(30 \text{ in.}) - D(20.3 \text{ in.}) = 0$$

$$D = +222 \text{ lb}$$

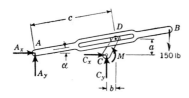

Member CD. The internal force D is resolved into its x and y components.

$$D_x = (222 \text{ lb}) \sin 9.8° = 37.8 \text{ lb} \rightarrow$$

$$D_y = (222 \text{ lb}) \cos 9.8° = 218 \text{ lb} \downarrow$$

We then write

$+\!\!\downarrow \Sigma M_C = 0$: $(218 \text{ lb})(2 \text{ in.})$
$$+ (37.8 \text{ lb})(3.46 \text{ in.}) - M = 0$$

$$M = +567 \text{ lb-in.} \qquad M = 567 \text{ lb-in.} \;\rangle$$

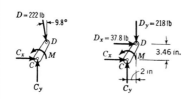

From the free-body diagram of the crank we may also obtain $C_y = 218 \text{ lb}$.

Entire Mechanism (Check). Considering the entire mechanism as a free body, we check that $\Sigma M_A = 0$.

$+\!\!\downarrow \Sigma M_A = (150 \text{ lb})(30 \text{ in.}) - C_y(18 \text{ in.}) - M = 4{,}500 - (218)(18) - 567 = 9$

Although ΣM_A is equal to 9 instead of zero, it is small compared with the quantities involved (4,500) and provides a satisfactory check.

PROBLEMS

6.80. A horizontal force $P = 125$ lb is applied to the toggle vise shown. If $a = 5$ in. and $l = 13$ in., determine the force Q exerted by the vise on the block.

6.81. It is desired to have the toggle vise exert a force $Q = 2,000$ lb on the block. Determine the force P which must be applied if $a = 3.5$ in. and $l = 12$ in.

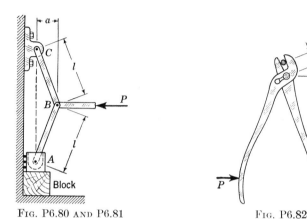

FIG. P6.80 AND P6.81   FIG. P6.82

6.82. Determine the forces Q exerted by the pliers on the rod if two forces $P = 80$ lb are applied as shown on the handles.

6.83. A force $P = 100$ lb is applied to the piston of a Scotch crosshead mechanism as shown. Determine the magnitude of the couple M which is required to maintain equilibrium.

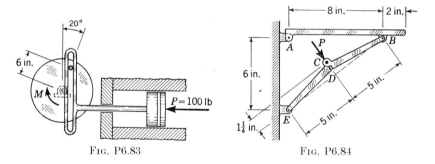

FIG. P6.83   FIG. P6.84

6.84. A shelf is held horizontally by a self-locking brace which consists of two parts EDC and CDB hinged at C and bearing against each other at D. If the shelf is 10 in. wide and weighs 24 lb, determine the force P required to release the brace. (*Hint.* To release the brace, the forces of contact at D must be zero.)

6.85. A cylinder weighs 500 lb and is lifted by a pair of tongs as shown. Determine the forces exerted at D and C on the tong BCD.

6.86. If the toggle shown is added to the tongs of Prob. 6.85 and the load is lifted by applying a single force at G, determine the forces exerted at D and C on tong BCD.

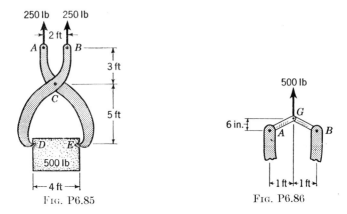

FIG. P6.85   FIG. P6.86

6.87. The automobile front wheel assembly shown supports 750 lb. Determine the force exerted by the spring and the components of the forces exerted on the frame at points A and D.

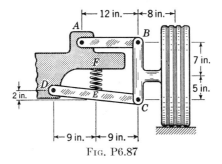

FIG. P6.87

6.88. A couple of moment $M = 300$ lb-ft is applied to the crank of the engine system shown. Determine the force P required to hold the system in equilibrium.

6.89. If a force $P = 400$ lb is applied to the piston of the engine system shown, determine the moment of the couple M required to hold the system in equilibrium.

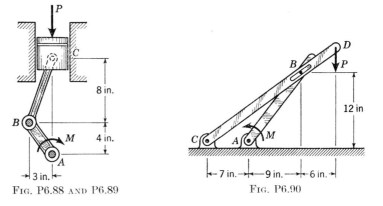

FIG. P6.88 AND P6.89   FIG. P6.90

6.90. Members AB and CD are connected by a pin attached to AB which slides freely in a slot in member CD. If a couple of moment $M = 450$ lb-in. is applied to AB as shown, determine the force P required to maintain equilibrium.

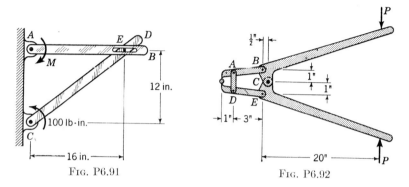

Fig. P6.91   Fig. P6.92

6.91. Two machine parts are connected at E by a pin which is attached to member CD and slides freely in a slot cut in member AB. If a couple of moment 100 lb-in. is applied to member CD, determine the moment of the couple M required for equilibrium.

6.92. In using the bolt cutter shown, a man applies two forces $P = 125$ lb. Determine the forces Q exerted by the cutter on the bolt.

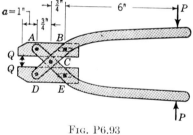

Fig. P6.93

6.93. In the pliers shown, the clamping jaws remain parallel as objects of various sizes are held. If a gripping force $Q = 450$ lb is desired, determine the forces P which must be applied. Assume that pins B and E slide freely in the slots cut in the jaws.

6.94. In Prob. 6.93, show that the required forces P are independent of the position of the object gripped by the jaws. (*Hint.* Determine P in terms of the distance a.)

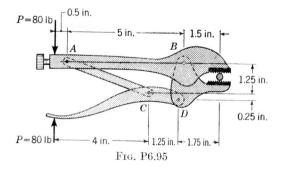

Fig. P6.95

6.95. Determine the gripping forces Q produced when two forces $P = 80$ lb are applied as shown.

6.96. Determine the force P required to maintain the quick-return mechanism in equilibrium if $M = 1,800$ lb-in. and $\alpha = 60°$.

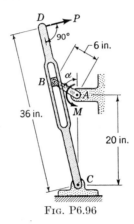

FIG. P6.96

6.97. Solve Prob. 6.96 assuming (*a*) $\alpha = 0°$ and (*b*) $\alpha = 180°$.

6.98. The Whitworth mechanism shown is used to produce a quick-return motion. Members AB and CDE rotate freely about points A and D, respectively. The block at B is attached to member AB by a pin and slides freely along member CDE. If $\alpha = 60°$ and $M = 800$ lb-in., determine the force P required to maintain the mechanism in equilibrium.

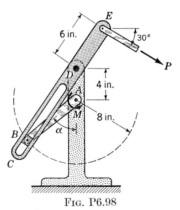

FIG. P6.98

6.99. Solve Prob. 6.98 assuming (*a*) $\alpha = 90°$ and (*b*) $\alpha = 0°$.

7. Forces in Beams and Cables

7.1. Introduction. Internal Forces in Members. In preceding chapters, two basic problems involving structures were considered, (1) the determination of the external forces acting on a structure (Chaps. 3 and 4) and (2) the determination of the forces which hold together the various members forming a structure (Chap. 6). We shall now consider the problem

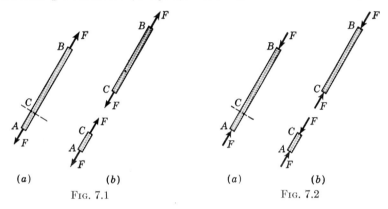

(a)   (b)   (a)   (b)

FIG. 7.1   FIG. 7.2

of determining the internal forces which hold together the various parts of a given member.

We shall first consider a *straight two-force member* AB (Fig. 7.1a). From Sec. 3.16, we know that the forces acting at A and B must be directed along AB in opposite sense and have the same magnitude F. Let us cut, now, the member at C. To maintain the equilibrium of each of the two parts obtained, we must apply to each part a force F as shown in Fig. 7.1b. These forces are directed along AB in opposite sense and are equal in magnitude to the forces applied at A and B. Since the two parts AC and CB were in equilibrium before the member was cut, *internal forces* equivalent to the forces F must have existed in the member itself. We see that, in the case of a straight two-force member, the internal forces acting on each part of the member are equivalent to an axial force F. This force does not depend upon the location of the section C and is referred to as the *force in member AB*. In the case considered, the member is in tension and will elongate under the action of the internal forces. In the case represented in Fig. 7.2, the member is in compression and will decrease in length under the action of the internal forces.

Next we shall consider a *multiforce member*. Take, for instance, member AD of the crane analyzed in Sec. 6.10. This crane is shown again in

211

Fig. 7.3a, and the free-body diagram of member AD is drawn in Fig. 7.3b. We now cut member AD at J and draw a free-body diagram for each of the portions JD and AJ of the member (Fig. 7.3c and d). Considering the free body JD, we find that its equilibrium will be maintained if we apply at J a force F to balance the vertical component of T, a force V to balance the horizontal component of T, and a couple of moment M to balance the moment of T about J. Again we conclude that internal

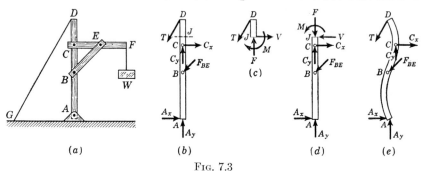

(a)   (b)   (c)   (d)   (e)

FIG. 7.3

forces must have existed at J before member AD was cut. The internal forces acting on the portion JD of member AD are equivalent to the force-couple system shown in Fig. 7.3c. According to Newton's third law, the internal forces acting on AJ must be equivalent to an equal and opposite force-couple system, as shown in Fig. 7.3d. It clearly appears that the action of the internal forces in member AD *is not limited to producing tension or compression* as in the case of straight two-force members; the internal forces *also produce shear and bending.* The force F is again called an *axial force;* the force V is called a *shearing force,* or simply *shear;* and the moment M of the couple is known as the *bending moment* at J. We note that, when determining internal forces in a member, we should clearly indicate on which portion of the member the forces are supposed to act. The deformation which will occur in member AD is sketched in Fig. 7.3e. The actual analysis of such a deformation is part of the study of mechanics of materials.

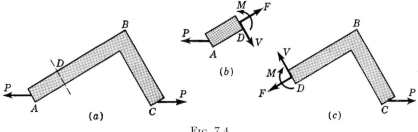

(a)   (b)   (c)

FIG. 7.4

It should be noted that, in a *two-force member which is not straight,* the internal forces are also equivalent to a force-couple system. This is shown in Fig. 7.4, where the two-force member ABC has been cut at D.

In the frame shown, determine the internal forces (a) in member ACF at point J and (b) in member BCD at point K. This frame has been previously considered in Sample Prob. 6.6.

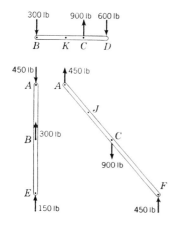

Solution. The reactions and the forces acting on each member of the frame are determined; this has been previously done in Sample Prob. 6.6, and the results are repeated here.

a. Internal Forces at J. Member ACF is cut at point J, and the two parts shown are obtained. The internal forces at J are represented by an equivalent force-couple system and may be determined by considering the equilibrium of either part. Considering the *free body AJ*, we write

$$+\!\!\smallfrown\; \Sigma M_J = 0: \quad (450 \text{ lb})(4 \text{ ft}) - M = 0$$

$$M = +1{,}800 \text{ lb-ft} \qquad M = \textbf{1,800 lb-ft} \;\smallfrown$$

$$+\!\!\searrow\; \Sigma F_x = 0: \quad F - (450 \text{ lb}) \cos 41.7° = 0$$

$$F = +336 \text{ lb} \qquad F = \textbf{336 lb} \;\searrow$$

$$+\!\!\nearrow\; \Sigma F_y = 0: \quad -V + (450 \text{ lb}) \sin 41.7° = 0$$

$$V = +299 \text{ lb} \qquad V = \textbf{299 lb} \;\nearrow$$

The internal forces at J are therefore equivalent to a couple of moment M, an axial force F, and a shear force V. The internal force-couple system acting on part JCF is equal and opposite.

b. Internal Forces at K. We cut member BCD at K and obtain the two parts shown. Considering the *free body BK*, we write

$$+\!\!\smallfrown\; \Sigma M_K = 0: \quad -(300 \text{ lb})(5 \text{ ft}) - M' = 0$$

$$M' = -1{,}500 \text{ lb-ft} \qquad M' = \textbf{1,500 lb-ft} \;\smallfrown$$

$$\xrightarrow{+}\; \Sigma F_x = 0: \qquad F' = 0$$

$$+\!\!\uparrow\; \Sigma F_y = 0: \quad -300 \text{ lb} - V' = 0$$

$$V' = -300 \text{ lb} \qquad V' = \textbf{300 lb} \;\uparrow$$

213

PROBLEMS

7.1 through 7.6. Determine the internal forces (axial force, shear, and bending moment) at point J of the frame indicated:

    7.1. Frame and loading of Prob. 6.53.
    7.2. Frame and loading of Prob. 6.54.
    7.3. Frame and loading of Prob. 6.55.
    7.4. Frame and loading of Prob. 6.62a.
    7.5. Frame and loading of Prob. 6.63.
    7.6. Frame and loading of Prob. 6.62b.

    7.7. A steel channel section forms one side of a flight of stairs. If the total weight of one channel section is 300 lb, determine the internal forces at the center of one channel due to its own weight.

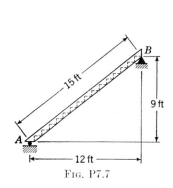

Fɪɢ. P7.7

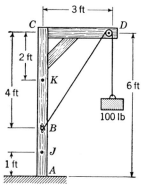

Fɪɢ. P7.8

    7.8. A load $W = 100$ lb is held by a rope which passes over a pulley at D and is tied to a cleat at B. Determine the internal forces at points J and K.

    ***7.9.** The weight of the half section of pipe shown is w lb/ft. If the half section rests on a horizontal surface, determine the internal forces per foot of pipe at point J in terms of w, r, and θ.

    7.10. A half section of pipe 1 ft long rests on a horizontal surface as shown. If the half section of pipe weighs 30 lb and has a diameter of 20 in., determine the bending moment at point J when $\theta = 90°$.

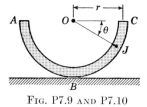

Fɪɢ. P7.9 ᴀɴᴅ P7.10

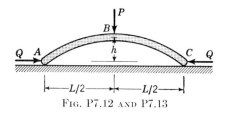

Fɪɢ. P7.12 ᴀɴᴅ P7.13

    ***7.11.** In Prob. 7.9, determine the magnitude and location of the maximum internal axial force.

    7.12. The axis of the curved member ABC is parabolic. If the member rests on a smooth horizontal surface and is subjected to the forces $P = 100$ lb and $Q = 200$ lb, determine the internal forces at a distance $L/4$ from the left end. Assume $h = 4$ in. and $L = 24$ in.

7.13. If the parabolic member shown rests on a smooth surface and is subjected to the forces P and Q shown, determine (a) the internal forces just to the left of point B and (b) the magnitude of Q for which the bending moment at B is zero.

BEAMS

7.2. Various Types of Loading and Support. A structural member designed to support loads applied at various points along the member is known as a *beam*. In most cases, the loads are perpendicular to the axis of the beam and will cause only shear and bending in the beam. When the loads are not at a right angle to the beam, they will also produce axial forces in the beam. Axial forces, however, may usually be neglected in the design of beams, since the ability of a beam to resist shear and especially bending is more critical than its ability to resist axial forces.

Beams are usually long, straight prismatic bars. Designing a beam consists essentially in selecting the cross section which will provide the

(*a*) Concentrated loads   (*b*) Distributed loads

FIG. 7.5. Types of loading.

most effective resistance to the shear and bending moment produced by the applied loads. The design of the beam, therefore, includes two distinct parts. In the first part, the shear and bending moment produced by the loads are determined. The second part is concerned with the selection of the cross section best suited to resist the shears and bending moments determined in the first part. This portion of the chapter, Beams, deals with the first part of the problem of beam design, namely, the determination of the shear and bending moment in beams subjected to various loading conditions and supported in various ways. The second part of the problem belongs to the study of mechanics of materials.

A beam may be subjected to *concentrated loads* (Fig. 7.5a), to *distributed loads* (Fig. 7.5b), or to a combination of both. When the load w per unit length has a constant value over part of the beam (as between A and B in Fig. 7.5b), the load is said to be *uniformly distributed* over that part of the beam. The determination of the reactions at the supports may be considerably simplified if distributed loads are replaced by equivalent concentrated loads, as explained in Sec. 5.6. This substitution, however, should not be performed, or at least should be performed with care, when internal forces are being computed (see Sample Prob. 7.3).

Beams are classified according to the way in which they are supported. Several types of beams frequently used are shown in Fig. 7.6. The distance L between supports is called the *span*. It should be noted that the reactions will be determinate if the supports involve only three unknowns. The reactions will be statically indeterminate if more unknowns are involved; the methods of statics are not sufficient then to determine the reactions, and the properties of the beam with regard to its resistance to bending must be taken into consideration. Beams supported by two rollers are not shown here; such beams are unstable and will move under certain loading conditions.

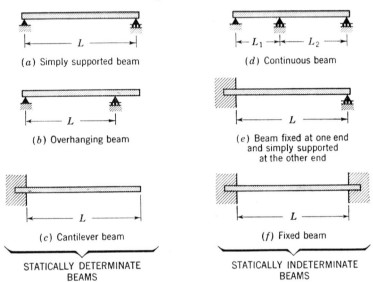

(a) Simply supported beam

(d) Continuous beam

(b) Overhanging beam

(e) Beam fixed at one end and simply supported at the other end

(c) Cantilever beam

(f) Fixed beam

STATICALLY DETERMINATE BEAMS

STATICALLY INDETERMINATE BEAMS

Fig. 7.6. Types of beams.

Sometimes two or more beams are connected by hinges to form a single continuous structure. Two examples of beams hinged at a point H are shown in Fig. 7.7. It will be noted that the reactions at the supports involve four unknowns and cannot be determined from the free-body diagram of the two-beam system. They can be determined, however, by considering the free-body diagram of each beam separately; six unknowns are involved (including two force components at the hinge), and six equations are available.

(a)

(b)

Fig. 7.7. Combined beams.

7.3. Shear and Bending Moment in a Beam. Consider a beam AB subjected to various concentrated and distributed loads (Fig. 7.8a). We propose to determine the shear and bending moment at any point of the beam. In the example considered here, the beam is simply supported, but the method used could be applied to any type of statically determinate beam.

First we determine the reactions at A and B by choosing the entire beam as a free body (Fig. 7.8b); writing $\Sigma M_A = 0$ and $\Sigma M_B = 0$, we obtain, respectively, R_B and R_A.

To determine the internal forces at C, we cut the beam at C and draw the free-body diagrams of the portions AC and CB of the beam (Fig. 7.8c). Equating to zero the sum of the vertical components of all the forces acting on AC, we find that *the shear V at C is equal in magnitude to the algebraic sum of the vertical components of the external forces acting to the*

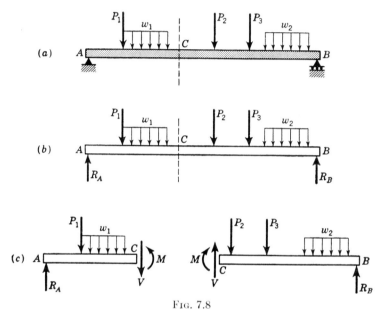

Fig. 7.8

left of C but is opposite in sense. These external forces include the reaction R_A and all the loads applied to the portion AC of the beam. Equating to zero the sum of the moments about C of all the forces acting on AC, we find that *the bending moment M at C is equal in magnitude to the algebraic sum of the moments about C of the external forces acting to the left of C but is opposite in sense.* Again, the moment of the reaction R_A should be included, as well as the moments of all the loads applied to AC.

The shear and bending moment at C can also be obtained from the free-body diagram of the portion CB of the beam. They are found, respectively, equal in magnitude to the algebraic sum of the vertical components and to the algebraic sum of the moments about C of the external forces *acting to the right of C*. This result is identical to the result obtained previously; the sums of the components and the sums of the moments of the external forces acting to the left and to the right of C are *numerically equal* since the beam is in equilibrium.

While this possible choice of alternate free bodies (AC or CB) will facilitate the computation of the numerical values of the shear and bending moment, it makes it necessary to indicate on which portion of the beam the internal forces considered are acting. The internal forces V acting on AC and CB have same magnitude but opposite sense; similarly, the internal couples acting on AC and CB have moments M of same magnitude but of opposite sense. If the shear and bending moment, however, are to be computed at every point of the beam and efficiently recorded, we should not have to specify every time which portion of the beam is used as a free body. We shall adopt, therefore, the following *sign convention:* The shear and bending moment at point C *are said to be positive if the internal forces acting on each portion of the beam are directed as*

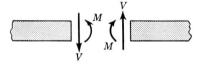

(*a*) Internal forces at section
(positive shear and positive bending moment)

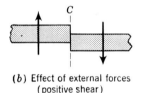

(*b*) Effect of external forces
(positive shear)

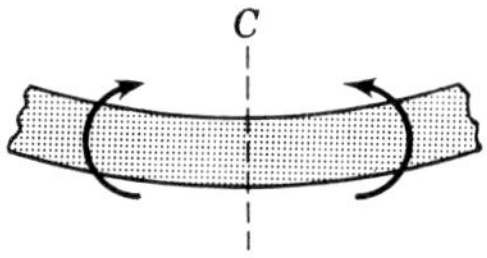

(*c*) Effect of external forces
(positive bending moment)

Fig. 7.9

shown in Figs. 7.8*c* and 7.9*a*. This convention will be more easily remembered if we note that:

1. *The shear at C is positive when the* external *forces (loads and reactions) acting on the beam tend to shear off the beam at C as indicated in Fig.* 7.9*b*.

2. *The bending moment at C is positive when the* external *forces acting on the beam tend to bend the beam at C as indicated in Fig.* 7.9*c*.

7.4. Shear and Bending-moment Diagrams. Now that shear and bending moment have been clearly defined in sense as well as in magnitude, we may easily record their values at any point of a beam by plotting these values against the distance x measured from one end of the beam. The graphs obtained in this way are called, respectively, the *shear diagram* and the *bending-moment diagram.* As an example, consider a simply supported beam AB of span L subjected to a single concentrated load P applied at its mid-point D (Fig. 7.10*a*). We first determine the reactions at the supports from the free-body diagram of the entire beam (Fig. 7.10*b*); we find that each reaction is equal to $P/2$.

Next we cut the beam at a point C between A and D and draw the free-body diagrams of AC and CB (Fig. 7.10*c*). *Assuming that shear* *and bending moment are positive*, we direct the internal forces V and the internal couples M as indicated in Fig. 7.9a. Considering the free body AC and writing that the sum of the vertical components and the sum of the moments about C of the forces acting on the free body are zero, we find $V = +P/2$ and $M = +Px/2$. Both the shear and the bending moment are therefore positive; this may be checked by observing that the reaction at A tends to shear off and to bend the beam at C as indicated in Fig. 7.9b and c. We may plot V and M between A and D (Fig. 7.10e and f); the shear has a constant value $V = P/2$, while the bending moment increases linearly from $M = 0$ at $x = 0$ to $M = PL/4$ at $x = L/2$.

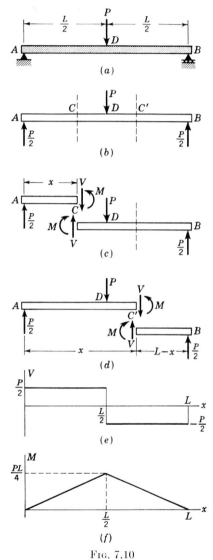

Cutting, now, the beam at a point C' between D and B and considering the free body $C'B$ (Fig. 7.10d), we write that the sum of the vertical components and the sum of the moments about C' of the forces acting on the free body are zero. We obtain $V = -P/2$ and $M = P(L - x)/2$. The shear is therefore negative and the bending moment positive; this may be checked by observing that the reaction at B bends the beam at C' as indicated in Fig. 7.9c but tends to shear it off in a manner opposite to that shown in Fig. 7.9b. We can complete, now, the shear and bending-moment diagrams of Fig. 7.10e and f; the shear has a constant value $V = -P/2$ between D and B, while the bending moment decreases linearly from $M = PL/4$ at $x = L/2$ to $M = 0$ at $x = L$.

We shall note that, when a beam is subjected only to concentrated loads, the shear is of constant value between loads and the bending moment varies linearly between loads. On the other hand, when a beam is subjected to distributed loads, the shear and bending moment vary quite differently (see Sample Prob. 7.3).

Fig. 7.10

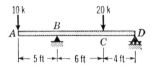

Draw the shear and bending-moment diagram for the beam and loading shown.

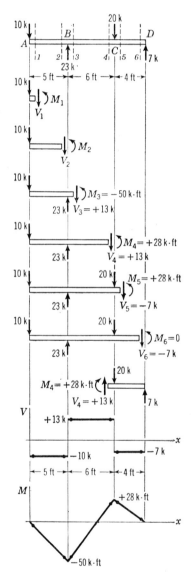

Solution. The reactions are determined by considering the entire beam as a free body; they are

$$R_B = 23 \text{ kips} \uparrow \qquad R_D = 7 \text{ kips} \uparrow$$

We first determine the internal forces just to the right of the 10-kip load at A. Considering the stub of beam to the left of section 1 as a free body and assuming V and M to be positive (according to the standard convention), we write

$$+\uparrow \Sigma F_y = 0: \quad -10 \text{ kips} - V_1 = 0$$
$$V_1 = -10 \text{ kips}$$
$$+\rotatebox{0}{)}\ \Sigma M_1 = 0: \quad -(10 \text{ kips})(0 \text{ ft}) - M_1 = 0$$
$$M_1 = 0$$

We next consider as a free body the portion of beam to the left of section 2 and write

$$+\uparrow \Sigma F_y = 0: \quad -10 \text{ kips} - V_2 = 0$$
$$V_2 = -10 \text{ kips}$$
$$+\rotatebox{0}{)}\ \Sigma M_2 = 0: \quad -(10 \text{ kips})(5 \text{ ft}) - M_2 = 0$$
$$M_2 = -50 \text{ kip-ft}$$

The shear and bending moment at sections 3, 4, 5, and 6 are determined in a similar way from the free-body diagrams shown. For several of the latter sections, the results may be more easily obtained by considering as a free body the portion of the beam to the right of the section. For example, considering the portion of the beam to the right of section 4, we write

$$+\uparrow \Sigma F_y = 0: \quad V_4 - 20 \text{ kips} + 7 \text{ kips} = 0$$
$$V_4 = +13 \text{ kips}$$
$$+\rotatebox{0}{)}\ \Sigma M_4 = 0: \quad +M_4 - (7 \text{ kips})(4 \text{ ft}) = 0$$
$$M_4 = +28 \text{ kip-ft}$$

We may now plot the six points shown on the shear and bending-moment diagrams. As indicated in Sec. 7.4, the shear is of constant value between concentrated loads, and the bending moment varies linearly; we obtain therefore the shear and bending-moment diagrams shown.

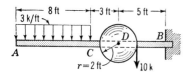

Draw the shear and bending-moment diagrams for the cantilever beam AB. The distributed load of 3 kips/ft extends over 8 ft of the beam and the 10-kip load is applied to a pulley, the shaft of which is rigidly attached to the beam at D.

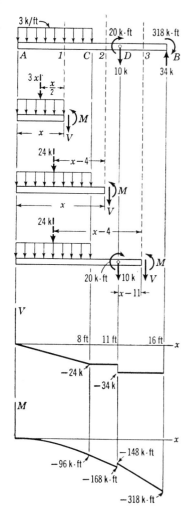

Solution. The 10-kip load is replaced by an equivalent force-couple system acting on the beam at point D. The reaction at B is determined by considering the entire beam as a free body.

From A to C. We determine the internal forces at a distance x from point A by considering the portion of beam to the left of section *1*. That part of the distributed load acting on the free body is replaced by its resultant, and we write

$$+\uparrow \ \Sigma F_y = 0: \quad -3x - V = 0$$
$$V = -3x \text{ kips}$$
$$+\downarrow \ \Sigma M_1 = 0: \quad -3x(\tfrac{1}{2}x) - M = 0$$
$$M = -1.5x^2 \text{ kip-ft}$$

Since the free-body diagram shown may be used for all values of x smaller than 8 ft, the expressions obtained for V and M are valid in the region $0 < x < 8$ ft.

From C to D. Considering the portion of beam to the left of section *2* and again replacing the distributed load by its resultant, we obtain

$$+\uparrow \ \Sigma F_y = 0: \quad -24 - V = 0$$
$$V = -24 \text{ kips}$$
$$+\downarrow \ \Sigma M_2 = 0: \quad -24(x - 4) - M = 0$$
$$M = 96 - 24x \quad \text{kip-ft}$$

These expressions are valid in the region 8 ft $< x <$ 11 ft.

From D to B. Using the portion of beam to the left of section *3*, we obtain for the region 11 ft $< x <$ 16 ft

$$V = -34 \text{ kips} \qquad M = 226 - 34x \qquad \text{kip-ft}$$

The shear and bending-moment diagrams for the entire beam may now be plotted. We note that the couple of moment 20 kip-ft applied at point D introduces a discontinuity into the bending-moment diagram.

221

PROBLEMS

7.14 through 7.17. Draw the shear and bending-moment diagrams for the given beam and loading.

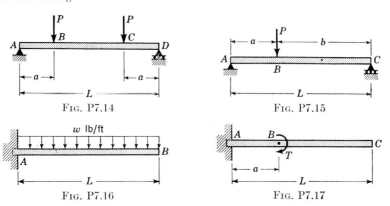

FIG. P7.14

FIG. P7.15

FIG. P7.16

FIG. P7.17

7.18. Draw the shear and bending-moment diagrams for the simple beam shown when $P = 20$ kips and $Q = 30$ kips.

7.19. Draw the shear and bending-moment diagrams for the simple beam shown when $P = 40$ kips and $Q = 15$ kips.

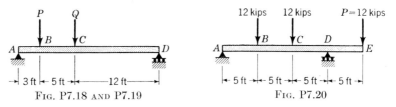

FIG. P7.18 AND P7.19

FIG. P7.20

7.20. Draw the shear and bending-moment diagrams for the overhanging beam shown.

7.21. Solve Prob. 7.20 if the magnitude of the load P is increased to 36 kips.

7.22 through 7.24. Draw the shear and bending-moment diagrams for the beam AB.

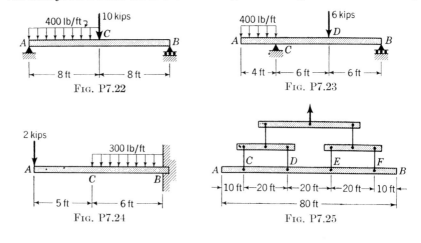

FIG. P7.22

FIG. P7.23

FIG. P7.24

FIG. P7.25

7.25. Concrete piles are designed primarily to resist axial loads, and their bending resistance is relatively small. To lessen the possibility of breaking them, piles are often lifted at several points along their length. By using the arrangement shown, the concrete pile AB is lifted by four equal forces applied at points C, D, E, and F. If the total weight of the pile is 16,000 lb, draw the shear and bending-moment diagrams of the pile. Assume the weight of the pile to be uniformly distributed.

7.26. Draw the shear and bending-moment diagrams for the combined beam shown.

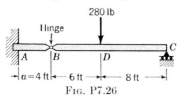

FIG. P7.26

*__7.27.__ For the combined beam of Prob. 7.26, determine the distance a from the left end at which the hinge should be placed to make the maximum bending moment in the beam as small as possible. Assume that the total length of the beam remains equal to 18 ft and that DC remains equal to 8 ft.

7.28. Draw the shear and bending-moment diagrams for the combined beam of Prob. 6.70.

7.29. Draw the shear and bending-moment diagrams for the combined beam of Prob. 6.71.

7.30 and 7.31. Assuming the upward reaction of the ground to be uniformly distributed, draw the shear and bending-moment diagrams for the beam AB.

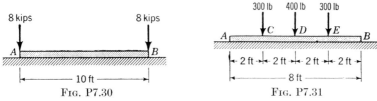

FIG. P7.30   FIG. P7.31

7.32 and 7.33. Draw the shear and bending-moment diagrams for the beam AB. In addition to the vertical loading, couples are applied at each end of the beam as shown.

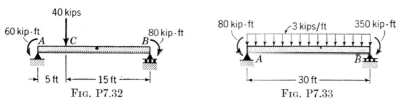

FIG. P7.32   FIG. P7.33

7.34 and 7.35. Draw the shear and bending-moment diagrams for the beam AB. The axle of each pulley is rigidly attached to the beam.

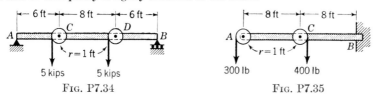

FIG. P7.34   FIG. P7.35

*7.36. A uniform beam (w lb/ft) is to be picked up by cranes at two points A and B. Determine the distance a from the ends of the beam to the points where the crane cables should be attached if the maximum bending moment in the beam is to be as small as possible. (*Hint.* Draw the bending-moment diagram in terms of a, L, and w, and then equate the maximum positive and negative bending moments obtained.)

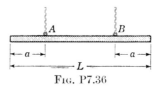

Fig. P7.36

*7.5. Relations between Load, Shear, and Bending Moment. When a beam carries more than two or three concentrated loads, or when it carries distributed loads, the method outlined in Sec. 7.4 for plotting shear and bending moment may prove quite cumbersome. The construction of the shear diagram and, especially, of the bending-moment diagram

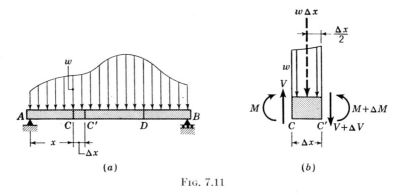

(a)   (b)

Fig. 7.11

will be greatly facilitated if certain relations existing between load, shear, and bending moment are taken into consideration.

Let us consider a simply supported beam AB carrying a distributed load w per unit length (Fig. 7.11a), and let C and C' be two points of the beam at a distance Δx from each other. The shear and bending moment at C will be denoted by V and M, respectively, and will be assumed positive; the shear and bending moment at C' will be denoted by $V + \Delta V$ and $M + \Delta M$.

We now shall detach the portion of beam CC' and draw its free-body diagram (Fig. 7.11b). The forces exerted on the free body include the load $w \Delta x$ and internal forces at C and C'. The forces acting at C consist of the shear V and of a couple of moment M; the forces acting at C' consist of the shear $V + \Delta V$ and of a couple of moment $M + \Delta M$. Shear and bending moment having been assumed positive, the forces and couples will be directed as shown in the figure.

Relations between Load and Shear. Writing that the sum of the vertical components of the forces acting on the free body CC' is zero, we obtain

$$V - (V + \Delta V) - w \, \Delta x = 0$$
$$\Delta V = -w \, \Delta x$$

Dividing both members of the equation by Δx and letting Δx approach zero, we obtain

$$\frac{dV}{dx} = -w \tag{7.1}$$

Formula (7.1) indicates that, for a beam loaded as shown in Fig. 7.11a, the slope dV/dx of the shear curve is negative; the numerical value of the slope at any point is equal to the load per unit length at that point.

Integrating (7.1) between points C and D, we obtain

$$V_D - V_C = -\int_{x_C}^{x_D} w \, dx \tag{7.2}$$
$$\boldsymbol{V_D - V_C = -(\text{area under load curve between } C \text{ and } D)} \tag{7.2'}$$

Note that this result could also have been obtained by considering the equilibrium of the portion of beam CD, since the area under the load curve represents the total load applied between C and D.

It should be observed that formula (7.1) *is not valid* at a point where a concentrated load is applied; the shear curve is discontinuous at such a point, as seen in Sec. 7.4. Similarly, formulas (7.2) and (7.2') cease to be valid when concentrated loads are applied between C and D, since they do not take into account the sudden change in shear caused by a concentrated load. Formulas (7.2) and (7.2'), therefore, should be applied only between successive concentrated loads.

Relations between Shear and Bending Moment. Returning to the free-body diagram of Fig. 7.11b, and writing now that the sum of the moments about C' is zero, we obtain

$$M - (M + \Delta M) + V \, \Delta x - w \, \Delta x \frac{\Delta x}{2} = 0$$
$$\Delta M = V \, \Delta x - \tfrac{1}{2} w (\Delta x)^2$$

Dividing both members of the equation by Δx and letting Δx approach zero, we obtain,

$$\frac{dM}{dx} = V \tag{7.3}$$

Formula (7.3) indicates that the slope dM/dx of the bending-moment curve is equal to the value of the shear. This is true at any point where the shear has a well-defined value, i.e., at any point where no concentrated load is applied. Formula (7.3) also shows that the shear is zero at points where the bending moment is maximum. This property facilitates the determination of the points where the beam is likely to fail under bending.

Integrating (7.3) between points C and D, we obtain

$$M_D - M_C = \int_{x_C}^{x_D} V \, dx \qquad (7.4)$$

$$M_D - M_C = \textbf{area under shear curve between } C \textbf{ and } D \qquad (7.4')$$

Note that the area under the shear curve should be considered positive where the shear is positive and negative where the shear is negative. Formulas (7.4) and (7.4′) are valid even when concentrated loads are applied between C and D, as long as the shear curve has been correctly drawn. The formulas cease to be valid, however, if a *couple* is applied at a point between C and D, since they do not take into account the sudden change in bending moment caused by a couple (see Sample Prob. 7.7).

Example. Let us consider a simply supported beam AB of span L carrying a uniformly distributed load w (Fig. 7.12a). From the free-body diagram of the entire beam we determine the reactions at the supports: $R_A = R_B = wL/2$ (Fig. 7.12b). Next, we draw the shear diagram. Close to the end A of the beam, the shear is equal to R_A, that is, to $wL/2$, as we may check by considering as a free body a very small portion of the beam. Using formula (7.2), we may then determine the shear V at any distance x from A; we write

$$V - V_A = -\int_0^x w \, dx = -wx$$

$$V = V_A - wx = \frac{wL}{2} - wx = w\left(\frac{L}{2} - x\right)$$

The shear curve is thus an oblique straight line which crosses the x axis at $x = L/2$ (Fig. 7.12c). Considering, now, the bending moment, we first observe that $M_A = 0$. The value M of the bending moment at any distance x from A may then be obtained from formula (7.4); we have

$$M - M_A = \int_0^x V \, dx$$

$$M = \int_0^x w\left(\frac{L}{2} - x\right) dx = \frac{w}{2}(Lx - x^2)$$

The bending-moment curve is a parabola. The maximum value of the bending moment occurs when $x = L/2$, since V (and thus dM/dx) is zero for that value of x. Substituting $x = L/2$ in the last equation, we obtain $M_{\max} = wL^2/8$.

In most engineering applications, the value of the bending moment needs to be known only at a few specific points. Once the shear diagram has been drawn, and after M has been determined at one of the ends of the beam, the value of the bending moment may then be obtained at any given point by computing the area under the shear curve and using formula (7.4′). For instance, since $M_A = 0$ in the example considered, the maximum value of the bending moment will be obtained simply by measuring the area of the shaded triangle in Fig. 7.12c. We have

$$M_{\max} = \frac{1}{2}\frac{L}{2}\frac{wL}{2} = \frac{wL^2}{8}$$

We note that, in this example, the load curve is a horizontal straight line, the shear curve an oblique straight line, and the bending-moment curve a parabola. If the load curve had been an oblique straight line

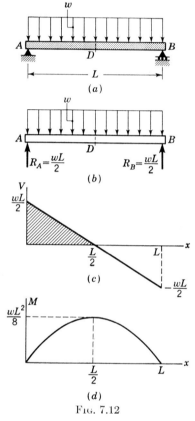

Fig. 7.12

(first degree), the shear curve would have been a parabola (second degree) and the bending-moment curve a cubic (third degree). The shear and bending-moment curves will always be, respectively, one and two degrees higher than the load curve. With this in mind, we should be able to sketch the shear and bending-moment diagrams without actually determining the functions $V(x)$ and $M(x)$, once a few values of the shear and bending moment have been computed. The sketches obtained will be more accurate if we make use of the fact that, at any point where the curves are continuous, the slope of the shear curve is equal to $-w$ and the slope of the bending-moment curve is equal to V.

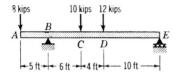

Draw the shear and bending-moment diagrams for the beam and loading shown.

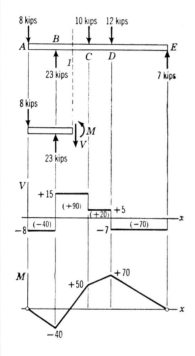

Solution. Considering the entire beam as a free body, we obtain the reactions

$$R_B = 23 \text{ kips} \uparrow \qquad R_E = 7 \text{ kips} \uparrow$$

We also note that at both A and E the bending moment is zero; thus two points (indicated by dots) are obtained on the bending-moment diagram.

Shear Diagram. Since $dV/dx = w$, we find that between loads the slope of the shear diagram is zero (i.e., the shear is constant). The shear at any point is determined by dividing the beam into two parts and considering either part as a free body. For example, using the portion of beam to the left of section *1*, we obtain

$$+\uparrow \Sigma F_y = 0: \quad -8 + 23 - V = 0$$
$$V = +15 \text{ kips}$$

Bending-moment Diagram. We recall that the area under the shear curve between two points is equal to the change in bending moment between the same two points. For convenience, the area of each portion of the shear diagram is computed and is indicated on the diagram. Since the bending moment at the free end M_A is known to be zero, we write

$$M_B - M_A = -40 \qquad M_B = -40 \text{ kip-ft}$$
$$M_C - M_B = +90 \qquad M_C = +50 \text{ kip-ft}$$
$$M_D - M_C = +20 \qquad M_D = +70 \text{ kip-ft}$$
$$M_E - M_D = -70 \qquad M_E = 0 \text{ kip-ft}$$

Since M_E is known to be zero, a check of the computations is obtained.

The shear being constant between successive loads, the slope dM/dx is constant and the bending-moment diagram is obtained by connecting the known points with straight lines. From the V and M diagrams we note that $V_{max} = 15$ kips, and $M_{max} = 70$ kip-ft.

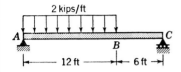

Draw the shear and bending-moment diagrams for the beam and loading shown.

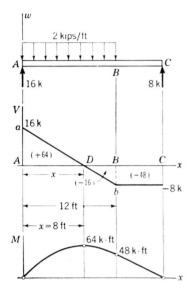

Solution. Considering the entire beam as a free body, we obtain the reactions

$$R_A = 16 \text{ kips} \uparrow \qquad R_C = 8 \text{ kips} \uparrow$$

Shear Diagram. The shear just to the right of A is $V_A = +16$ kips. Since the change in shear between two points is equal to *minus* the area under the load curve between the same two points, we obtain V_B by writing

$$V_B - V_A = -(2)(12) = -24$$

$$V_B = -24 + V_A = -24 + 16 = -8 \text{ kips}$$

The slope $dV/dx = -w$ being constant between A and B, the shear diagram between these two points is represented by a straight line. Between B and C, the area under the load curve is zero; therefore,

$$V_C - V_B = 0 \qquad V_C = V_B = -8 \text{ kips}$$

and the shear is constant between B and C.

Bending-moment Diagram. We note that the bending moment at each end of the beam is zero. In order to determine the maximum bending moment, we locate the section D of the beam where $V = 0$. Considering the portion of the shear diagram between A and B, we note that the triangles DAa and DBb are similar; thus,

$$\frac{x}{16 \text{ kips}} = \frac{12 - x}{8 \text{ kips}} \qquad x = 8 \text{ ft}$$

The maximum bending moment occurs at point D, where $dM/dx = V = 0$. The areas of the various portions of the shear diagram are computed and are given (in parentheses) on the diagram. Since the area of the shear diagram between two points is equal to the change in bending moment between the same two points, we write

$$M_D - M_A = +64 \text{ kip-ft} \qquad M_D = +64 \text{ kip-ft}$$

$$M_B - M_D = -16 \text{ kip-ft} \qquad M_B = +48 \text{ kip-ft}$$

$$M_C - M_B = -48 \text{ kip-ft} \qquad M_C = 0$$

The bending-moment diagram consists of an arc of parabola followed by a segment of straight line; the slope of the parabola at A is equal to the value of V at that point.

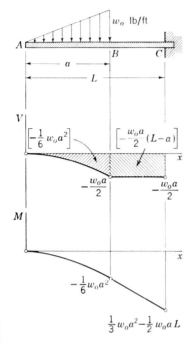

Sketch the shear and bending-moment diagrams for the cantilever beam shown.

Solution. *Shear Diagram.* At the free end of the beam, we find $V_A = 0$. Between A and B, the area under the load curve is $\frac{1}{2}w_0a$; we find V_B by writing

$$V_B - V_A = -\tfrac{1}{2}w_0a \qquad V_B = -\tfrac{1}{2}w_0a$$

Between B and C, the beam is not loaded; thus $V_C = V_B$. At A, we have $w = 0$, and therefore $dV/dx = 0$; between A and B, the loading increases linearly, and the shear diagram is parabolic. Between B and C, $w = 0$, and the shear diagram is a horizontal line.

Bending-moment Diagram. The bending moment at the free end of the beam is zero. We compute the area under the shear curve and write

$$M_B - M_A = -\tfrac{1}{6}w_0a^2 \qquad M_B = -\tfrac{1}{6}w_0a^2$$

$$M_C - M_B = -\tfrac{1}{2}w_0a(L - a)$$

$$M_C = \tfrac{1}{3}w_0a^2 - \tfrac{1}{2}w_0aL$$

The sketch of the bending-moment diagram is completed by recalling that $dM/dx = V$. We find that between A and B the diagram is represented by a cubic curve and between B and C by a straight line

---

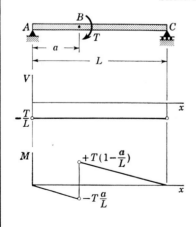

The simple beam AC is loaded by a couple of moment T applied at point B. Draw the shear and bending-moment diagrams of the beam.

Solution. The entire beam is taken as a free body, and we obtain

$$R_A = \frac{T}{L} \downarrow \qquad R_C = \frac{T}{L} \uparrow$$

The shear at any section is constant and equal to $-T/L$. Since a couple is applied at B, the bending-moment diagram is discontinuous at B; the bending moment increases suddenly by an amount equal to T.

PROBLEMS

7.37. Using the methods of Sec. 7.5, solve Prob. 7.15.
7.38. Using the methods of Sec. 7.5, solve Prob. 7.16.
7.39. Using the methods of Sec. 7.5, solve Prob. 7.19.
7.40. Using the methods of Sec. 7.5, solve Prob. 7.18.
7.41. Using the methods of Sec. 7.5, solve Prob. 7.20.
7.42. Using the methods of Sec. 7.5, solve Prob. 7.22.
7.43. Using the methods of Sec. 7.5, solve Prob. 7.23.
7.44. Using the methods of Sec. 7.5, solve Prob. 7.24.
7.45 through 7.50. Draw the shear and bending-moment diagrams for the given beam and loading.

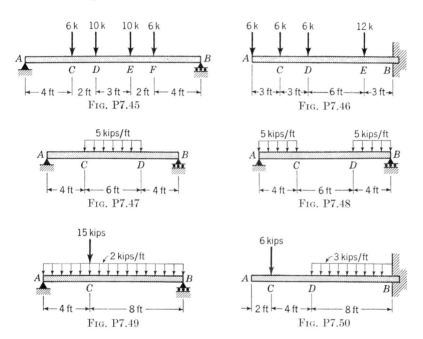

Fig. P7.45   Fig. P7.46

Fig. P7.47   Fig. P7.48

Fig. P7.49   Fig. P7.50

7.51 and 7.52. For the given beam and loading, draw the shear and bending-moment diagrams, and determine the magnitude and location of the maximum positive bending moment.

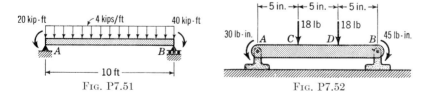

Fig. P7.51   Fig. P7.52

7.53 and 7.54. Determine the equations of the shear and bending-moment curves for the given beam and loading.

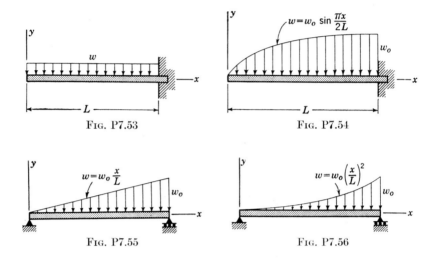

FIG. P7.53   FIG. P7.54

FIG. P7.55   FIG. P7.56

*7.55 and 7.56. Determine the equations of the shear and bending-moment curves for the given beam and loading. Also determine the magnitude and location of the maximum bending moment in the beam. (*Hint.* Use the formula $dM/dx = V$ to find the location of the maximum bending moment.)

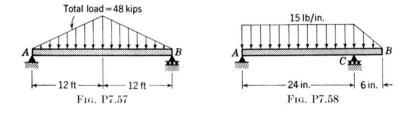

FIG. P7.57   FIG. P7.58

7.57 and 7.58. Draw the shear and bending-moment diagrams, and determine the magnitude and location of the maximum bending moment for the beam and loading shown.

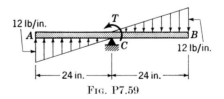

FIG. P7.59

7.59. Determine the couple T required to maintain the beam in equilibrium, and draw the shear and bending-moment diagrams.

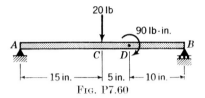

Fig. P7.60

7.60. Draw the shear and bending-moment diagrams for the beam and loading shown.

CABLES

*7.6. Cables with Concentrated Loads. Cables are used in many engineering applications, such as suspension bridges, transmission lines, aerial tramways, guy wires for high towers, etc. Cables may be divided

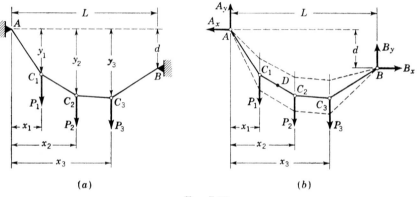

(a)   (b)

Fig. 7.13

into two categories, according to their loading: (1) cables supporting concentrated loads; (2) cables supporting distributed loads. In this section, we shall examine cables of the first category.

Consider a cable attached to two fixed points A and B and supporting n given vertical concentrated loads P_1, P_2, . . . , P_n (Fig. 7.13a). We assume that the cable is *flexible*, i.e., that its resistance to bending is small and may be neglected. We further assume that the *weight of the cable is negligible* compared with the loads supported by the cable. Any portion of cable between successive loads may therefore be considered as a two-force member, and the internal forces at any point in the cable reduce to a *force of tension directed along the cable*.

We assume that each of the loads lies in a given vertical line, i.e., that the horizontal distance from support A to each of the loads is known; we also assume that the horizontal and vertical distances between the supports are known. We propose to determine the shape of the cable, i.e., the vertical distance from A to each of the points $C_1, C_2, \ldots, C_n$, and also the tension T in each portion of the cable.

We first draw the free-body diagram of the entire cable (Fig. 7.13b). Since the slope of the portions of cable attached at A and B is not known, the reactions at A and B must be represented by two components each. Thus, four unknowns are involved, and the three equations of equilibrium are not sufficient to determine the reactions at A and B.† We must therefore obtain an additional equation by considering the equilibrium of a portion of the cable. This is possible if we know the coordinates x and y of a point D of the cable. Drawing the free-body diagram of the portion of cable AD (Fig. 7.14a) and writing $\Sigma M_D = 0$, we obtain an additional relation between A_x and A_y and may determine the reactions

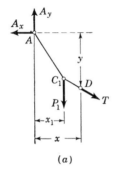 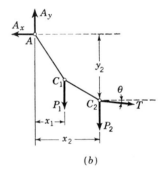

(a)   (b)

Fig. 7.14

at A and B. The problem would remain indeterminate, however, if we did not know the coordinates of D, unless some other relation between A_x and A_y (or between B_x and B_y) were given. The cable might hang in any of various possible ways, as indicated by the dashed lines in Fig. 7.13b.

Once A_x and A_y have been determined, the vertical distance from A to any point of the cable may be easily found. Considering point C_2, for example, we draw the free-body diagram of the portion of cable AC_2 (Fig. 7.14b). Writing $\Sigma M_{C_2} = 0$, we obtain an equation which may be solved for y_2. Writing $\Sigma F_x = 0$ and $\Sigma F_y = 0$, we obtain the components of the tension T in the portion of cable to the right of C_2. We observe that $T \cos \theta = A_x$; *the horizontal component of the tension is the same at any point of the cable.* It follows that the tension T is maximum when $\cos \theta$ is minimum, i.e., in the portion of cable which has the largest angle of inclination θ. Clearly, this portion of cable must be adjacent to one of the two supports of the cable.

† Clearly, the cable is not a rigid body; the equilibrium equations represent therefore *necessary but not sufficient conditions* (see Sec. 6.11).

7.7. Cables with Distributed Loads. Consider a cable attached to two fixed points A and B and carrying a *distributed load* (Fig. 7.15a). We saw in the preceding section that, for a cable supporting concentrated loads, the internal force at any point is a force of tension directed along the cable. In the case of a cable carrying a distributed load, the cable hangs in the shape of a curve, and the internal force at a point D is a force of tension *directed along the tangent to the curve.* Given a certain distributed load, we propose in this section to determine the tension at any point of the cable. We shall also see in the following sections how the shape of the cable may be determined for two particular types of distributed loads.

Considering the most general case of distributed load, we draw the free-body diagram of the portion of cable extending from the lowest point C to a given point D of the cable (Fig. 7.15b). The forces acting on the

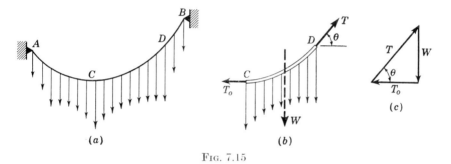

(a)   (b)   (c)

Fig. 7.15

free body are the tension T_0 at C, which is horizontal, the tension T at D, directed along the tangent to the cable at D, and the resultant W of the distributed load supported by the portion of cable CD. Drawing the corresponding force triangle (Fig. 7.15c), we obtain the following relations:

$$T \cos \theta = T_0 \qquad T \sin \theta = W \qquad (7.5)$$

$$T = \sqrt{T_0^2 + W^2} \qquad \tan \theta = \frac{W}{T_0} \qquad (7.6)$$

From the relations (7.5), it appears that the horizontal component of the tension is the same at any point and that the vertical component of the tension is equal to the load W measured from the lowest point. Relations (7.6) show that the tension is minimum at the lowest point and maximum at one of the two points of support.

7.8. Parabolic Cable. Let us assume, now, that the cable AB carries a load *uniformly distributed along the horizontal* (Fig. 7.16a). Cables of suspension bridges may be assumed loaded in this way, since the weight of the cables is small compared with the weight of the roadway. Denoting by w the load per unit length (*measured horizontally*) and choosing coordinate axes with origin at the lowest point C of the cable, we find that the total load W carried by the portion of cable extending from C to the point D of coordinates x and y is $W = wx$. The relations (7.6) defining the magnitude and direction of the tension at D become

$$T = \sqrt{T_0^2 + w^2 x^2} \qquad \tan \theta = \frac{wx}{T_0} \tag{7.7}$$

Moreover, the distance from D to the line of action of the resultant W is equal to half the horizontal distance from C to D (Fig. 7.16b). Summing moments about D, we write

$$+\,\underset{\displaystyle \lrcorner}{} \Sigma\, M_D = 0: \qquad y T_0 - \frac{x}{2}\, wx = 0$$

$$\boldsymbol{y = \frac{wx^2}{2T_0}} \tag{7.8}$$

This is the equation of a *parabola* with a vertical axis and its vertex at the origin of coordinates. The curve formed by cables loaded uniformly along the horizontal is thus a parabola.†

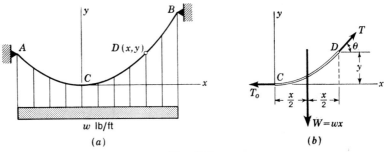

Fig. 7.16

When the supports A and B of the cable have the same elevation, the distance L between the supports is called the *span* of the cable and the vertical distance h from the supports to the lowest point is called the *sag* of the cable (Fig. 7.17a). If the span and sag of a cable are known, and if the load w per unit horizontal length is given, the minimum tension T_0 may be found by substituting $x = L/2$ and $y = h$ in formula (7.8).

† Cables hanging under their own weight are not loaded uniformly along the horizontal, and they do not form a parabola. The error introduced by assuming a parabolic shape for cables hanging under their own weight, however, is small when the cable is sufficiently taut. A complete discussion of cables hanging under their own weight is given in the next section.

Formulas (7.7) and (7.8) will then define the tension at any point and the shape of the cable.

When the supports have different elevations, the position of the lowest point of the cable is not known and the coordinates x_A, y_A and x_B, y_B of the supports must be determined. To this effect, we express that the coordinates of A and B satisfy Eq. (7.8) and that $x_B - x_A = L$, $y_B - y_A = d$, where L and d denote, respectively, the horizontal and vertical distances between the two supports (Fig. 7.17b and c).

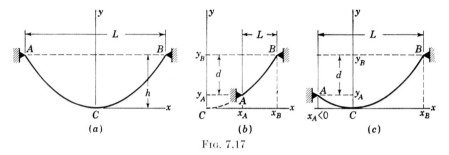

Fɪɢ. 7.17

The length of the cable from its lowest point C to its support B may be obtained from the formula

$$s_B = \int_0^{x_B} \sqrt{1 + \left(\frac{dy}{dx}\right)^2}\, dx \tag{7.9}$$

Differentiating (7.8), we obtain the derivative $dy/dx = wx/T_0$; substituting into (7.9) and using the binomial theorem to expand the radical in an infinite series, we have

$$
\begin{aligned}
s_B &= \int_0^{x_B} \sqrt{1 + \frac{w^2 x^2}{T_0^2}}\, dx \\
&= \int_0^{x_B} \left(1 + \frac{w^2 x^2}{2 T_0^2} - \frac{w^4 x^4}{8 T_0^4} + \cdots\right) dx \\
&= x_B \left(1 + \frac{w^2 x_B^2}{6 T_0^2} - \frac{w^4 x_B^4}{40 T_0^4} + \cdots\right)
\end{aligned}
$$

and since $wx_B^2/2T_0 = y_B$,

$$s_B = x_B \left[1 + \frac{2}{3}\left(\frac{y_B}{x_B}\right)^2 - \frac{2}{5}\left(\frac{y_B}{x_B}\right)^4 + \cdots\right] \tag{7.10}$$

The series converges for values of the ratio y_B/x_B less than 0.5; in most cases, this ratio is much smaller, and only the first two terms of the series need be computed.

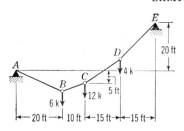

The cable AE supports three vertical loads from the points indicated. If point C is 5 ft below the left support, determine (a) the elevations of points B and D, (b) the maximum slope and the maximum tension in the cable.

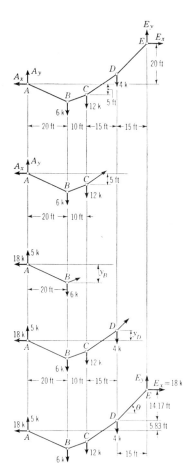

Solution. The reaction components A_x and A_y are determined as follows:

Free body: Entire cable

$+\circlearrowleft \Sigma M_E = 0:$ $A_y(60 \text{ ft}) + A_x(20 \text{ ft})$
$- (6 \text{ kips})(40 \text{ ft}) - (12 \text{ kips})(30 \text{ ft})$
$- (4 \text{ kips})(15 \text{ ft}) = 0$

$$60A_y + 20A_x - 660 = 0$$

Free body: ABC

$+\circlearrowleft \Sigma M_C = 0:$ $A_y(30 \text{ ft}) - A_x(5 \text{ ft})$
$- (6 \text{ kips})(10 \text{ ft}) = 0$

$$30A_y - 5A_x - 60 = 0$$

Solving the two equations simultaneously, we obtain

$$A_x = 18 \text{ kips} \leftarrow \qquad A_y = 5 \text{ kips} \uparrow$$

a. Elevation of Point B. Considering the portion of cable AB as a free body, we write

$+\circlearrowleft \Sigma M_B = 0:$ $-(18 \text{ kips})y_B$
$+ (5 \text{ kips})(20 \text{ ft}) = 0$

$$y_B = \textbf{5.56 ft} \qquad \textbf{below } A$$

Elevation of Point D. Using the portion of cable $ABCD$ as a free body and writing $\Sigma M_D = 0$, we obtain

$$y_D = \textbf{5.83 ft} \qquad \textbf{above } A$$

b. Maximum Slope and Maximum Tension. We observe that the maximum slope occurs in portion DE. Since the horizontal component of the tension is constant and equal to 18 kips, we write

$$\tan \theta = \frac{14.17 \text{ ft}}{15 \text{ ft}} \qquad \theta = \textbf{43.4°}$$

$$T_{\max} = \frac{18 \text{ kips}}{\cos \theta} \qquad T_{\max} = \textbf{24.8 kips}$$

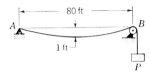

A light cable weighing 40 lb is attached to a support at A, passes over a small pulley at B, and supports a load P. Knowing that the sag of the cable is 1 ft, determine (a) the load P and (b) the total length of the cable from A to B. Since the ratio of the sag to the span is small, assume the cable to be parabolic. Also neglect the weight of the portion of cable from B to P.

a. **Load** P. The lowest point O of the cable is chosen as the origin of coordinates; the equation of the cable is given by Eq. (7.8),

$$y = \frac{wx^2}{2T_0}$$

Assuming the load to be uniformly distributed along the horizontal, we have

$$w = \frac{40 \text{ lb}}{80 \text{ ft}} = 0.5 \text{ lb/ft}$$

Since the cable passes through point B, we may determine T_0 as follows:

$$x_B = 40 \text{ ft} \qquad y_B = 1 \text{ ft}$$

$$y_B = \frac{wx_B^2}{2T_0} \qquad 1 = \frac{(0.5)(40)^2}{2T_0} \qquad T_0 = 400 \text{ lb}$$

Using Eq. (7.7), we find that the tension at B is

$$T_B = \sqrt{T_0^2 + w^2x_B^2}$$
$$= \sqrt{(400)^2 + (0.5)^2(40)^2} = 400.5 \text{ lb}$$

Since the tension on each side of the pulley is the same, we find

$$P = T_B = \textbf{400.5 lb}$$

b. **Length of Cable.** We consider the right half of the cable and apply Eq. (7.10),

$$s_B = x_B \left[1 + \frac{2}{3}\left(\frac{y_B}{x_B}\right)^2 + \cdots \right]$$
$$= 40 \left[1 + (\tfrac{2}{3})(\tfrac{1}{40})^2 + \cdots \right] = 40.0167 \text{ ft}$$

The total length of the cable between A and B is twice this value,

$$\text{Length} = 2s_B = \textbf{80.033 ft}$$

SAMPLE PROBLEM 7.10

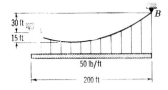

Cable AB supports a load distributed uniformly along the horizontal as shown. The lowest point of the cable is 15 ft below the support A. Determine the maximum and minimum values of the tension in the cable.

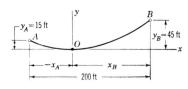

Solution. Since the load is distributed uniformly along the horizontal, the cable is parabolic; choosing the origin of coordinates at the lowest point O, the equation of the cable is given by Eq. (7.8),

$$y = \frac{wx^2}{2T_0} \tag{1}$$

From the geometry of the sketch, we note that x_A is negative as drawn and write

$$y_A = 15 \text{ ft} \qquad y_B = 45 \text{ ft}$$

$$x_B - x_A = 200 \text{ ft} \qquad \text{or} \qquad x_A = x_B - 200 \text{ ft}$$

Substituting successively the coordinates of A and B into Eq. (1), we obtain

Point A:
$$y_A = \frac{wx_A^2}{2T_0} \qquad 15 = \frac{w(x_B - 200)^2}{2T_0} \tag{2}$$

Point B:
$$y_B = \frac{wx_B^2}{2T_0} \qquad 45 = \frac{wx_B^2}{2T_0} \tag{3}$$

Dividing (2) by (3) member by member and solving for x_B, we obtain

$$\frac{15}{45} = \frac{(x_B - 200)^2}{x_B^2} \qquad x_B = 473 \text{ ft} \qquad \text{and} \qquad \mathbf{x_B = 126.8 \text{ ft}}$$

The first root is discarded since it is larger than 200 ft.

Minimum Tension. The minimum tension occurs at O and equals T_0. Substituting the computed coordinates of point B into Eq. (1), we find

$$y = \frac{wx^2}{2T_0} \qquad 45 = \frac{(50)(126.8)^2}{2T_0} \qquad \mathbf{T_0 = 8,930 \text{ lb}}$$

Maximum Tension. Since the slope is maximum at B, the maximum tension T_{max} occurs at B. Substituting the coordinates of B into Eq. (7.7), we find

$$T_{max} = \sqrt{T_0^2 + w^2x^2} = \sqrt{(8,930)^2 + (50)^2(126.8)^2} \qquad \mathbf{T_{max} = 10,950 \text{ lb}}$$

PROBLEMS

7.61. Two vertical loads are suspended as shown from the cable $ABCD$. Determine the components of the reaction at A and the difference in elevation between A and B.

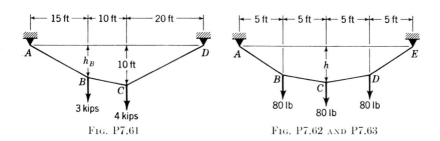

Fig. P7.61   Fig. P7.62 and P7.63

7.62. Three 80-lb loads are suspended from the cable AE. If $h = 4$ ft, determine the components of the reaction at A and the maximum value of the tension in the cable.

7.63. For the cable and loading shown, determine the sag h if the maximum value of the tension in the cable is 200 lb.

7.64. Determine the components of the reaction at each support for the cable and loading shown.

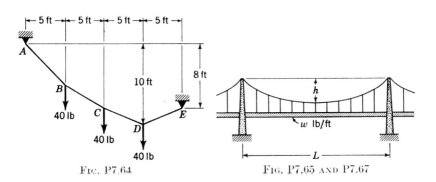

Fig. P7.64   Fig. P7.65 and P7.67

7.65. The center span of a suspension bridge consists of a uniform roadway suspended from cables. The uniform load supported by each cable is $w = 4$ kips/ft along the horizontal. If $L = 400$ ft and $h = 50$ ft, determine the maximum and minimum values of the tension in each cable.

7.66. Solve Prob. 7.65 if $w = 3$ kips/ft, $L = 200$ ft, and $h = 30$ ft.

7.67. The horizontal component of the cable tension is $T_0 = 32$ kips for the bridge shown. If $L = 350$ ft and $h = 40$ ft, determine the load supported by each cable and the length of the cables.

7.68. A force $T_0 = 80$ lb is required to hold the cable shown so that it is horizontal at A. Determine the weight per foot of the cable and the maximum tension. (Assume the cable to be parabolic.)

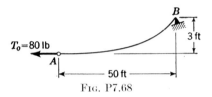

FIG. P7.68

7.69. A cable hangs between two supports at the same elevation and 200 ft apart. If the sag is 30 ft and the maximum cable tension is limited to 50,000 lb, determine the allowable load per foot along the horizontal which may be suspended from the cable. Also determine the length of the cable.

7.70. The maximum tension in the chain shown is to be 750 lb. If the chain weighs 5 lb/ft, determine the required value of the sag. (Assume the chain to be parabolic.)

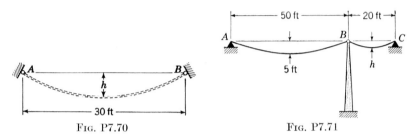

FIG. P7.70   FIG. P7.71

7.71. Two cables, each weighing w lb/ft, are attached to a tower at B as shown. In order to avoid bending in the tower, the horizontal component of the resultant of the forces exerted by the cables at B must be zero. Determine the required sag of cable BC. Assume the cables to be parabolic.

*7.72. A cable of total length 420 ft is suspended between two points at the same elevation and 400 ft apart. Assuming the cable to be parabolic, determine the approximate sag. [*Hint.* Use only the first two terms of Eq. (7.10).]

7.73. For the cable and loading shown, determine the location of the lowest point C and the maximum cable tension.

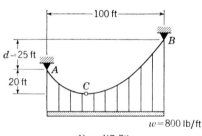

FIG. P7.73

7.74. Solve Prob. 7.73 assuming that the value of d is changed to 15 ft.

7.75. The loading of a cable varies linearly from zero at the lowest point to w_0 at each support. Determine the equation of the curve assumed by each half of the cable.

7.76. The cable AB supports a uniform load of w lb/ft as shown. Determine the sag at the quarter point and the components of the reaction at A in terms of L, w, and h.

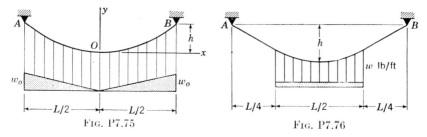

FIG. P7.75   FIG. P7.76

*7.77. Show that the curve assumed by a cable carrying a distributed load $w(x)$ is defined by the differential equation $d^2y/dx^2 = w(x)/T_0$, where T_0 is the tension at the lowest point.

*7.78. Using the property indicated in Prob. 7.77, determine the curve assumed by a cable of span L and sag h carrying a distributed load $w = w_0 \cos(\pi x/L)$, where x is measured from mid-span. Also determine the maximum and minimum values of the tension.

*7.9. Catenary. We shall consider now a cable AB carrying a load *uniformly distributed along the cable itself* (Fig. 7.18a). Cables hanging

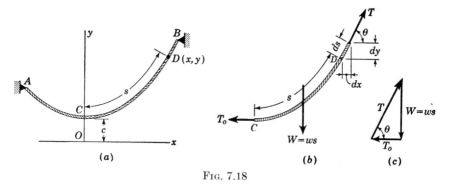

FIG. 7.18

under their own weight are loaded in this way. Denoting by w the load per unit length (*measured along the cable*), we find that the total load W carried by a portion of cable of length s extending from the lowest point C to a point D is $W = ws$. Substituting this value for W in formula (7.6), we obtain the tension at D,

$$T = \sqrt{T_0^2 + w^2 s^2}$$

In order to simplify the subsequent computations, we shall introduce the constant $c = T_0/w$. We thus write

$$T_0 = wc \qquad W = ws \qquad T = w\sqrt{c^2 + s^2} \qquad (7.11)$$

The free-body diagram of the portion of cable CD is shown in Fig. 7.18b. This diagram, however, cannot be used to obtain directly the equation of the curve assumed by the cable, since we do not know the horizontal distance from D to the line of action of the resultant W of the load. To obtain this equation, we shall write first that the horizontal projection of a small element of cable of length ds is $dx = ds \cos \theta$. Observing from Fig. 7.18c that $\cos \theta = T_0/T$ and using (7.11), we write

$$dx = ds \cos \theta = \frac{T_0}{T} ds = \frac{wc\, ds}{w \sqrt{c^2 + s^2}} = \frac{ds}{\sqrt{1 + s^2/c^2}}$$

Selecting the origin O of the coordinates at a distance c directly below C (Fig. 7.18a) and integrating from $C(0,c)$ to $D(x,y)$, we obtain†

$$x = \int_0^s \frac{ds}{\sqrt{1 + s^2/c^2}} = c \left[\sinh^{-1} \frac{s}{c} \right]_0^s = c \sinh^{-1} \frac{s}{c}$$

This equation, which relates the length s of the portion of cable CD and the horizontal distance x, may be written in the form

$$s = c \sinh \frac{x}{c} \tag{7.15}$$

The relation between the coordinates x and y may now be obtained by writing $dy = dx \tan \theta$. Observing from Fig. 7.18c that $\tan \theta = W/T_0$ and using (7.11) and (7.15), we write

$$dy = dx \tan \theta = \frac{W}{T_0} dx = \frac{s}{c} dx = \sinh \frac{x}{c} dx$$

† This integral may be found in all standard integral tables. The function

$$z = \sinh^{-1} u$$

(read "arc hyperbolic sine u") is the *inverse* of the function $u = \sinh z$ (read "hyperbolic sine z"). This function and the function $v = \cosh z$ (read "hyperbolic cosine z") are defined as follows:

$$u = \sinh z = \tfrac{1}{2}(e^z - e^{-z}) \qquad v = \cosh z = \tfrac{1}{2}(e^z + e^{-z})$$

Numerical values of these functions are found in *tables of hyperbolic functions*. The student is referred to any calculus text for a complete description of the properties of these functions. In this section, we shall make use only of the following properties, which may be easily derived from the above definitions:

$$\frac{d \sinh z}{dz} = \cosh z \qquad \frac{d \cosh z}{dz} = \sinh z \tag{7.12}$$

$$\sinh 0 = 0 \qquad \cosh 0 = 1 \tag{7.13}$$

$$\cosh^2 z - \sinh^2 z = 1 \tag{7.14}$$

Integrating from $C(0,c)$ to $D(x,y)$ and using (7.12) and (7.13), we obtain

$$y - c = \int_0^x \sinh \frac{x}{c}\, dx = c \left[\cosh \frac{x}{c} \right]_0^x = c \left(\cosh \frac{x}{c} - 1 \right)$$

$$y = c \cosh \frac{x}{c} \qquad \qquad \text{(7.16)}$$

This is the equation of a *catenary* with vertical axis. The ordinate c of the lowest point C is called the *parameter* of the catenary. Squaring both sides of Eqs. (7.15) and (7.16), subtracting, and taking (7.14) into account, we obtain the following relation between y and s:

$$y^2 - s^2 = c^2 \qquad \qquad \text{(7.17)}$$

Solving (7.17) for s^2 and carrying into the last of the relations (7.11), we write these relations as follows:

$$T_0 = wc \qquad W = ws \qquad T = wy \qquad \text{(7.18)}$$

The last relation indicates that the tension at any point D of the cable is proportional to the vertical distance from D to the horizontal line representing the x axis.

When the supports A and B of the cable have the same elevation, the distance L between the supports is called the *span* of the cable and the vertical distance h from the supports to the lowest point C is called the *sag* of the cable. These definitions are the same that were given in the case of parabolic cables, but it should be noted that, because of our choice of coordinate axes, the sag h is now

$$h = y_A - c \qquad \qquad \text{(7.19)}$$

It should also be observed that certain catenary problems involve transcendental equations which must be solved by successive approximations (see Sample Prob. 7.11). When the cable is fairly taut, however, the load may be assumed uniformly distributed *along the horizontal* and the catenary may be replaced by a parabola. The solution of the problem is thus greatly simplified, while the error introduced is small.

When the supports A and B have different elevations, the position of the lowest point of the cable is not known. The problem may be solved then in a manner similar to that used for parabolic cables, by expressing that the cable must pass through the supports and that $x_B - x_A = L$, $y_B - y_A = d$, where L and d denote, respectively, the horizontal and vertical distances between the two supports.

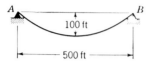

A uniform cable weighing 3 lb/ft is suspended between two points A and B as shown. Determine (a) the maximum and minimum values of the tension in the cable and (b) the length of the cable.

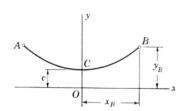

Solution. Equation of Cable. The origin of coordinates is placed at a distance c below the lowest point of the cable. The equation of the cable is given by Eq. (7.16),

$$y = c \cosh \frac{x}{c}$$

The coordinates of point B are

$$x_B = 250 \text{ ft} \qquad y_B = 100 + c$$

Substituting these coordinates into the equation of the cable, we obtain

$$100 + c = c \cosh \frac{250}{c}$$

$$\frac{100}{c} + 1 = \cosh \frac{250}{c}$$

The value of c is determined by assuming successive trial values, as shown in the following table:

c	$\dfrac{250}{c}$	$\dfrac{100}{c}$	$\dfrac{100}{c}+1$	$\cosh\dfrac{250}{c}$
300	0.833	0.333	1.333	1.367
350	0.714	0.286	1.286	1.266
330	0.758	0.303	1.303	1.301
328	0.762	0.305	1.305	1.305

Taking $c = 328$, we have

$$y_B = 100 + c = 428 \text{ ft}$$

a. Maximum and Minimum Values of the Tension. Using Eqs. (7.18), we obtain

$$T_{\min} = T_0 = wc = (3 \text{ lb/ft})(328 \text{ ft}) \qquad T_{\min} = \textbf{984 lb}$$

$$T_{\max} = T_B = wy_B = (3 \text{ lb/ft})(428 \text{ ft}) \qquad T_{\max} = \textbf{1,284 lb}$$

b. Length of Cable. One-half the length of the cable is found by solving Eq. (7.17),

$$y_B^2 - s_{CB}^2 = c^2 \qquad s_{CB}^2 = y_B^2 - c^2 = (428)^2 - (328)^2 \qquad s_{CB} = 275 \text{ ft}$$

The total length of the cable is therefore

$$s_{AB} = 2s_{CB} = 2(275 \text{ ft}) \qquad s_{AB} = \textbf{550 ft}$$

PROBLEMS

7.79. A cable of total length 400 ft and weighing 3 lb/ft is suspended between two supports at the same elevation. If the sag of the cable is observed to be 100 ft, determine the span L and the maximum tension.

7.80. A 200-ft cable is hung between two supports A and B at the same elevation. With a sag of 40 ft, the maximum tension is found to be 500 lb. Determine the horizontal distance from A to B and the total weight of the cable.

7.81. A 200-ft steel surveying tape weighs 4 lb. If the tape is stretched between two points at the same elevation and pulled until the tension at each end is 16 lb, determine the horizontal distance between the ends of the tape. Neglect the elongation of the tape due to the tension.

7.82. A cable weighing 2 lb/ft is suspended between two supports at the same elevation and 300 ft apart. If the horizontal component of the cable tension is 700 lb, determine the total length of the cable and the maximum tension.

7.83. A cable weighing 4 lb/ft is suspended between two points at the same elevation and 750 ft apart. If the sag is 100 ft, determine the total length of the cable and the maximum tension.

7.84. The maximum tension is to be 1,500 lb in a cable hanging between two points at the same elevation located 300 ft apart. If the sag is 90 ft, determine the total length and the total weight of the cable.

7.85. The total weight of a 300-ft cable is 450 lb. The cable is suspended between two points at the same elevation and 200 ft apart. Determine the sag and the maximum tension.

7.86. A 300-ft cable is suspended between two points at the same elevation and 250 ft apart. If the maximum tension is 500 lb, determine the sag and the total weight of the cable.

*7.87. The cable shown weighs 800 lb. Determine the location of the lowest point of the cable and the maximum tension.

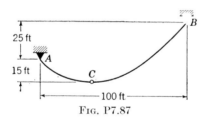

Fig. P7.87

7.88. Solve Prob. 7.87 assuming that the 800-lb load is distributed uniformly along the horizontal.

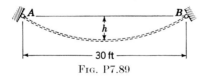

Fig. P7.89

7.89. The chain shown weighs 5 lb/ft. Determine the *smaller* of the two values of h for which the maximum tension is 200 lb.

*7.90. A cable weighing 2 lb/ft is suspended between supports at the same elevation and 100 ft apart. Determine the sag h for which the maximum tension in the cable is as small as possible.

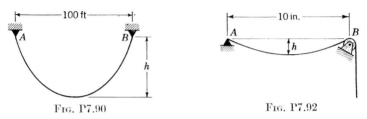

FIG. P7.90   FIG. P7.92

*7.91. Solve Prob. 7.71 assuming the cables to be catenaries.

*7.92. A uniform cord 30 in. long passes over a frictionless pulley at B and is attached to a rigid support at A. Determine the smaller of the two values of h for which the cord is in equilibrium.

8. Friction

8.1. Introduction. In the preceding chapters, it was assumed that surfaces in contact were either *smooth* or *rough*. If they were smooth, it was assumed that the force each surface exerted on the other was normal to the surfaces and that the two surfaces could move freely with respect to each other. If they were rough, it was assumed that tangential forces could develop to prevent the motion of one surface with respect to the other.

This view was a simplified one. Actually, no perfectly smooth surface exists. When two surfaces are in contact, tangential forces, called *friction forces*, will always develop if one attempts to move one surface with respect to the other. On the other hand, these friction forces are limited in magnitude and will not prevent motion if sufficiently large forces are applied. The distinction between smooth and rough surfaces is thus a matter of degree. This will be seen more clearly in the present chapter, which is devoted to the study of friction and of its applications to common engineering situations.

There are two types of friction: *dry friction*, sometimes called *Coulomb friction*, and *fluid friction*. Fluid friction develops between layers of fluid moving at different velocities. Fluid friction is of great importance in problems involving the flow of fluids through pipes and orifices or dealing with bodies immersed in moving fluids. It is also basic in the analysis of the motion of *lubricated mechanisms*. Such problems are considered in texts on fluid mechanics. We shall limit our present study to dry friction, i.e., to problems involving rigid bodies which are in contact along *nonlubricated* surfaces.

8.2. The Laws of Dry Friction. Coefficients of Friction. The laws of dry friction are best understood by the following experiment. A block of weight W is placed on a horizontal plane surface (Fig. 8.1a). The forces acting on the block are its weight W and the reaction of the surface. Since the weight has no horizontal component, the reaction of the surface also has no horizontal component; the reaction is therefore *normal* to the surface and is represented by N in Fig. 8.1a. Suppose, now, that a horizontal force P is applied to the block (Fig. 8.1b). If P is small, the block will not move; some other horizontal force must there-

fore exist, which balances P. This other force is the *static-friction force*
F, which is actually the resultant of a great number of forces acting over
the entire surface of contact between the block and the plane. The
nature of these forces is not known exactly, but it is generally assumed
that these forces are due to the irregularities of the surfaces in contact
and also, to a certain extent, to molecular attraction.

If the force P is increased, the friction force F also increases, continuing
to oppose P, until it reaches a certain *maximum value* F_m (Fig. 8.1c).
If P is further increased, the friction force cannot balance it any more and
the block starts sliding. As soon as the block has been set in motion,
the value of F drops from F_m to a lower value F_k, called the *kinetic-friction
force*. This is because there is less interpenetration between the irregularities of the surfaces in contact when these surfaces move with respect

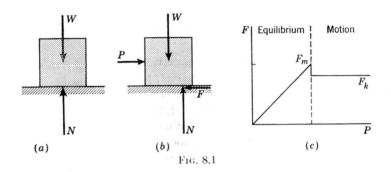

FIG. 8.1

to each other. From then on, the block keeps sliding with increasing
velocity; the value of the friction force, however, remains approximately
constant.

Experimental evidence shows that the maximum value F_m of the static-
friction force is proportional to the normal force N. We have

$$F_m = \mu_s N \qquad (8.1)$$

where μ_s is a constant called the *coefficient of static friction*. Similarly,
the value F_k of the kinetic-friction force may be put in the form

$$F_k = \mu_k N \qquad (8.2)$$

where μ_k is a constant called the *coefficient of kinetic friction*. The coefficients of friction μ_s and μ_k do not depend upon the area of the surfaces
in contact. Both coefficients, however, depend strongly on the *nature*

of the surfaces in contact. Since they also depend upon the exact condition of the surfaces, their value is seldom known with an accuracy greater than 5 per cent. Approximate values of coefficients of static friction are given in Table 8.1 for various dry surfaces. The corresponding values of the coefficient of kinetic friction would be about 25 per cent smaller.

TABLE 8.1. APPROXIMATE VALUES OF COEFFICIENT OF STATIC FRICTION FOR DRY SURFACES

Metal on metal	0.15–0.60
Metal on wood	0.20–0.60
Metal on stone	0.30–0.70
Metal on leather	0.30–0.60
Wood on wood	0.25–0.50
Wood on leather	0.25–0.50
Stone on stone	0.40–0.70
Earth on earth	0.20–1.00
Rubber on concrete	0.60–0.90

From the description given above, it appears that four different situations may occur when a rigid body is in contact with a horizontal surface:

1. The forces applied to the body do not tend to move it along the surface of contact; there is no friction force (Fig. 8.2a).

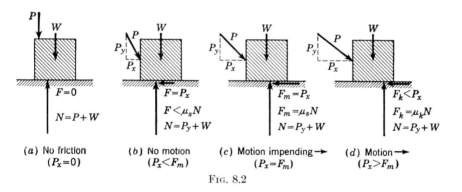

(a) No friction
($P_x=0$)

(b) No motion
($P_x<F_m$)

(c) Motion impending →
($P_x=F_m$)

(d) Motion →
($P_x>F_m$)

FIG. 8.2

2. The applied forces tend to move the body along the surface of contact but are not large enough to set it in motion. The friction force F which has developed may be found by solving the equations of equilibrium for the body. Since there is no evidence that the maximum value of the static-friction force has been reached, the equation $F_m = \mu_s N$ *cannot be used* to determine the friction force (Fig. 8.2b).

3. The applied forces are such that the body is just about to slide. We say that *motion is impending*. The friction force F has reached its maximum value F_m and, together with the normal force N, balances the applied forces. Both the equations of equilibrium and the equation $F_m = \mu_s N$ *may be used*. We also note that the friction force has a sense opposite to the sense of impending motion (Fig. 8.2c).

4. The body is sliding under the action of the applied forces, and the equations of equilibrium do not apply any more. However, F, now equal to F_k, may be obtained from the formula $F_k = \mu_k N$, and its sense is opposite to the sense of motion (Fig. 8.2d).

8.3. Angles of Friction. It is sometimes found convenient to replace the normal force N and the friction force F by their resultant R. Let

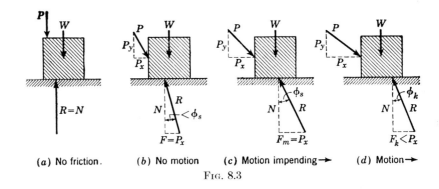

(a) No friction.   **(b)** No motion   **(c)** Motion impending →   **(d)** Motion →

Fig. 8.3

us consider again a block of weight W resting on a horizontal plane surface. If no horizontal force is applied to the block, the resultant R reduces to the normal force N (Fig. 8.3a). However, if the applied force P has a horizontal component P_x which tends to move the block, the force R will have a horizontal component F and, thus, will form a certain angle with the vertical (Fig. 8.3b). If P_x is increased until motion becomes impending, the angle between R and the vertical grows and reaches a maximum value (Fig. 8.3c). This value is called the *angle of static friction* and is denoted by ϕ_s. From the force triangle shown in Fig. 8.3c, we note that

$$\tan \phi_s = \frac{F_m}{N} = \frac{\mu_s N}{N}$$

$$\tan \phi_s = \mu_s \tag{8.3}$$

If motion actually takes place, the value of the friction force drops to F_k; similarly, the angle between R and N drops to a lower value ϕ_k, called the *angle of kinetic friction* (Fig. 8.3d). Using the force triangle of

Fig. 8.3d, we write

$$\tan \phi_k = \frac{F_k}{N} = \frac{\mu_k N}{N}$$
$$\mathbf{\tan \phi_k = \mu_k} \qquad\qquad (8.4)$$

Another example will show how the angle of friction may be used to advantage in the analysis of certain types of problems. Consider a block resting on a board which may be given any desired inclination; the block is subjected to no other force than its weight W and the reaction R of the board. If the board is horizontal, the force R exerted by the board on the block is perpendicular to the board and balances the weight W (Fig. 8.4a). If the board is given a small angle of inclination θ, the force R will deviate from the perpendicular to the board by the angle θ and will

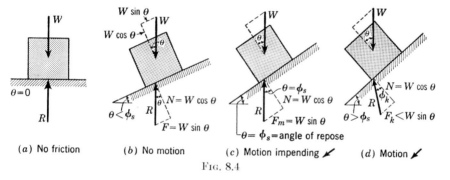

(a) No friction   (b) No motion   (c) Motion impending �’   (d) Motion ✓

Fig. 8.4

keep balancing W (Fig. 8.4b); it will then have a normal component $N = W \cos \theta$ and a tangential component $F = W \sin \theta$.

If we keep increasing the angle of inclination, motion will soon become impending. At that time, the angle between R and the normal will have reached its maximum value ϕ_s (Fig. 8.4c). The value of the angle of inclination corresponding to impending motion is called the *angle of repose*. Clearly, the angle of repose is equal to the angle of static friction ϕ_s. If the angle of inclination θ is further increased, motion starts and the angle between R and the normal drops to the lower value ϕ_k (Fig. 8.4d). The reaction R is not vertical any more, and the forces acting on the block are unbalanced.

8.4. Problems Involving Dry Friction. Problems involving dry friction are found in many engineering applications. Some deal with simple situations such as the block sliding on a plane described in the preceding sections. Others involve more complicated situations as in Sample Prob. 8.3; many deal with the stability of rigid bodies in accelerated motion and will be studied in dynamics. Also, a number of common machines and mechanisms may be analyzed by applying the laws of dry friction. These include wedges, screws, journal and thrust bearings, and belt transmissions. They will be studied in the following sections.

The *methods* which should be used to solve problems involving dry friction are the same that were used in the preceding chapters. If a problem involves only a motion of translation, with no possible rotation, the body under consideration may usually be treated as a particle and the methods of Chap. 2 may be used. If the problem involves a possible rotation, the body must be considered as a rigid body and the methods of Chap. 3 should be used. If the structure considered is made of several parts, the principle of action and reaction must be used as was done in Chap. 6.

If the body considered is acted upon by more than three forces (including the reactions at the surfaces of contact), the reaction at each surface

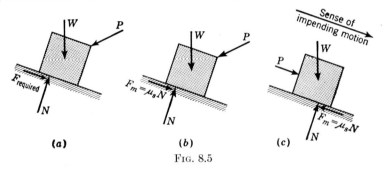

(a)   (b)   (c)

FIG. 8.5

will be represented by its components N and F and the problem will be solved from the equations of equilibrium. If only three forces act on the body under consideration, it may be found more convenient to represent each reaction by the resultant R of N and F and to solve the problem by drawing a force triangle.

Most problems involving friction fall into one of the following *three groups*: In the *first group* of problems, all applied forces are given, and the coefficients of friction are known; we are to determine whether the body considered will remain at rest or slide. The friction force F *required to maintain equilibrium* is unknown (it is *not* equal to $\mu_s N$) and should be determined, together with the normal force N, by drawing a free-body diagram and *solving the equations of equilibrium* (Fig. 8.5a). The value found for F is then compared with the maximum friction force $F_m = \mu_s N$. If F is smaller than or equal to F_m, the body remains at rest. If the value found for F is larger than F_m, equilibrium cannot be maintained and motion takes place; the actual value of the friction force is then $F_k = \mu_k N$.

In problems of the *second group*, all applied forces are given, and the motion is known to be impending; we are to determine the value of the coefficient of static friction.   Here again, we determine the friction force and the normal force by drawing a free-body diagram and solving the equations of equilibrium (Fig. 8.5b).   Since we know that the value found for F is the maximum value F_m, the coefficient of friction may be found by writing and solving the equation $F_m = \mu_s N$.

In problems of the *third group*, the coefficient of static friction is given, and it is known that motion is impending in a given direction; we are to determine the magnitude or the direction of one of the applied forces. The friction force may then be assumed equal to $F_m = \mu_s N$ and should be shown in the free-body diagram with a *sense opposite to that of the impending motion* (Fig. 8.5c).   The equations of equilibrium may then be written, and the desired force may be determined.

As noted above, it may be more convenient, when only three forces are involved, to represent the reaction of the surface by a single force

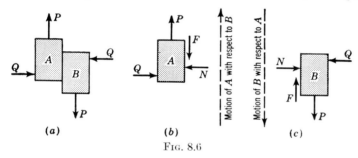

(a)   (b)   (c)

FIG. 8.6

R and to solve the problem by drawing a force triangle.   Such a solution is used in Sample Prob. 8.2.

When two bodies A and B are in contact (Fig. 8.6a), the forces of friction exerted, respectively, by A on B and by B on A are equal and opposite (Newton's third law).   It is important, in drawing the free-body diagram of one of the bodies, to include the appropriate friction force with its correct sense.   The following rule should then be observed: *The sense of the friction force acting on A is opposite to that of the motion (or impending motion) of A as observed from B* (Fig. 8.6b).†   The sense of the friction force acting on B is determined in a similar way (Fig. 8.6c). Note that the motion of A as observed from B is a *relative motion*.   Body A may be fixed; yet it will have a relative motion with respect to B if B itself moves.   Also, A may actually move down yet be observed from B to move up if B moves down faster than A.

† It is therefore *the same as that of the motion of B as observed from A.*

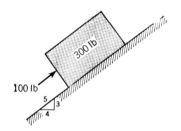

A 100-lb force acts as shown on a 300-lb block placed on an inclined plane. The coefficients of friction between the block and the plane are $\mu_s = 0.25$ and $\mu_k = 0.20$. Determine whether the block is in equilibrium, and find the value of the friction force.

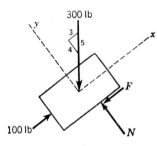

Force Required for Equilibrium. We first determine the value of the friction force *required to maintain equilibrium*. Assuming that F is directed down and to the left, we draw the free-body diagram of the block and write

$+\nearrow \Sigma F_x = 0:$
$$100 \text{ lb} - \tfrac{3}{5}(300 \text{ lb}) - F = 0$$
$$F = -80 \text{ lb} = 80 \text{ lb} \nearrow$$
$+\nwarrow \Sigma F_y = 0: \quad N - \tfrac{4}{5}(300 \text{ lb}) = 0$
$$N = +240 \text{ lb} = 240 \text{ lb} \nwarrow$$

The force F required to maintain equilibrium is an 80-lb force directed up and to the right; the tendency of the block is thus to move down the plane.

Maximum Friction Force. The maximum friction force which may be developed is

$$F_{\max} = \mu_s N \qquad F_{\max} = 0.25(240 \text{ lb}) = 60 \text{ lb}$$

Since the value of the force required to maintain equilibrium (80 lb) is larger than the maximum value which may be obtained (60 lb), equilibrium will not be maintained and the *block will slide down the plane.*

Actual Value of Friction Force. The value of the actual friction force is obtained as follows:

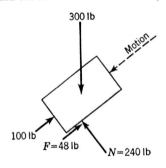

$$F_{\text{actual}} = F_k = \mu_k N$$
$$= 0.20(240 \text{ lb}) = 48 \text{ lb}$$

The sense of this force is opposite to the sense of motion; the force is thus directed up and to the right,

$$F_{\text{actual}} = \textbf{48 lb} \nearrow$$

It should be noted that the forces acting on the block are not balanced; their resultant is a force equal to

$$\tfrac{3}{5}(300 \text{ lb}) - 100 \text{ lb} - 48 \text{ lb} = 32 \text{ lb} \swarrow$$

SAMPLE PROBLEM 8.2

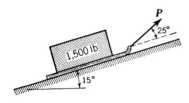

A wooden sled supporting a large stone is pulled up a track inclined at 15°. The combined weight of the sled and stone is 1,500 lb, and the coefficients of friction between the sled and the track are $\mu_s = 0.40$ and $\mu_k = 0.30$. Determine the force P required (a) to start the sled up the track, (b) to keep the sled moving up after it has been started, and (c) to keep the sled from sliding down.

Solution. Since the normal component of the reaction of the track depends upon the unknown force P as well as upon the 1,500-lb weight, it would not be convenient to resolve the reaction into components. We shall instead draw a force triangle including the 1,500-lb weight, the force P, and the reaction R. The direction of the reaction R must be redetermined in each part of the problem. The law of sines is used to determine the value of P in each part of the problem.

a. Force P to Start Sled Moving Up

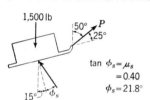

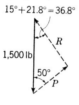

$$15° + 21.8° = 36.8°$$

$$\frac{P}{\sin 36.8°} = \frac{1{,}500 \text{ lb}}{\sin [180° - (50° + 36.8°)]}$$

$$P = 900 \text{ lb} \; \nearrow$$

$$\tan \phi_s = \mu_s$$
$$= 0.40$$
$$\phi_s = 21.8°$$

b. Force P to Keep Sled Moving

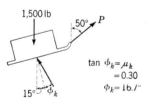

$$15° + 16.7° = 31.7°$$

$$\frac{P}{\sin 31.7°} = \frac{1{,}500 \text{ lb}}{\sin [180° - (50° + 31.7°)]}$$

$$P = 796 \text{ lb} \; \nearrow$$

$$\tan \phi_k = \mu_k$$
$$= 0.30$$
$$\phi_k = 16.7°$$

c. Force P to Keep Sled from Sliding Down

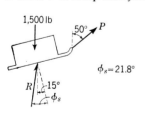

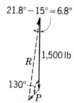

$$21.8° - 15° = 6.8°$$

$$\frac{P}{\sin 6.8°} = \frac{1{,}500 \text{ lb}}{\sin [180° - (130° + 6.8°)]}$$

$$P = 260 \text{ lb} \; \swarrow$$

$$\phi_s = 21.8°$$

Since the force P is directed downward, the sled will not slide down under its own weight.

257

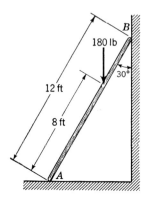

A 12-ft ladder weighing 40 lb is placed against a vertical wall as shown. As a 180-lb man reaches a point 8 ft from the lower end A, the ladder is just about to slip. Knowing that the coefficient of static friction between the ladder and the wall is 0.20, determine the coefficient of friction μ_s between the ladder and the floor.

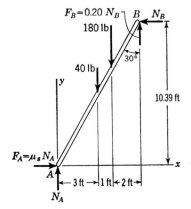

Solution. We draw the free-body diagram of the ladder. Since the ladder is about to slip, the forces of friction at A and B have reached their maximum values, equal to $\mu_s N_A$ and $0.20 N_B$, respectively. The values of N_B, N_A, and μ_s are successively obtained from the equations of equilibrium,

$$+\!\!\!\downarrow \ \Sigma M_A = 0: \quad -(6 \text{ ft})0.20 N_B - (10.39 \text{ ft}) N_B + (3 \text{ ft})(40 \text{ lb}) + (4 \text{ ft})(180 \text{ lb}) = 0$$

$$N_B = 72.5 \text{ lb}$$

$$+\!\!\uparrow \ \Sigma F_y = 0: \quad N_A + 0.20 N_B - 40 \text{ lb} - 180 \text{ lb} = 0$$

$$N_A + 0.20(72.5 \text{ lb}) - 40 \text{ lb} - 180 \text{ lb} = 0$$

$$N_A = 205 \text{ lb}$$

$$\xrightarrow{+} \ \Sigma F_x = 0: \quad \mu_s N_A - N_B = 0$$

$$\mu_s(205 \text{ lb}) - 72.5 \text{ lb} = 0$$

$$\mu_s = \frac{72.5 \text{ lb}}{205 \text{ lb}} \qquad \mu_s = \mathbf{0.35}$$

PROBLEMS

8.1. A 200-lb block resting on a 30° incline is acted upon by a horizontal force P as shown. Determine the value of P required to start the block up the plane.

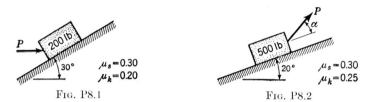

FIG. P8.1   FIG. P8.2

8.2. A 500-lb block rests on a 20° incline as shown. Determine the magnitude and direction of the smallest force P which will prevent the block from sliding down the plane.

8.3. Determine the magnitude and direction of the smallest force P which will start the block of Prob. 8.2 moving up the plane.

8.4. A 300-lb block rests on a plate. The coefficient of static friction is 0.25 between all surfaces in contact. Determine the smallest force P required to move the plate for each of the arrangements shown.

8.5. A 300-lb block rests on a plate. The coefficients of friction between all surfaces are $\mu_s = 0.25$ and $\mu_k = 0.20$. Determine, for each of the two arrangements shown, whether the plate moves when $P = 100$ lb, and find the resultant of the friction forces.

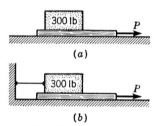

(a)

(b)

FIG. P8.4 AND P8.5

8.6. Determine whether the block of Prob. 8.1 moves, and find the value of the friction force (a) when $P = 40$ lb, (b) when $P = 60$ lb.

8.7. Determine whether the block of Prob. 8.2 moves, and find the value of the friction force (a) when $P = 200$ lb and $\alpha = 0°$, (b) when $P = 400$ lb and $\alpha = 0°$.

8.8. A 40-lb block rests on a 30° incline and is attached to a weight W by a cable ABC. The pulley at B is frictionless. Determine whether the 40-lb block moves, and find the value of the friction force (a) when $W = 12$ lb, (b) when $W = 15$ lb.

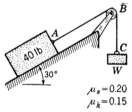

FIG. P8.8

8.9. A cabinet weighing 70 lb is pulled by a horizontal force P as shown. The coefficient of static friction is 0.30. Determine (*a*) the force P required to move the cabinet and (*b*) the largest allowable value of h if the cabinet is not to tip over.

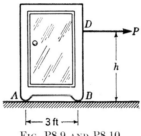

FIG. P8.9 AND P8.10

8.10. A 70-lb cabinet is acted upon by a horizontal force P as shown. The coefficient of static friction between the cabinet and the floor is 0.30. The magnitude of the force P is gradually increased until motion impends; determine whether the cabinet will tip or slide if $h = 6$ ft.

8.11. Solve Prob. 8.10 when $h = 4$ ft.

8.12. A 15-lb triangular block rests on a rough floor as shown. The coefficient of static friction between the block and the floor is 0.25. Determine the smallest allowable width of the base x if the block is to slide rather than tip as the magnitude of the force P is gradually increased.

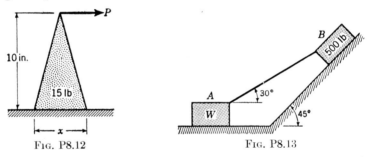

FIG. P8.12   FIG. P8.13

8.13. Block B weighs 500 lb and is held in place by means of a rod connecting it to block A. The coefficient of static friction is 0.35 between all surfaces in contact. Determine the minimum value of the weight W of block A which will assure equilibrium.

8.14. If the weight of block A in Prob. 8.13 is $W = 30$ lb, determine the magnitude of the horizontal force P which should be applied to block A to maintain equilibrium.

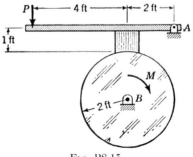

FIG. P8.15

8.15. In the brake shown, the coefficient of static friction between the brake shoe and the flywheel is 0.30. Determine the smallest value of P which will prevent rotation of the flywheel if a clockwise couple of moment $M = 500$ lb-ft is applied to the flywheel.

8.16. Same as Prob. 8.15 assuming, now, that a counterclockwise couple of moment $M = 500$ lb-ft is applied to the flywheel.

8.17. A window sash weighs 10 lb and is normally supported by two 5-lb sash weights. It is observed that the window remains open after one sash cord has broken. What is the smallest possible value of the coefficient of static friction? (Assume that the sash is slightly smaller than the frame and will bind only at points A and D.)

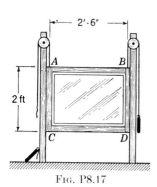

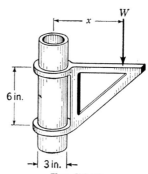

Fig. P8.17   Fig. P8.18

8.18. The movable bracket shown may be placed at any height on the 3-in.-diameter pipe. If the coefficient of static friction between the pipe and bracket is 0.25, determine the minimum distance x at which the load W can be supported. Neglect the weight of the bracket.

8.19. Determine the value of the coefficient of static friction between the floor and the ladder if the ladder is just about to slip. Assume that the wall at B is smooth.

8.20. A 13-ft ladder rests against a wall as shown. The coefficient of static friction at both the wall and the ground is 0.30. Determine how high a 175-lb man can climb before the ladder slips. Neglect the weight of the ladder.

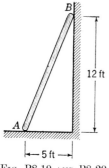
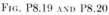

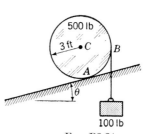

Fig. P8.19 and P8.20   Fig. P8.21

8.21. Determine the inclination of the plane and the minimum value of the coefficient of static friction which are necessary to maintain equilibrium.

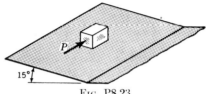

Fig. P8.23

8.22. Determine the minimum required value of the coefficient of static friction if the cylinder of Sample Prob. 3.13 is to be raised over the obstruction A.

8.23. A 50-lb block rests on a 15° incline. The coefficients of static and kinetic friction between block and incline are both assumed equal to 0.30. If a horizontal force P parallel to the incline is applied as shown, determine the value of P required to move the block and the direction in which the block moves.

Fig. P8.24

8.24. Determine the smallest value of the coefficient of static friction for which three identical cylindrical rods may be placed as shown.

8.25. A shaft of radius r and weight W is placed as shown; the coefficient of static friction between all surfaces is μ_s. Determine the moment M of the couple required to start the shaft rotating in terms of r, W, and μ_s, when $\theta = 90°$.

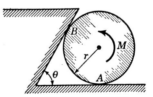

Fig. P8.25 and P8.26

8.26. The shaft shown weighs 50 lb and has a diameter of 6 in. If $\theta = 60°$ and if the coefficient of static friction is 0.20, determine the moment M of the couple required to start the shaft rotating.

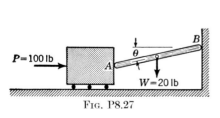

Fig. P8.27

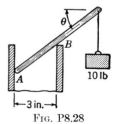

Fig. P8.28

*8.27. A 20-lb rod is placed between a movable block and a wall as shown. The coefficient of static friction at A and B is 0.25. If a force $P = 100$ lb acts on the block as shown, determine the angle θ for which slipping is impending.

*8.28. A small steel rod, 10 in. long, is placed inside a pipe as shown. The coefficient of static friction between the rod and the pipe is 0.20. Determine the limiting values of θ if the rod is to remain in equilibrium.

8.5. Wedges. Wedges are simple machines used to raise large stone blocks and other heavy loads. These loads may be raised by applying to the wedge a force usually considerably smaller than the weight of the load. Besides, because of the friction existing between the surfaces in contact, a wedge, if properly shaped, will remain in place after being forced under the load. Wedges may thus be used advantageously to make small adjustments in the position of heavy pieces of machinery.

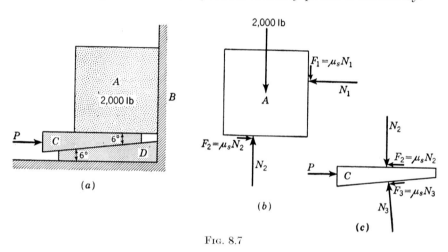

FIG. 8.7

Consider the 2,000-lb block A shown in Fig. 8.7a. This block rests against a vertical wall B and is to be raised a few inches by forcing a wedge C between block A and a second wedge D. We want to find the minimum value of the force P which must be applied to the wedge C to move the block.

The free-body diagrams of block A and of wedge C have been drawn in Fig. 8.7b and c. The forces acting on the block include its weight and the normal and friction forces at the surfaces of contact with wall B and wedge C. The friction forces F_1 and F_2 are equal, respectively, to $\mu_s N_1$ and $\mu_s N_2$ since the motion of the block must be started. It is important to show the friction forces with their correct sense. Since the block will move upward, the force F_1 exerted by the wall on the block must be directed downward. On the other hand, since the wedge C moves to the right, the relative motion of A with respect to C is to the left and the force F_2 exerted by C on A must be directed to the right.

Considering now the free body C in Fig. 8.7c, we note that the forces acting on C include the applied force P and the normal and friction forces at the surfaces of contact with A and D. The weight of the wedge is small compared with the other forces involved and may be neglected. The forces N_2 and F_2 acting on C are equal and opposite to the forces N_2 and F_2 acting on A; the friction force F_2 must therefore be directed to the left. We check that the force F_3 is also directed to the left.

The total number of unknowns involved in the two free-body diagrams may be reduced to four if the friction forces are expressed in terms of the normal forces. Expressing that block A and wedge C are in equilibrium will provide four equations which may be solved to obtain P. It should be noted that, in the example considered here, it will be more convenient to replace each pair of normal and friction forces by their resultant. Each free body is then subjected to only three forces, and the problem may be solved by drawing the corresponding force triangles. The actual solution of the problem has been carried out in this way in Sample Prob. 8.4.

8.6. Square-threaded Screws. Square-threaded screws are frequently used in jacks, presses, and other mechanisms. Their analysis is similar to that of a block sliding along an inclined plane.

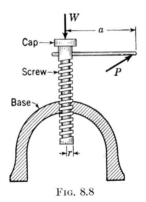

FIG. 8.8

Consider the jack shown in Fig. 8.8. The screw carries a load W and is supported by the base of the jack. Contact between screw and base takes place along a portion of their threads. By applying a force P on the handle, the screw may be made to turn and to raise the load W.

The thread of the base has been unwrapped and shown as a straight line in Fig. 8.9a. The correct slope was obtained by plotting horizontally the product $2\pi r$, where r is the mean radius of the thread, and vertically the *lead* L of the screw, i.e., the distance through which the screw advances in one turn. The angle θ this line forms with the horizontal

is the *lead angle*. Since the force of friction between two surfaces in
contact does not depend upon the area of contact, the two threads may
be assumed to be in contact over a much smaller area than they actually
are and the screw may be represented by the block shown in Fig. 8.9a.
It should be noted, however, that, in this analysis of the jack, the friction
between cap and screw is neglected.

The free-body diagram of the block should include the load W, the
reaction R of the base thread, and a horizontal force Q having the same
effect as the force P exerted on the handle. The force Q should have the
same moment as P about the axis of the screw and should thus be equal
to $Q = Pa/r$. The force Q, and thus the force P required to raise the
load W, may be obtained from the free-body diagram shown in Fig. 8.9a.
The friction angle is taken equal to ϕ_s since the load will presumably be

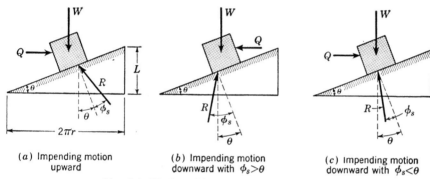

(*a*) Impending motion   (*b*) Impending motion   (*c*) Impending motion
        upward   downward with $\phi_s > \theta$ downward with $\phi_s < \theta$

Fig. 8.9. Block-and-incline analysis of a screw.

raised through a succession of short strokes. In mechanisms providing
for the continuous rotation of a screw, it may be desirable to distinguish
between the force required to start motion (using ϕ_s) and that required
to maintain motion (using ϕ_k).

If the friction angle ϕ_s is larger than the lead angle θ, the screw is said
to be *self-locking;* it will remain in place under the load. To lower the
load, we must then apply the force shown in Fig. 8.9b. If ϕ_s is smaller
than θ, the screw will unwind under the load; it is then necessary to apply
the force shown in Fig. 8.9c to maintain equilibrium.

The lead of a screw should not be confused with its *pitch*. The lead
was defined as the distance through which the screw advances in one turn;
the pitch is the distance measured between two consecutive threads.
While lead and pitch are equal in the case of *single-threaded* screws, they
are different in the case of *multiple-threaded* screws, i.e., screws having
several independent threads. It is easily verified that, for double-
threaded screws, the lead is twice as large as the pitch; for triple-threaded
screws, it is three times as large as the pitch; etc.

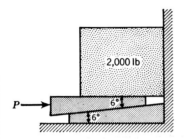

A 2,000-lb block is raised by forcing a wedge under it as shown. Determine the minimum value of the force P which must be applied to the wedge. The coefficient of static friction is 0.30 at all surfaces of contact.

Solution. The free-body diagrams of the block and of the upper wedge are shown below; the corresponding force triangles are also shown. The sense in which friction takes place is obtained by considering the *relative motion* of the surfaces in contact (see Sec. 8.5). The force R_2 exerted by the wedge on the block is obtained by applying the law of sines to the force triangle of the block. The force R_2 exerted by the block on the wedge is equal and opposite; its value is used to draw the force triangle of the wedge, from which P is obtained.

Free Body: Block

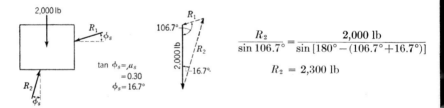

$$\frac{R_2}{\sin 106.7°} = \frac{2,000 \text{ lb}}{\sin [180° - (106.7° + 16.7°)]}$$

$$R_2 = 2,300 \text{ lb}$$

Free Body: Wedge

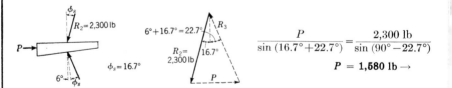

$$\frac{P}{\sin (16.7° + 22.7°)} = \frac{2,300 \text{ lb}}{\sin (90° - 22.7°)}$$

$$P = 1,580 \text{ lb} \rightarrow$$

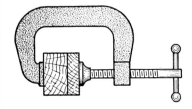

SAMPLE PROBLEM 8.5

A clamp is used to hold two pieces of wood together as shown. The clamp has a double square thread of mean diameter equal to 0.50 in. and with a pitch of 0.10 in. The coefficient of friction between threads is $\mu_s = 0.30$. If a maximum torque of 30 lb-ft is applied in tightening the clamp, determine (a) the force exerted on the pieces of wood and (b) the torque required to loosen the clamp.

a. Force Exerted by Clamp. Since the screw is double-threaded, the lead L is equal to twice the pitch, i.e., to $2(0.10$ in.$) = 0.20$ in. The lead angle θ and the friction angle ϕ_s are obtained by writing

$$\tan \theta = \frac{L}{2\pi r} = \frac{0.20 \text{ in.}}{0.50\pi \text{ in.}} = 0.1273 \qquad \theta = 7.3°$$

$$\tan \phi_s = \mu_s = 0.30 \qquad\qquad\qquad \phi_s = 16.7°$$

The force Q which should be applied to the block representing the screw is obtained by expressing that its moment Qr about the axis of the screw is equal to the applied torque

$$Q(0.25 \text{ in.}) = 30 \text{ lb-ft} \qquad Q = \frac{30 \text{ lb-ft}}{0.25 \text{ in.}} = \frac{360 \text{ lb-in.}}{0.25 \text{ in.}} = 1,440 \text{ lb}$$

The free-body diagram and the corresponding force triangle may now be drawn for the block; the value of the force W exerted on the pieces of wood is obtained by solving the triangle.

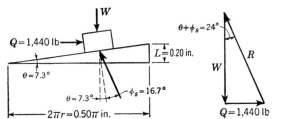

$$W = \frac{Q}{\tan (\theta + \phi_s)}$$

$$= \frac{1,440 \text{ lb}}{\tan 24°}$$

$$W = 3,230 \text{ lb}$$

b. Torque Required to Loosen Clamp. The force Q required to loosen the clamp and the corresponding torque are obtained from the following free-body diagram and force triangle.

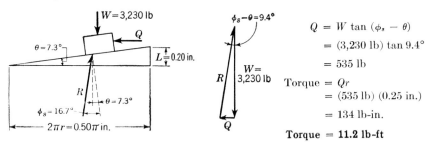

$$Q = W \tan (\phi_s - \theta)$$
$$= (3,230 \text{ lb}) \tan 9.4°$$
$$= 535 \text{ lb}$$
$$\text{Torque} = Qr$$
$$= (535 \text{ lb}) (0.25 \text{ in.})$$
$$= 134 \text{ lb-in.}$$

$$\text{Torque} = 11.2 \text{ lb-ft}$$

PROBLEMS

8.29. Determine the force P required to raise the 500-lb weight. The coefficient of static friction is 0.30 at all surfaces.

8.30. If the rollers are removed, determine the force P required to raise the 500-lb weight. The coefficient of static friction is 0.30 at all surfaces.

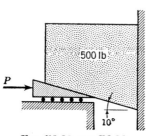

Fig. P8.29 and P8.30

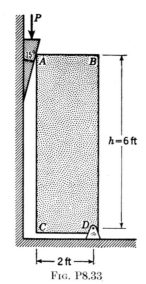

Fig. P8.31

8.31. The coefficient of static friction at all surfaces of contact is 0.20. Determine the magnitude of the force P required to start the 20-lb wedge moving if both blocks are free to move.

8.32. Solve Prob. 8.31 assuming that block A is bolted to the ground.

8.33. The block $ABCD$ weighs 200 lb and is hinged at D. The coefficient of static friction is 0.20 at all surfaces, including corner A. Determine the force P required to move the wedge.

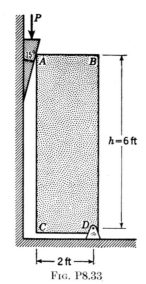

Fig. P8.33

8.34. If the height h of the block in Prob. 8.33 is reduced, the force required to move the wedge will increase. Determine for what height h it becomes impossible to move the wedge downward.

8.35. The coefficient of static friction at all surfaces is 0.20. If $\theta = 10°$, determine the force P required to move the wedge.

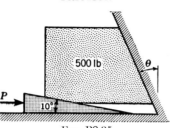

FIG. P8.35

8.36. Determine the angle θ in Prob. 8.35 at which it becomes impossible to move the wedge. (The system is then said to be self-locking.)

8.37. A wedge is being forced under the base of an 800-lb machine at point A. The coefficient of static friction at all surfaces is 0.10. Determine the force P required to move the wedge, and indicate whether the machine will move.

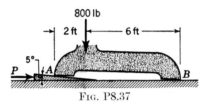

FIG. P8.37

8.38. Solve Prob. 8.37 assuming the wedge to be forced under the machine at point B instead of at A.

8.39. A force P is applied to the handle of a jackscrew at a distance of 12 in. from the center of the screw. The mean radius of the screw is 1 in., the pitch is $\frac{3}{16}$ in., and the screw is single-threaded. If the coefficient of static friction is 0.10, determine the force P required (a) to raise a load of 2 tons, (b) to lower a load of 2 tons.

8.40. Derive the following formulas relating the load W and the force P exerted on the handle of the jack discussed in Sec. 8.6: (a) $P = (Wr/a) \tan (\theta + \phi_s)$, to raise the load; (b) $P = (Wr/a) \tan (\phi_s - \theta)$, to lower the load if the screw is self-locking; (c) $P = (Wr/a) \tan (\theta - \phi_s)$, to hold the load if the screw is not self-locking.

8.41. The vise shown consists of two members connected by two double-threaded screws of mean radius 0.20 in. and pitch 0.04 in. The lower member is threaded at A and B ($\mu_s = 0.25$), but the upper member is not threaded. It is desired to apply two equal and opposite forces of 100 lb on the blocks held between the jaws. (a) What screw should be tightened first? (b) What is the maximum torque applied in tightening the second screw?

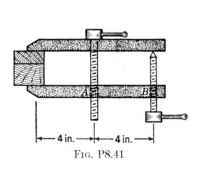

FIG. P8.41

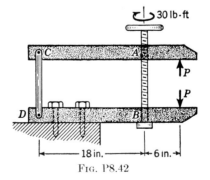

FIG. P8.42

8.42. In the vise shown, the screw is single-threaded in the upper member, passes through the lower member, and is held by a frictionless washer. The pitch of the screw is $\frac{1}{8}$ in., and the mean radius is $\frac{1}{2}$ in. If a torque of 30 lb-ft is applied to the screw, determine the force P. The coefficient of static friction is 0.10.

8.43. Solve Prob. 8.42 assuming that the screw is single-threaded at both A and B (a right-hand thread at B and a left-hand thread at A).

*8.7. Journal Bearings. Axle Friction.

Journal bearings are used to provide lateral support to rotating shafts and axles. *Thrust bearings,* which will be studied in the next section, are used to provide axial support

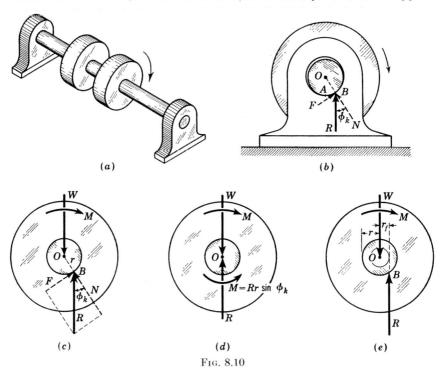

FIG. 8.10

to shafts and axles. If the journal bearing is fully lubricated, the frictional resistance depends upon the speed of rotation, the clearance between axle and bearing, and the viscosity of the lubricant. As indicated in Sec. 8.1, such problems are studied in fluid mechanics. The methods of this chapter, however, may be applied to the study of axle friction when the bearing is not lubricated or only partially lubricated. We may then assume that the axle and the bearing are in direct contact along a single straight line.

Consider two wheels, each of weight W, rigidly mounted on an axle supported symmetrically by two journal bearings (Fig. 8.10a). If the wheels rotate, we find that, to keep them rotating at constant speed, it is necessary to apply to each of them a couple of moment M. A free-body diagram has been drawn in Fig. 8.10c, which represents one of the wheels and the corresponding half axle in projection on a plane perpendicular to the axle. The forces acting on the free body include the weight W of the wheel, the couple M required to maintain its motion, and a force R representing the reaction of the bearing. This force is vertical, equal, and opposite to W but does not pass through the center O of the axle. R is located to the right of O at a distance such that its moment about O balances the moment M of the couple. Contact between axle and bearing, therefore, does not take place at the lowest point A when the axle rotates. It takes place at point B (Fig. 8.10b) or, rather, along a straight line intersecting the plane of the figure at B. Physically, this is explained by the fact that, when the wheels are set in motion, the axle "climbs" in the bearings until slippage occurs. After sliding back slightly, the axle settles more or less in the position shown. This position is such that the angle between the reaction R and the normal to the surface of the bearing is equal to the angle of kinetic friction ϕ_k. The distance from O to the line of action of R is thus $r \sin \phi_k$, where r is the radius of the axle. Writing that $\Sigma M_O = 0$ for the forces acting on the free body considered, we obtain the following expression for the moment M of the couple required to overcome the frictional resistance of one of the bearings:

$$M = Rr \sin \phi_k \qquad (8.5)$$

Observing that, for small values of the angle of friction, $\sin \phi_k$ may be replaced by $\tan \phi_k$, that is, by μ_k, we write the approximate formula

$$M \approx Rr\mu_k \qquad (8.6)$$

In the solution of certain problems, it may be more convenient to let the line of action of R pass through O, as it does when the axle does not rotate. A couple of moment M defined by formula (8.5) or (8.6) must then be added to the reaction R (Fig. 8.10d). This couple represents the frictional resistance of the bearing.

In case a graphical solution is preferred, the line of action of R may be readily drawn (Fig. 8.10e) if we note that it must be tangent to a circle centered at O and of radius

$$r_f = r \sin \phi_k \approx r\mu_k \qquad (8.7)$$

This circle is called the *circle of friction* of the axle and bearing and is independent of the loading conditions of the axle.

8.8. Thrust Bearings. Disk Friction. Thrust bearings are used to provide axial support to rotating shafts and axles. They are of two types: (1) *end bearings* and (2) *collar bearings* (Fig. 8.11). In the case of collar bearings, friction forces develop between the two ring-shaped areas which are in contact. In the case of end bearings, friction takes place over full circular areas, or over ring-shaped areas when the end of the shaft is hollow. Friction between circular areas, called *disk friction*, also occurs in other mechanisms, such as *disk clutches.*

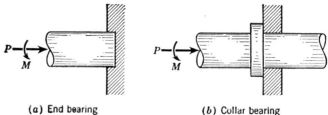

(a) End bearing   (b) Collar bearing

FIG. 8.11. Thrust bearings.

To obtain a formula which is valid in the most general case of disk friction, we shall consider a rotating hollow shaft. A couple of moment M keeps the shaft rotating at constant speed while a force P maintains it in contact with a fixed bearing (Fig. 8.12). Contact between the shaft and the bearing takes place over a ring-shaped area of inner radius R_1 and outer radius R_2. Assuming that the pressure between the two surfaces in contact is uniform, we find that the normal force ΔN exerted on an element of area ΔA is $\Delta N = P \, \Delta A / A$, where $A = \pi(R_2^2 - R_1^2)$, and that the friction force ΔF acting on ΔA is $\Delta F = \mu_k \, \Delta N$. Denoting by r the distance from the axis of the shaft to the element of area ΔA, we express as follows the moment ΔM of ΔF about the axis of the shaft:

$$\Delta M = r \, \Delta F = \frac{r \mu_k P \, \Delta A}{\pi(R_2^2 - R_1^2)}$$

The equilibrium of the shaft requires that the moment M of the couple applied to the shaft be equal in magnitude to the sum of the moments ΔM of the friction forces. Replacing ΔA by the infinitesimal element $dA = r \, d\theta \, dr$ used with polar coordinates, and integrating over the area of contact, we thus obtain the following expression for the moment M of the couple required to overcome the frictional resistance of the bearing:

$$M = \frac{\mu_k P}{\pi(R_2^2 - R_1^2)} \int_0^{2\pi} \int_{R_1}^{R_2} r^2 \, dr \, d\theta = \frac{\mu_k P}{\pi(R_2^2 - R_1^2)} \int_0^{2\pi} \tfrac{1}{3} (R_2^3 - R_1^3) \, d\theta$$

$$M = \tfrac{2}{3} \mu_k P \frac{R_2^3 - R_1^3}{R_2^2 - R_1^2} \tag{8.8}$$

When contact takes place over a full circle of radius R, formula (8.8) reduces to

$$M = \tfrac{2}{3} \mu_k P R \tag{8.9}$$

The value of M is then the same as would be obtained if contact between shaft and bearing took place at a single point located at a distance $2R/3$ from the axis of the shaft.

The largest torque which may be transmitted by a disk clutch without causing slippage is given by a formula similar to (8.9), where μ_k has been replaced by the coefficient of static friction μ_s.

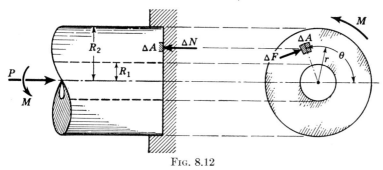

FIG. 8.12

*8.9. Wheel Friction. Rolling Resistance. The wheel is one of the most important inventions of our civilization. Its use makes it possible to move heavy loads with relatively little effort. Because the point of the wheel in contact with the ground at any given instant has no relative motion with respect to the ground, the wheel eliminates the large friction forces which would arise if the load were in direct contact with the ground. In practice, however, the wheel is not perfect, and some resistance to its motion exists. This resistance has two distinct causes. It is due (1) to a combined effect of axle friction and friction at the rim and (2) to the fact that the wheel and the ground deform, with the result that contact between wheel and ground takes place, not at a single point, but over a certain area.

To better understand the first cause of resistance to the motion of a wheel, we shall consider a railroad car supported by eight wheels mounted on axles and bearings. The car is assumed to be moving to the right at constant speed along a straight horizontal track. The free-body diagram of one of the wheels is shown in Fig. 8.13a. The forces acting on the free body include the load W supported by the wheel and the normal reaction N of the track. Since W is drawn through the center O of the axle, the frictional resistance of the bearing should be represented by a counterclockwise couple of moment M (see Sec. 8.7). To keep the free body in equilibrium, we must add two equal and opposite forces P and F forming a clockwise couple of moment M. The force F is the friction force exerted by the track on the wheel, and P represents the force which should be applied to the wheel to keep it rolling at constant speed. Note that the forces P and F would not exist if there were no friction between wheel and track. The couple M representing the axle friction would then be zero; the wheel would slide on the track without turning in its bearing.

The couple M and the forces P and F also reduce to zero when there is no axle friction. For example, a wheel which is not held in bearings and rolls freely and at constant speed on horizontal ground (Fig. 8.13b) will be subjected to only two forces: its own weight W and the normal reaction N of the ground. No friction force will act on the wheel, regardless of the value of the coefficient of friction between wheel and ground. A wheel rolling freely on a horizontal ground should thus keep rolling indefinitely.

Experience, however, indicates that the wheel will slow down and eventually come to rest. This is due to the second type of resistance mentioned at the beginning of this section, known as the *rolling resistance*. Under the load W, both the wheel and the ground deform slightly, causing the contact between wheel and ground to take place over a certain area. Experimental evidence shows that the resultant of the forces

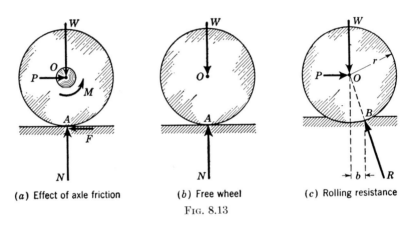

(a) Effect of axle friction   (b) Free wheel   (c) Rolling resistance

Fig. 8.13

exerted by the ground on the wheel over this area is a force R applied at a point B, which is not located directly under the center O of the wheel, but slightly in front of it (Fig. 8.13c). To balance the moment of W about B and to keep the wheel rolling at constant speed, it is necessary to apply a horizontal force P at the center of the wheel. Writing $\Sigma M_B = 0$, we obtain

$$Pr = Wb \qquad (8.10)$$

where r = radius of wheel

b = horizontal distance between O and B

The distance b is commonly called the *coefficient of rolling resistance*. It should be noted that b is not a dimensionless coefficient since it represents a length; b is usually expressed in inches. The value of b depends upon several parameters in a manner which has not yet been clearly established. Values of the coefficient of rolling resistance vary from about 0.01 in. for a steel wheel on a steel rail to 5.0 in. for the same wheel on soft ground; the value of b for an automobile tire on a good road is approximately 0.02 in.

SAMPLE PROBLEM 8.6

A pulley of diameter 4 in. can rotate about a fixed shaft of diameter 2 in. The coefficients of static and kinetic friction between the pulley and shaft are both assumed equal to 0.20. Determine the least force P required (a) to raise a 500-lb load, (b) to hold a 500-lb load.

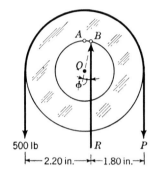

500 lb R P

|←—— 2.20 in.——→|←—1.80 in.—→|

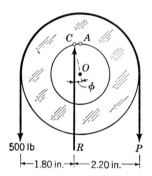

500 lb R P

|←—1.80 in.—→|←—— 2.20 in.——→|

a. Force P Required to Raise Load. When the forces in both parts of the rope are equal, contact between the pulley and shaft takes place at A. When P is increased, the pulley rolls around the shaft slightly and contact takes place at B. The free-body diagram of the pulley when motion is impending is drawn. The perpendicular distance from the center O of the pulley to the line of action of R is

$$r_f = r \sin \phi \approx r\mu \qquad r_f \approx (1 \text{ in.})0.20 = 0.20 \text{ in.}$$

Summing moments about B, we write

$+\!\downarrow \Sigma M_B = 0: \quad (1.80 \text{ in.})P$
$$- (2.20 \text{ in.})(500 \text{ lb}) = 0$$

$$P = \textbf{611 lb}$$

b. Force P to Hold the Load. As the force P is decreased, the pulley rolls around the shaft and contact takes place at C. Considering the pulley as a free body and summing moments about C, we write

$+\!\downarrow \Sigma M_C = 0: \quad (2.20 \text{ in.})P$
$$- (1.80 \text{ in.})(500 \text{ lb}) = 0$$

$$P = \textbf{409 lb}$$

PROBLEMS

8.44. A 5-lb pulley supports two 20-lb blocks as shown. Adding an 8-oz weight to one of the loads will just cause the pulley to start rotating. The diameter of the pulley is 12 in., and the diameter of the shaft is 3 in. Determine the coefficient of friction between the shaft and bearing.

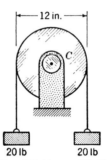

FIG. P8.44 AND P8.45

8.45. Determine the weight which should be added to one of the loads to cause the pulley to rotate. The diameter of the pulley is 12 in., the diameter of the shaft is 3 in., and the coefficient of friction between the shaft and bearing is 0.30.

8.46. A windlass, of diameter 6 in., is used to raise a 100-lb load. It is supported by two axles and bearings of diameter 2 in., poorly lubricated ($\mu_s = 0.40$). Determine the force P required to raise the load for each of the two positions shown.

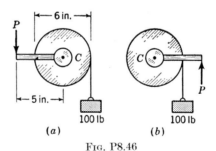

FIG. P8.46

8.47. The diameter of the pulley is 8 in., and the diameter of the shaft is 2 in. A 214-lb force is required to raise the 200-lb load. Determine the coefficient of friction between axle and bearing.

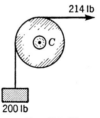

FIG. P8.47

8.48. A scooter is designed to roll down a 2 per cent slope at constant speed. Assuming that the coefficient of kinetic friction between the 1-in. axles and the bearings is 0.10, determine the diameter of the wheels. Neglect the rolling resistance between the wheels and the ground.

***8.49.** An old cart carries a 500-lb load. The two wheels are 4 ft in diameter, and the axles are 4 in. in diameter. The coefficient of friction between axles and bearings is 0.40. Determine the minimum force P required to pull the cart along a horizontal road. Neglect rolling resistance between the wheels and the road.

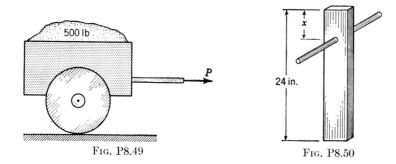

FIG. P8.49   FIG. P8.50

***8.50.** A uniform bar which is 24 in. long hangs loosely on a horizontal shaft of diameter 1 in. The shaft is rotated slowly. If the distance $x = 2$ in., determine the angle at which the bar initially slips. The coefficient of friction is 0.10.

***8.51.** Determine the minimum value of x for which the bar of Prob. 8.50 will not slip when the shaft is rotated slowly through a full turn.

8.52. The coefficients of friction between the collar and the bearing plate in the thrust bearing shown are $\mu_s = 0.15$ and $\mu_k = 0.10$. Determine the moment of the couple required (a) to set the shaft in motion, (b) to maintain the shaft in motion.

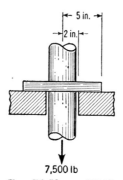

7,500 lb

FIG. P8.52 AND P8.53

8.53. A torque of 250 lb-ft is required to set in motion the shaft shown. Determine the coefficient of static friction between the collar and the bearing plate.

8.54. A force $P = 8$ kips is exerted on a 3-in. solid rod resting in an end bearing as shown in Fig. 8.11a. If the coefficient of static friction between the rod and the bearing is 0.15, determine the moment of the couple M required to start rotating the rod.

8.55. The coefficient of static friction is 0.20 between all surfaces. If a force $P = 1,000$ lb is exerted by the spring, determine the moment of the couple M required to rotate the shaft.

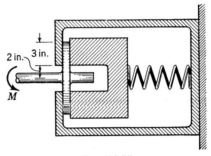

FIG. P8.55

8.56. Determine the magnitude of the force P which is required if the shaft of Prob. 8.55 is not to rotate when $M = 100$ lb-ft.

8.57. In the clutch shown, disks A and B are keyed to the shaft but are free to slide along it. Disks C, D, and E are free to move parallel to the shaft but cannot rotate. The coefficient of static friction is 0.25 between all surfaces in contact. If disks C and E are pressed against the other disks by forces of 300 lb, determine the moment of the couple M required to rotate the shaft.

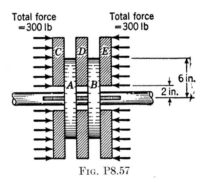

FIG. P8.57

8.58. The clutch of Prob. 8.57 is to prevent rotation of the shaft when $M = 50$ lb-ft. Determine the forces with which disks C and E must be pressed against the other disks.

***8.59.** As the surfaces of shaft and bearing wear out, the frictional resistance of a thrust bearing decreases. It is generally assumed that the wear is directly proportional to the distance traveled by any given point of the shaft, and thus to the distance r from the point to the axis of the shaft. Assuming, then, that the normal force per unit area is inversely proportional to r, show that the moment M measuring the frictional resistance of a worn-out end bearing (with contact over full circular area) is equal to 75 per cent of the value given by formula (8.9) for a new bearing.

***8.60.** Assuming that bearings wear out as indicated in Prob. 8.59, show that the moment M required to overcome the frictional resistance of a worn-out collar bearing is

$$M = \tfrac{1}{2}\mu_k P(R_1 + R_2)$$

where P = total axial force
R_1, R_2 = inner and outer radius of collar

8.61. A steel disk of diameter 6 in. rolls freely on an incline. If the coefficient of rolling resistance is 0.01 in., determine the slope of the incline if the disk is to roll at a constant velocity.

8.62. Determine the horizontal force required to move a 4,000-lb automobile along a horizontal road at constant velocity. Neglect all forms of friction except rolling resistance, and assume the coefficient of rolling resistance to be 0.02 in. The diameter of each tire is 25 in.

8.63. Solve Prob. 8.48 assuming the coefficient of rolling resistance to be 0.06 in.

*8.64. Solve Prob. 8.49 assuming the coefficient of rolling resistance to be 1.50 in.

8.10. Belt Friction. Consider a flat belt passing over a fixed cylindrical drum (Fig. 8.14a). We propose to determine the relation existing between the tensions T_1 and T_2 in the two parts of the belt when the belt is just about to slide toward the right.

Let us detach from the belt a small element PP' subtending an arc $\Delta\theta$. Denoting by T the tension at P and by $T + \Delta T$ the tension at P', we

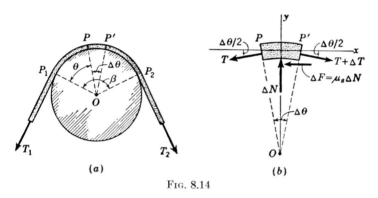

FIG. 8.14

draw the free-body diagram of the element of the belt (Fig. 8.14b). Besides the tensions T and $T + \Delta T$, the forces acting on the free body are the normal component ΔN of the reaction of the drum and the friction force ΔF. Since motion is assumed to be impending, we have $\Delta F = \mu_s \, \Delta N$. It should be noted that if $\Delta\theta$ is made to approach zero, the forces ΔN, ΔF, and the *difference* ΔT between the tension at P and the tension at P' will also approach zero; the value T of the tension at P, however, will remain unchanged. This observation helps in understanding our choice of notations.

Choosing the coordinate axes shown in Fig. 8.14b, we write the equations of equilibrium for the element PP':

$$\Sigma F_x = 0: \qquad (T + \Delta T) \cos \frac{\Delta\theta}{2} - T \cos \frac{\Delta\theta}{2} - \mu_s \, \Delta N = 0 \qquad (8.11)$$

$$\Sigma F_y = 0: \qquad \Delta N - (T + \Delta T) \sin \frac{\Delta\theta}{2} - T \sin \frac{\Delta\theta}{2} = 0 \qquad (8.12)$$

Solving Eq. (8.12) for ΔN and substituting into (8.11), we obtain after reductions

$$\Delta T \cos \frac{\Delta\theta}{2} - \mu_s(2T + \Delta T) \sin \frac{\Delta\theta}{2} = 0$$

We shall now divide both terms by $\Delta\theta$; as far as the first term is concerned, this will be simply done by dividing ΔT by $\Delta\theta$. The division of the second term is carried out by dividing the terms in the parentheses by 2 and the sine by $\Delta\theta/2$. We write

$$\frac{\Delta T}{\Delta\theta} \cos \frac{\Delta\theta}{2} - \mu_s \left(T + \frac{\Delta T}{2}\right) \frac{\sin (\Delta\theta/2)}{\Delta\theta/2} = 0$$

If we now let $\Delta\theta$ approach 0, the cosine approaches 1 and $\Delta T/2$ approaches zero as noted above. On the other hand, the quotient of $\sin (\Delta\theta/2)$ over $\Delta\theta/2$ approaches 1, according to a lemma derived in all calculus textbooks. Since the limit of $\Delta T/\Delta\theta$ is by definition equal to the derivative $dT/d\theta$, we write

$$\frac{dT}{d\theta} - \mu_s T = 0 \qquad \frac{dT}{T} = \mu_s \, d\theta$$

We shall now integrate both members of the last equation obtained from P_1 to P_2 (Fig. 8.14a). At P_1, we have $\theta = 0$ and $T = T_1$; at P_2, we have $\theta = \beta$ and $T = T_2$. Integrating between these limits, we write

$$\int_{T_1}^{T_2} \frac{dT}{T} = \int_0^\beta \mu_s \, d\theta$$
$$\ln T_2 - \ln T_1 = \mu_s \beta$$
$$\ln \frac{T_2}{T_1} = \mu_s \beta \qquad (8.13)$$

This relation may also be written in the form

$$\frac{T_2}{T_1} = e^{\mu_s \beta} \qquad (8.14)$$

The formulas we have derived apply equally well to problems involving flat belts passing over fixed cylindrical drums and to problems involving ropes wrapped around a post or capstan. They may also be used to solve problems involving band brakes. In such problems, it is the drum which is about to rotate, while the band remains fixed. The formulas may also be applied to problems involving belt drives. In these problems, both the pulley and the belt rotate; our concern is then to find whether the belt will slip, i.e., whether it will move *with respect* to the pulley.

Formulas (8.13) and (8.14) should be used only if the belt, rope, or brake is *about to slip*. Formula (8.14) will be used if T_1 or T_2 is desired; formula (8.13) will be preferred if either μ_s or the angle of contact β is desired.† We should note that T_2 is always larger than T_1; T_2 therefore represents the tension in that part of the belt or rope which *pulls*, while T_1 is the tension in the part which *resists*. We should also observe that the angle of contact β must be expressed in *radians*. The angle β may be larger than 2π; for example, if a rope is wrapped n times around a post, β is equal to $2\pi n$.

If the belt, rope, or brake is actually slipping, formulas similar to (8.13) and (8.14), but involving the coefficient of kinetic friction μ_k, should be used. If the belt, rope, or brake does not slip and is not about to slip, none of these formulas may be used.

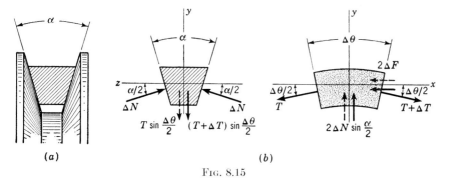

FIG. 8.15

The belts used in belt drives are often V-shaped. Such a belt, called a "V belt," is shown in Fig. 8.15a. It is seen that contact between belt and pulley takes place along the sides of the groove. The relation existing between the tensions T_1 and T_2 in the two parts of the belt when the belt is just about to slip may again be obtained by drawing the free-body diagram of an element of belt (Fig. 8.15b). Equations similar to (8.11) and (8.12) are derived, but the total friction force acting on the element is now $2\,\Delta F$, and the sum of the y components of the normal forces is $2\,\Delta N \sin(\alpha/2)$. Proceeding as above, we obtain

$$\frac{T_2}{T_1} = e^{\mu_s \beta / \sin(\alpha/2)} \tag{8.15}$$

† Since the determination of a power of e and that of a logarithm to the base e (ln) involves the use of the same scales on the slide rule, there is no need for distinguishing between formulas (8.13) and (8.14) in carrying out computations on the slide rule. In every case, the product $\mu_s\beta$ should be read on the D scale and the quotient T_2/T_1 on one of the LL scales.

SAMPLE PROBLEM 8.7

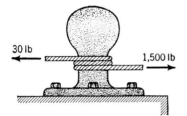

30 lb ←   1,500 lb →

A hawser thrown from a ship to a pier is wrapped two full turns around a capstan. The tension in the hawser is 1,500 lb; by exerting a force of 30 lb on its free end, a longshoreman can just keep the hawser from sliding. (*a*) Determine the coefficient of friction between the hawser and the capstan. (*b*) Determine the tension in the hawser that could be resisted by the 30-lb force if the hawser were wrapped three full turns around the capstan.

a. **Coefficient of Friction.** Since slipping of the hawser is impending, we use Eq. (8.13),

$$\ln \frac{T_2}{T_1} = \mu_s \beta$$

Since the hawser is wrapped two full turns around the capstan, we have

$$\beta = 2(2\pi \text{ radians}) = 12.6 \text{ radians}$$

$$T_1 = 30 \text{ lb} \qquad T_2 = 1,500 \text{ lb}$$

Therefore,

$$\mu_s \beta = \ln \frac{T_2}{T_1}$$

$$\mu_s(12.6 \text{ radians}) = \ln \frac{1,500 \text{ lb}}{30 \text{ lb}} = \ln 50 = 3.91$$

$$\mu_s = \mathbf{0.31}$$

b. **Hawser Wrapped Three Turns around Capstan.** Using the value of μ_s obtained in part *a*, we have now

$$\beta = 3(2\pi \text{ radians}) = 18.9 \text{ radians}$$

$$T_1 = 30 \text{ lb} \qquad \mu_s = 0.31$$

Substituting these values into Eq. (8.14), we obtain

$$\frac{T_2}{T_1} = e^{\mu_s \beta}$$

$$\frac{T_2}{30 \text{ lb}} = e^{(0.31)(18.9)} = e^{5.86} = 350$$

$$T_2 = \mathbf{10,500 \ lb}$$

Note. See the footnote on page 281 for the use of the slide rule in problems dealing with belt friction.

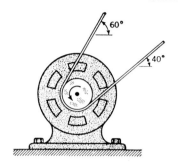

A flat belt is used to transmit the 25 lb-ft torque developed by an electric motor. The belt is in contact with a drum of diameter of 6 in. as shown. The coefficient of static friction between belt and drum is 0.30. Determine the minimum values of the tension in both parts of the belt which will assure no slippage.

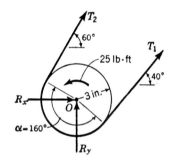

Solution. The free-body diagram of the drum is drawn. Summing moments about the center O of the drum, we write

$$+\!\!\downarrow \Sigma M_0 = 0: \quad T_2(3 \text{ in.}) - T_1(3 \text{ in.})$$
$$- 25 \text{ lb-ft} = 0$$

$$(T_2 - T_1)(3 \text{ in.}) = 300 \text{ lb-in.}$$

$$T_2 - T_1 = 100 \text{ lb} \qquad (1)$$

The angle of contact between belt and drum is

$$\beta = 160° = 160° \frac{2\pi \text{ radians}}{360°} = 2.79 \text{ radians}$$

Since the values of T_1 and T_2 corresponding to impending slippage are desired, we use Eq. (8.14).

$$\frac{T_2}{T_1} = e^{\mu_s \beta} \qquad \frac{T_2}{T_1} = e^{(0.30)(2.79)} = e^{0.837} = 2.31$$

$$T_2 = 2.31 T_1 \qquad (2)$$

Substituting T_2 from Eq. (2) into Eq. (1), we obtain

$$2.31 T_1 - T_1 = 100 \text{ lb} \qquad T_1 = \textbf{76.4 lb}$$

$$T_2 = T_1 + 100 \text{ lb} \qquad T_2 = \textbf{176.4 lb}$$

PROBLEMS

8.65. A seaman can exert a force of 75 lb on the free end of a hawser. The coefficient of static friction between the hawser and the capstan head is 0.30. How many times should he wrap the hawser around the capstan head in order to resist a force of 3 tons?

8.66. A rope weighing 0.5 lb/ft is wound $2\frac{1}{2}$ times around a horizontal bar. What length x of rope should be left hanging if a load of 100 lb is to be supported? The coefficient of static friction between the rope and bar is 0.25.

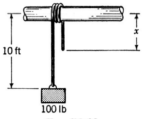

FIG. P8.66

8.67. A rope is wrapped four complete turns around a post. If a force of 8 lb is exerted on one end of the rope, determine the largest force which may be resisted by the other end of the rope. Assume $\mu_s = 0.25$.

8.68. A rope is wrapped around two posts as shown. If a 20-lb force must be exerted at A to resist a 2,000-lb force at B, determine the coefficient of static friction between the rope and the posts. Assume the coefficient of friction to be the same for each post.

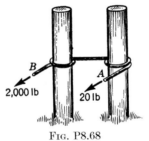

FIG. P8.68

8.69. A band brake is used to control the speed of a flywheel as shown. What torque must be applied to the flywheel in order to keep it rotating at a constant speed when $P = 10$ lb? Assume that the flywheel rotates clockwise.

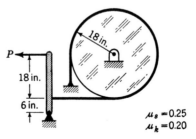

$\mu_s = 0.25$
$\mu_k = 0.20$

FIG. P8.69

8.70. Same as Prob. 8.69 assuming that the flywheel rotates counterclockwise.

8.71. A clockwise torque of 250 lb-ft is applied to the flywheel shown. Determine the force P required to prevent rotation of the flywheel.

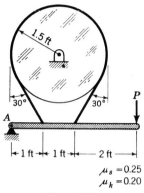

$\mu_s = 0.25$
$\mu_k = 0.20$

Fig. P8.71

8.72. Same as Prob. 8.71 assuming that the torque of 250 lb-ft is applied counterclockwise.

8.73. The arrangement shown is used to measure the power output of a small turbine. The coefficient of kinetic friction is 0.15. When the flywheel is at rest, the reading of each spring is 15 lb. What will be the reading of each spring when the flywheel is rotating? Assume that the belt is of constant length.

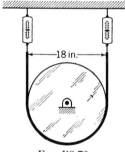

Fig. P8.73

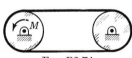

Fig. P8.74

8.74. What is the largest torque M which can be transmitted by the flat belt shown, if the maximum allowable tension in the belt is 400 lb? The diameter of each pulley is 12 in., and the coefficient of static friction between the belt and the drums is 0.20.

8.75. What coefficient of friction would allow the transmission of a 150 lb-ft torque without breaking the belt of Prob. 8.74?

8.76. A 50-ft rope passes over a small horizontal shaft; one end of the rope is attached to a bucket which weighs 5 lb. The excess rope is coiled inside the bucket. The coefficient of static friction between the rope and the shaft is 0.30, and the rope weighs 0.50 lb/ft. (a) If the shaft is held fixed, show that the system is in equilibrium. (b) If the shaft is slowly rotated, how far will the bucket rise before slipping? Neglect the diameter of the shaft.

8.77. Solve Prob. 8.74 assuming that a V belt and V-groove pulley are used.   The cross sections of the pulley and belt are as shown.

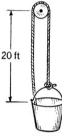

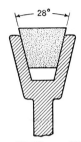

FIG. P8.76   FIG. P8.77 AND P8.78

8.78. Solve Prob. 8.75 assuming the pulley and flat belt are replaced by the V-belt system shown.

8.79. Complete the derivation of formula (8.15), which relates the values of the tension in both parts of a V belt.

9. Distributed Forces: Moments of Inertia

9.1. Second Moment, or Moment of Inertia, of an Area. In Chap. 5, we analyzed various systems of forces distributed over an area. The two main types of forces considered were (1) weights of homogeneous plates of uniform thickness (Secs. 5.2 to 5.4) and (2) distributed loads on beams and hydrostatic forces (Secs. 5.6 and 5.7). In the case of homogeneous plates, the weight ΔW of an element of plate was proportional to the area ΔA of the element. In the case of distributed loads on beams, each elementary weight ΔW was represented by an element of area $\Delta A = \Delta W$ under the load curve; in the case of hydrostatic forces on submerged rectangular surfaces, a similar procedure was followed. Thus, in all cases considered in Chap. 5, the distributed forces were proportional to the elementary areas associated with them. The resultant of these forces, therefore, could be obtained by summing the corresponding areas, and the moment of the resultant about any given axis could be determined by computing the first moments of the areas about that axis.

In this chapter, we shall consider distributed forces ΔF which depend not only upon the element of area ΔA on which they act but also upon the distance from ΔA to some given axis. More precisely, the force per unit area $\Delta F/\Delta A$ will vary linearly with the distance to the axis.

Consider, for example, a beam of uniform cross section, subjected to two equal and opposite couples applied at each end of the beam. Such a beam is said to be in *pure bending*, and it is shown in mechanics of materials that the internal forces in any section of the beam are distributed forces $\Delta F = ky\,\Delta A$ which vary linearly with the distance y from an axis passing through the centroid of the section. This axis, represented by the x axis in Fig. 9.1, is known as the *neutral axis* of the section. The forces on one side of the neutral axis are forces of compression, and on the other side forces of tension, while on the neutral axis itself the forces are zero.

The sum of the elementary forces ΔF over the entire section is

$$R = \int ky\,dA = k\int y\,dA$$

287

The last integral obtained is recognized as the *first moment* of the section about the x axis; it is equal to $\bar{y}A$ and to zero, since the centroid of the section is located on the x axis. The system of the forces ΔF thus reduces to a couple. The moment M of this couple (bending moment) must be equal to the sum of the moments $\Delta M = y\,\Delta F = ky^2\,\Delta A$ of the elementary forces. Integrating over the entire section, we obtain

$$M = \int ky^2\,dA = k\int y^2\,dA$$

The last integral is known as the *second moment*, or *moment of inertia*,† of the beam section with respect to the x axis and is denoted by I_x. It is obtained by multiplying each element of area dA by the *square of its*

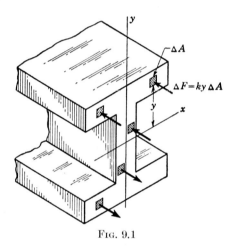

Fig. 9.1

distance from the x axis and integrating over the beam section. Since each product $y^2\,dA$ is positive, whether y is itself positive or negative (or zero if y is zero), the integral I_x will always be different from zero and positive.

Another example of second moment, or moment of inertia, of an area is provided by the following problem of hydrostatics: A vertical circular gate used to close the outlet of a large reservoir is submerged under water as shown in Fig. 9.2. What is the resultant of the forces exerted by the water on the gate, and what is the moment of the resultant about the line of intersection of the plane of the gate with the water surface (x axis)?

If the gate were rectangular, the resultant of the forces of pressure

---

† The term second moment is more proper than the term moment of inertia since, logically, the latter should be used only to denote integrals of mass (see Sec. 9.10). In common engineering practice, however, moment of inertia is used in connection with areas as well as masses.

could be determined from the pressure curve, as was done in Sec. 5.7. Since the gate is circular, however, a more general method must be used. Denoting by y the depth of an element of area ΔA and by γ the specific weight of water, the pressure at the element is $p = \gamma y$, and the elementary force exerted on ΔA is $\Delta F = p\,\Delta A = \gamma y\,\Delta A$. The resultant of the elementary forces is thus

$$R = \int \gamma y\,dA = \gamma \int y\,dA$$

and may be obtained by computing the first moment of the area of the gate with respect to the x axis. The moment M_x of the resultant must

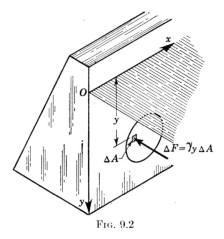

FIG. 9.2

be equal to the sum of the moments $\Delta M_x = y\,\Delta F = \gamma y^2\,\Delta A$ of the elementary forces. Integrating over the area of the gate, we have

$$M_x = \int \gamma y^2\,dA = \gamma \int y^2\,dA$$

Here again, the integral obtained represents the second moment, or moment of inertia, I_x of the area with respect to the x axis.

9.2. Determination of the Moment of Inertia of an Area by Integration. We have defined in the preceding section the second moment, or moment of inertia, of an area A with respect to the x axis. Defining in a similar way the moment of inertia I_y of the area A with respect to the y axis, we write (Fig. 9.3a)

$$I_x = \int y^2\,dA \qquad I_y = \int x^2\,dA \qquad (9.1)$$

These integrals, known as the *rectangular moments of inertia* of the area A, may be more easily computed if we choose for dA a thin strip parallel to one of the axes of coordinates. To compute I_x, the strip is chosen parallel to the x axis, so that all the points forming the strip are at the same distance y from the x axis (Fig. 9.3b); the moment of inertia dI_x of the strip is then obtained by multiplying the area dA of the strip by y^2. To compute I_y, the strip is chosen parallel to the y axis, so that all the points forming the strip are at the same distance x from the y axis (Fig. 9.3c); the moment of inertia dI_y of the strip is $x^2\, dA$.

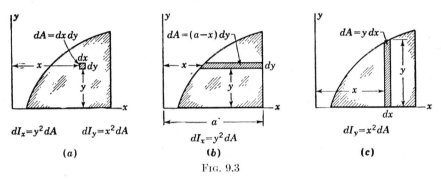

$dI_x = y^2\, dA$ $dI_y = x^2\, dA$

(a)

$dI_x = y^2\, dA$

(b)

$dI_y = x^2\, dA$

(c)

Fig. 9.3

Moment of Inertia of a Rectangular Area. As an example, we shall determine the moment of inertia of a rectangle with respect to its base

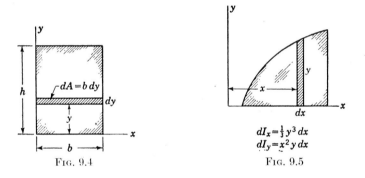

Fig. 9.4

$dI_x = \tfrac{1}{3} y^3\, dx$
$dI_y = x^2 y\, dx$

Fig. 9.5

(Fig. 9.4). Dividing the rectangle into strips parallel to the x axis, we obtain

$$dA = b\, dy \qquad dI_x = y^2 b\, dy \qquad I_x = \int_0^h b y^2\, dy = \tfrac{1}{3} b h^3 \qquad (9.2)$$

Computing I_x and I_y from the Same Elementary Strips. The formula just derived may be used to determine the moment of inertia dI_x with respect to the x axis of a rectangular strip parallel to the y axis such as the one shown in Fig. 9.3c and reproduced in Fig. 9.5. Making $b = dx$ and $h = y$ in formula (9.2), we write

$$dI_x = \tfrac{1}{3} y^3\, dx$$

On the other hand, we have

$$dI_y = x^2\, dA = x^2 y\, dx$$

The same element may thus be used to compute the moments of inertia I_x and I_y of a given area (see Sample Prob. 9.3).

9.3. Polar Moment of Inertia. An integral of great importance in problems concerning the torsion of cylindrical shafts and in problems dealing with the rotation of slabs is

$$J_O = \int r^2\, dA \tag{9.3}$$

where r is the distance from the element of area dA to the pole O (Fig.

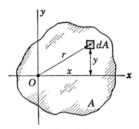

FIG. 9.6

9.6). This integral is the *polar moment of inertia* of the area A with respect to O.

The polar moment of inertia of a given area may be computed from the rectangular moments of inertia I_x and I_y of the area if these integrals are already known. Indeed, noting that $r^2 = x^2 + y^2$, we write

$$J_O = \int r^2\, dA = \int (x^2 + y^2)\, dA = \int y^2\, dA + \int x^2\, dA$$

that is,

$$J_O = I_x + I_y \tag{9.4}$$

9.4. Radius of Gyration of an Area. Consider an area A which has a moment of inertia I_x with respect to the x axis (Fig. 9.7a). Let us imagine that we concentrate this area into a thin strip parallel to the x axis (Fig. 9.7b). If the area A, thus concentrated, is to have the same

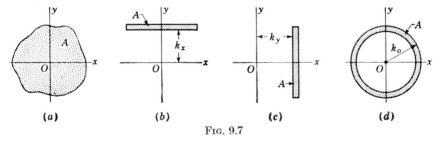

(a)   (b)   (c)   (d)

FIG. 9.7

moment of inertia with respect to the x axis, the strip should be placed at a distance k_x from the x axis, defined by the relation

$$I_x = k_x^2 A$$

Solving for k_x, we write

$$k_x = \sqrt{\frac{I_x}{A}} \tag{9.5}$$

The distance k_x is referred to as the *radius of gyration* of the area with

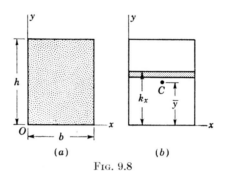

FIG. 9.8

respect to the x axis. We may define in a similar way the radii of gyration k_y and k_O; we write

$$I_y = k_y^2 A \qquad k_y = \sqrt{\frac{I_y}{A}} \tag{9.6}$$

$$J_O = k_O^2 A \qquad k_O = \sqrt{\frac{J_O}{A}} \tag{9.7}$$

Substituting for J_O, I_x, and I_y in terms of the radii of gyration in the relation (9.4), we observe that

$$k_O^2 = k_x^2 + k_y^2 \tag{9.8}$$

Example. As an example, let us compute the radius of gyration k_x of the rectangle shown in Fig. 9.4 and reproduced in Fig. 9.8a. Using formulas (9.5) and (9.2), we write

$$k_x^2 = \frac{I_x}{A} = \frac{\frac{1}{3}bh^3}{bh} = \frac{h^2}{3} \qquad k_x = \frac{h}{\sqrt{3}}$$

The radius of gyration k_x of the rectangle is shown in Fig. 9.8b. It should not be confused with the ordinate $\bar{y} = h/2$ of the centroid of the area. While k_x depends upon the *second moment*, or moment of inertia, of the area, the ordinate $\bar{y}$ is related to the *first moment* of the area.

SAMPLE PROBLEM 9.1

Determine the moment of inertia of a triangle with respect to its base.

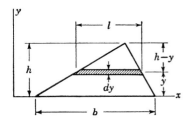

Solution. A triangle of base b and height h is drawn; the x axis is chosen to coincide with the base. A differential strip parallel to the x axis is chosen. Since all portions of the strip are at the same distance from the x axis, we write

$$dI_x = y^2 \, dA \qquad dA = l \, dy$$

From the similar triangles, we have

$$\frac{l}{b} = \frac{h-y}{h} \qquad l = b\,\frac{h-y}{h} \qquad dA = b\,\frac{h-y}{h}\,dy$$

Integrating dI_x from $y = 0$ to $y = h$, we obtain

$$I_x = \int y^2 \, dA = \int_0^h y^2 b\,\frac{h-y}{h}\,dy = \frac{b}{h}\int_0^h (hy^2 - y^3)\,dy = \frac{b}{h}\left[h\frac{y^3}{3} - \frac{y^4}{4}\right]_0^h = \boxed{\frac{bh^3}{12}}$$

SAMPLE PROBLEM 9.2

(a) Determine the centroidal polar moment of inertia of a circular area by direct integration. (b) Using the result of part a, determine the moment of inertia of a circular area with respect to a diameter.

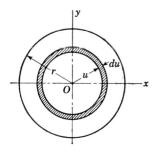

*a. **Polar Moment of Inertia.*** A circular differential element of area is chosen. Since all portions of this differential area are at the same distance from the origin, we write

$$dJ_0 = u^2 \, dA \qquad dA = 2\pi u \, du$$

$$J_0 = \int dJ_0 = \int_0^r u^2(2\pi u \, du) = 2\pi \int_0^r u^3 \, du$$

$$J_0 = \frac{\pi}{2} r^4$$

*b. **Moment of Inertia.*** Because of the symmetry of the circular area we have $I_x = I_y$. We then write

$$J_0 = I_x + I_y = 2I_x \qquad \frac{\pi}{2} r^4 = 2I_x \qquad I_x = \frac{\pi}{4} r^4 \qquad I_{\text{diameter}} = \frac{\pi}{4} r^4$$

293

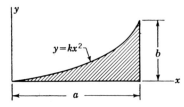

(*a*) Determine the moment of inertia of the shaded area shown with respect to each of the coordinate axes. This area has also been considered in Sample Prob. 5.4. (*b*) Using the results of part *a*, determine the radius of gyration of the shaded area with respect to each of the coordinate axes.

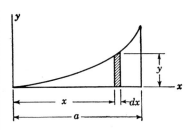

Solution. Referring to Sample Prob. 5.4, we obtain the following expressions for the equation of the curve and the total area:

$$y = \frac{b}{a^2} x^2 \qquad A = \tfrac{1}{3}ab$$

Moment of Inertia I_x. A vertical differential element of area is chosen. Since all portions of this element are *not* at the same distance from the x axis, we must treat the element as a thin rectangle. The moment of inertia of the element with respect to the x axis is

$$dI_x = \tfrac{1}{3}y^3\, dx = \frac{1}{3}\left(\frac{b}{a^2}x^2\right)^3 dx = \frac{1}{3}\frac{b^3}{a^6}x^6\, dx$$

$$I_x = \int dI_x = \int_0^a \frac{1}{3}\frac{b^3}{a^6}x^6\, dx = \left[\frac{1}{3}\frac{b^3}{a^6}\frac{x^7}{7}\right]_0^a \qquad \boxed{I_x = \frac{ab^3}{21}}$$

Moment of Inertia I_y. The same vertical differential element of area is used. Since all portions of the element are at the same distance from the y axis, we write

$$dI_y = x^2\, dA = x^2(y\, dx) = x^2\left(\frac{b}{a^2}x^2\right)dx = \frac{b}{a^2}x^4\, dx$$

$$I_y = \int dI_y = \int_0^a \frac{b}{a^2}x^4\, dx = \left[\frac{b}{a^2}\frac{x^5}{5}\right]_0^a \qquad \boxed{I_y = \frac{a^3b}{5}}$$

Radii of Gyration k_x and k_y

$$k_x^2 = \frac{I_x}{A} = \frac{ab^3/21}{ab/3} = \frac{b^2}{7} \qquad \boxed{k_x = \sqrt{\tfrac{1}{7}}\, b}$$

$$k_y^2 = \frac{I_y}{A} = \frac{a^3b/5}{ab/3} = \tfrac{3}{5}a^2 \qquad \boxed{k_y = \sqrt{\tfrac{3}{5}}\, a}$$

PROBLEMS

9.1. Determine by direct integration the moment of inertia of a rectangle of height h and width b with respect to an axis through its centroid parallel to the base.

9.2. Determine by direct integration the moment of inertia of a circular area of radius r with respect to a diameter.

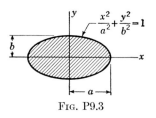

FIG. P9.3

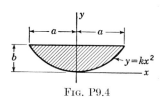

FIG. P9.4

9.3 through 9.6. Determine by direct integration the moment of inertia of the shaded area with respect to the y axis.

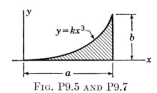

FIG. P9.5 AND P9.7

9.7 and 9.8. Determine by direct integration the moment of inertia of the shaded area with respect to the x axis.

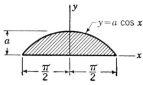

*FIG. P9.6 AND P9.8

9.9. Determine the radius of gyration of a rectangle of height h and base b with respect to an axis through its centroid parallel to the base.

9.10. Determine the polar radius of gyration of a circular area with respect to its centroid.

9.11. Determine the polar moment of inertia and the polar radius of gyration of a rectangle of height h and base b with respect to its centroid.

9.12. Determine the polar moment of inertia and the polar radius of gyration with respect to the origin for the area considered in Sample Prob. 9.3. (*Hint.* Make use of results obtained in the sample problem.)

9.13. (*a*) Determine by direct integration the polar moment of inertia of the annular area shown. (*b*) Using the results of part *a*, determine the moment of inertia of the given area with respect to the x axis.

9.14. Solve Prob. 9.13 assuming $R_1 = 3$ in. and $R_2 = 5$ in.

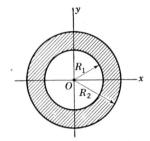

FIG. P9.13 AND P9.15

*9.15. Show that the polar radius of gyration k_O of the annular area shown is approximately equal to the mean radius $R_m = (R_1 + R_2)/2$ for small values of the thickness $t = R_2 - R_1$.

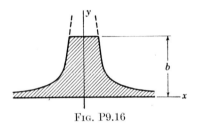

FIG. P9.16

*9.16. In the plane area shown, it is desired to have I_x directly proportional to the height b. Determine the equation of the curve bounding the area on the right.

9.5. Parallel-axis Theorem.

Consider the moment of inertia I of an area A with respect to an axis AA' (Fig. 9.9). Denoting by y the dis-

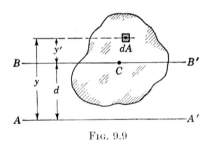

FIG. 9.9

tance from an element of area dA to AA', we write

$$I = \int y^2 \, dA$$

Let us now draw an axis BB' parallel to AA' through the centroid C of the area; this axis is called a *centroidal axis*. Denoting by y' the distance from the element dA to BB', we write $y = y' + d$, where d is the distance between the axes AA' and BB'. Substituting for y in the integral representing I, we write

$$I = \int y^2 \, dA = \int (y' + d)^2 \, dA$$
$$= \int y'^2 \, dA + 2d\int y' \, dA + d^2\int dA$$

The first integral represents the moment of inertia $\bar{I}$ of the area with respect to the centroidal axis BB'. The second integral represents the first moment of the area with respect to BB'; since the centroid C of the area is located on that axis, the second integral must be zero. Finally, we observe that the last integral is equal to the total area A. We write therefore

$$I = \bar{I} + Ad^2 \tag{9.9}$$

This formula expresses that the moment of inertia I of an area with respect to any given axis AA' is equal to the moment of inertia $\bar{I}$ of the area with respect to a centroidal axis BB' parallel to AA' *plus* the product Ad^2 of the area A and of the square of the distance d between the two axes. This theorem is known as the *parallel-axis theorem*. Substituting k^2A for I and $\bar{k}^2A$ for $\bar{I}$, the theorem may also be expressed in the following way:

$$k^2 = \bar{k}^2 + d^2 \tag{9.10}$$

A similar theorem may be used to relate the polar moment of inertia J_O of an area about a point O and the polar moment of inertia J_C of the same area about its centroid C. Denoting by d the distance between O and C, we write

$$J_O = J_C + Ad^2 \qquad \text{or} \qquad k_O^2 = k_C^2 + d^2 \tag{9.11}$$

Example 1. As an application of the parallel-axis theorem, we shall determine the moment of inertia I_T of a circular area with respect to a line tangent to the circle (Fig. 9.10). We found in Sample Prob. 9.2 that the moment of inertia of a circular area about a centroidal axis is $\bar{I} = \frac{1}{4}\pi r^4$. We may write, therefore,

$$I_T = \bar{I} + Ad^2 = \frac{1}{4}\pi r^4 + \pi r^2 r^2 = \frac{5}{4}\pi r^4$$

Example 2. The parallel-axis theorem may also be used to determine the centroidal moment of inertia of an area when the moment of inertia of this area with respect to some parallel axis is known. Consider, for instance, a triangular area (Fig. 9.11). We found in Sample Prob. 9.1 that the moment of inertia of a triangle with respect to its base AA' is equal to $\frac{1}{12}bh^3$. Using the parallel-axis theorem, we write

$$I_{AA'} = \bar{I}_{BB'} + Ad^2 \qquad \bar{I}_{BB'} = I_{AA'} - Ad^2 = \frac{1}{12}bh^3 - \frac{1}{2}bh(\frac{1}{3}h)^2 = \frac{1}{36}bh^3$$

It should be observed that the product Ad^2 was *subtracted* from the given moment of inertia in order to obtain the centroidal moment of inertia of the triangle. While this product is *added* in transferring *from* a centroidal axis to a parallel axis, it should be *subtracted* in transferring *to* a centroidal axis. In other words, the moment of inertia of an area is always smaller with respect to a centroidal axis than with respect to any other parallel axis.

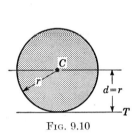

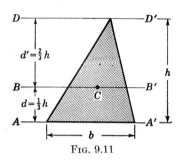

Fig. 9.10   Fig. 9.11

Returning to Fig. 9.11, we observe that the moment of inertia of the triangle with respect to a line DD' drawn through a vertex may be obtained by writing

$$I_{DD'} = \bar{I}_{BB'} + Ad'^2 = \tfrac{1}{36}bh^3 + \tfrac{1}{2}bh(\tfrac{2}{3}h)^2 = \tfrac{1}{4}bh^3$$

Note that $I_{DD'}$ *could not* have been obtained directly from $I_{AA'}$. The parallel-axis theorem can be applied only if one of the two parallel axes passes through the centroid of the area.

9.6. Moments of Inertia of Composite Areas. Consider a composite area A made of several component areas A_1, A_2, etc. Since the integral representing the moment of inertia of A may be subdivided into integrals computed over A_1, A_2, etc., the moment of inertia of A with respect to a given axis will be obtained by adding the moments of inertia of the areas A_1, A_2, etc., with respect to the same axis. The moment of inertia of an area made of several of the common shapes shown in Fig. 9.12 may thus be obtained from the formulas given in that figure. Before adding the moments of inertia of the component areas, however, the parallel-axis theorem should be used to transfer each moment of inertia to the desired axis. This is shown in Sample Probs. 9.4 and 9.5.

The properties of the cross sections of various structural shapes are given in Fig. 9.13. As noted in Sec. 9.1, the moment of inertia of a beam section about its neutral axis is closely related to the value of the internal forces. The determination of moments of inertia is thus a prerequisite to the analysis and design of structural members.

It should be noted that the radius of gyration of a composite area is *not* equal to the sum of the radii of gyration of the component areas. In order to determine the radius of gyration of a composite area, it is necessary first to compute the moment of inertia of the area.

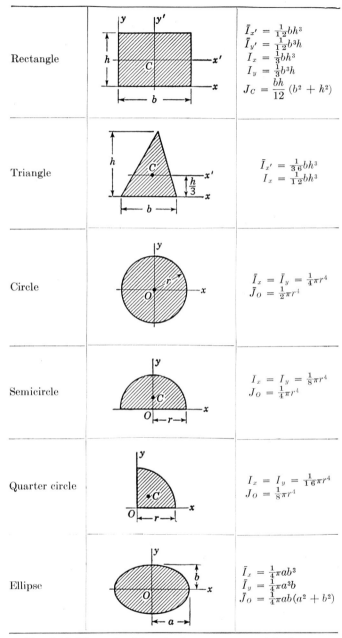

Rectangle	$\bar{I}_{x'} = \frac{1}{12}bh^3$ $\bar{I}_{y'} = \frac{1}{12}b^3h$ $I_x = \frac{1}{3}bh^3$ $I_y = \frac{1}{3}b^3h$ $J_C = \dfrac{bh}{12}\,(b^2 + h^2)$
Triangle	$\bar{I}_{x'} = \frac{1}{36}bh^3$ $I_x = \frac{1}{12}bh^3$
Circle	$\bar{I}_x = \bar{I}_y = \frac{1}{4}\pi r^4$ $\bar{J}_O = \frac{1}{2}\pi r^4$
Semicircle	$I_x = I_y = \frac{1}{8}\pi r^4$ $J_O = \frac{1}{4}\pi r^4$
Quarter circle	$I_x = I_y = \frac{1}{16}\pi r^4$ $J_O = \frac{1}{8}\pi r^4$
Ellipse	$\bar{I}_x = \frac{1}{4}\pi ab^3$ $\bar{I}_y = \frac{1}{4}\pi a^3b$ $\bar{J}_O = \frac{1}{4}\pi ab(a^2 + b^2)$

FIG. 9.12. Moments of inertia of common geometric shapes.

Shape		Nominal size, in.	Wt/ft, lb	Area, in.²	I_x, in.⁴	k_x, in.	$\bar{y}$, in.	I_y, in.⁴	k_y, in.	$\bar{x}$, in.
Wide-flange section		$16 \times 8\frac{1}{2}$†	64	18.80	833.8	6.66	....	68.4	1.91	
		14×8	43	12.65	429.0	5.82	....	45.1	1.89	
		8×8	31	9.12	109.7	3.47	....	37.0	2.01	
American Standard beam		18×6	70	20.46	917.5	6.70	....	24.5	1.09	
		12×5	35	10.20	227.0	4.72	....	10.0	0.99	
		$6 \times 3\frac{3}{8}$	12.5	3.61	21.8	2.46	....	1.8	0.72	
American Standard channel		$10 \times 2\frac{5}{8}$	25.0	7.33	90.7	3.52	....	3.4	0.68	0.62
		$8 \times 2\frac{1}{4}$	11.5	3.36	32.3	3.10	....	1.3	0.63	0.58
		6×2	8.2	2.39	13.0	2.34	....	0.7	0.54	0.52
Angles		$6 \times 6 \times 1$‡	37.4	11.00	35.5	1.80	1.86	35.5	1.80	1.86
		$4 \times 4 \times \frac{1}{2}$	12.8	3.75	5.6	1.22	1.18	5.6	1.22	1.18
		$8 \times 6 \times 1$	44.2	13.00	80.8	2.49	2.65	38.8	1.73	1.65
		$5 \times 3\frac{1}{2} \times \frac{1}{2}$	13.6	4.00	10.0	1.58	1.66	4.1	1.01	0.91

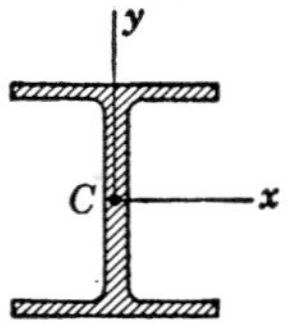

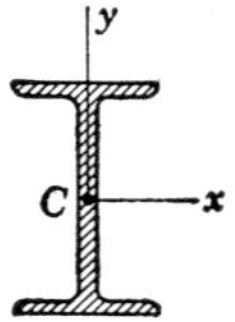

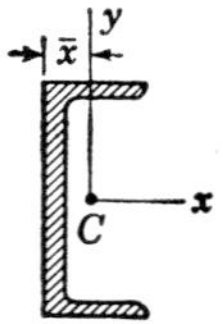

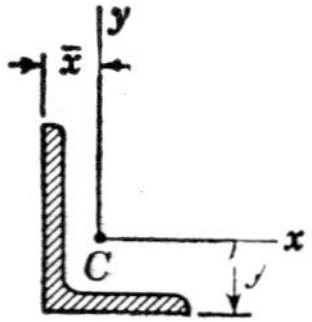

† Depth and width.

‡ The last figure represents the thickness.

Fig. 9.13. Properties of rolled-steel structural shapes.

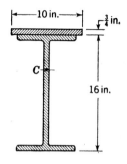

SAMPLE PROBLEM 9.4

The strength of a 16-in. 64-lb wide-flange beam is increased by attaching a 10- by $\frac{3}{4}$-in. plate to its upper flange as shown. Determine the moment of inertia and the radius of gyration of the composite section with respect to an axis through its centroid C and parallel to the plate.

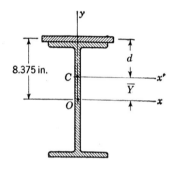

Solution. The origin of coordinates O is placed at the centroid of the wide-flange section, and the distance $\bar{Y}$ to the centroid of the composite section is computed by the methods of Chap. 5. The area of the wide-flange section is found by referring to Fig. 9.13.

Section	Area	$\bar{y}$	$\bar{y}A$
Plate................	7.5	8.375	62.8
Wide-flange section....	18.8	0	0
	26.3	.....	62.8

$$\bar{Y}\Sigma A = \Sigma \bar{y}A \qquad \bar{Y}(26.3) = 62.8 \qquad \bar{Y} = 2.39 \text{ in.}$$

Moment of Inertia. The parallel-axis theorem is used to determine the moments of inertia of the wide-flange section and of the plate with respect to the x' axis. This axis is a centroidal axis for the composite section, *but not* for either of the elements considered separately. The value of $\bar{I}_x$ for the wide-flange section is obtained from Fig. 9.13.

For the wide-flange section

$$I_{x'} = \bar{I}_x + A\bar{Y}^2 = 833.8 + (18.8)(2.39)^2 = 941 \text{ in.}^4$$

For the plate

$$I_{x'} = \bar{I}_x + Ad^2 = (\tfrac{1}{12})(10)(\tfrac{3}{4})^3 + (7.5)(8.375 - 2.39)^2 = 269 \text{ in.}^4$$

For the composite area

$$I_{x'} = 941 + 269 = 1,210 \text{ in.}^4 \qquad I_{x'} = \mathbf{1,210 \text{ in.}^4}$$

Radius of Gyration

$$k_{x'}^2 = \frac{I_{x'}}{A} = \frac{1,210 \text{ in.}^4}{26.3 \text{ in.}^2} \qquad k_{x'} = \mathbf{6.78 \text{ in.}}$$

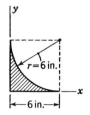

Determine the moment of inertia of the shaded area with respect to the y axis.

Solution. The given area may be obtained by subtracting a quarter circle from a square. The moments of inertia of the square and of the quarter circle are computed separately.

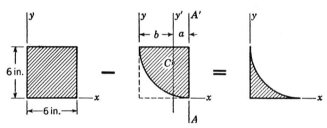

I_y *for Square.* Referring to Fig. 9.12, we obtain

$$I_y = \tfrac{1}{3}b^3h = (\tfrac{1}{3})(6)^3(6) = 432 \text{ in.}^4$$

I_y *for the Quarter Circle.* Referring to Fig. 5.8, we locate the centroid C of the quarter circle with respect to side AA'.

$$a = \frac{4r}{3\pi} = \frac{(4)(6)}{3\pi} = 2.546 \text{ in.}$$

The distance b from the centroid C to the y axis is

$$b = 6 \text{ in.} - a = 6 \text{ in.} - 2.546 \text{ in.} = 3.454 \text{ in.}$$

Referring now to Fig. 9.12, we compute the moment of inertia of the quarter circle with respect to side AA'; we also compute the area of the quarter circle.

$$I_{AA'} = \tfrac{1}{16}\pi r^4 = \tfrac{1}{16}\pi(6)^4 = 254.5 \text{ in.}^4 \qquad A = \tfrac{1}{4}\pi r^2 = \tfrac{1}{4}\pi(6)^2 = 28.27 \text{ in.}^2$$

Using the parallel-axis theorem, we obtain the value of $\bar{I}_{y'}$,

$$I_{AA'} = \bar{I}_{y'} + Aa^2 \qquad \bar{I}_{y'} = I_{AA'} - Aa^2 = 254.5 - (28.27)(2.546)^2 = 71.2 \text{ in.}^4$$

Again using the parallel-axis theorem, we obtain the value of I_y,

$$I_y = \bar{I}_{y'} + Ab^2 = 71.2 + (28.27)(3.454)^2 = 408.5 \text{ in.}^4$$

I_y *for Given Area.* Subtracting the moment of inertia of the quarter circle from that of the square, we obtain

$$I_y = 432.0 \text{ in.}^4 - 408.5 \text{ in.}^4 = 23.5 \text{ in.}^4 \qquad I_y = \textbf{23.5 in.}^4$$

PROBLEMS

9.17. For the area shown, it is known that $A = 20$ in.^{2} and $\bar{I}_{BB'} = 30$ in.^{4} Determine the distance d for which (a) $I_{AA'} = 60$ in.^{4}, (b) $I_{AA'} = 120$ in.^{4}

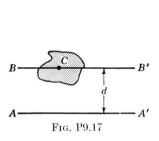

FIG. P9.17

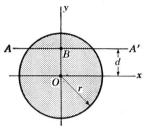

FIG. P9.18

9.18. For the circular area shown, determine the distance d for which (a) the value of the moment of inertia with respect to the axis AA' is twice the value of the moment of inertia with respect to the x axis, (b) the value of the polar moment of inertia with respect to B is twice the value of the centroidal polar moment of inertia.

9.19. For the shaded area shown, $I_{AA'} = 504$ in.^{4} and $I_{BB'} = 1,206$ in.^{4} Determine the area of the figure and its centroidal moment of inertia.

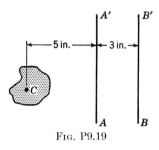

FIG. P9.19

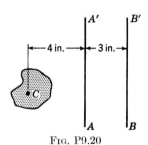

FIG. P9.20

9.20. For the shaded area shown, it is known that $I_{BB'} = 936$ in.^{4} and that the area is 18 in.^{2} Determine the moment of inertia with respect to the axis AA'.

9.21 through 9.23. For the plane area shown, determine the moment of inertia and the radius of gyration with respect to the x axis.

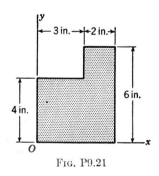

FIG. P9.21

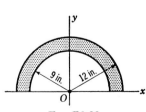

FIG. P9.22

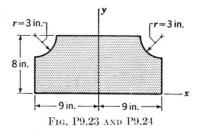

FIG. P9.23 AND P9.24

9.24. For the plane area shown, determine the moment of inertia and the radius of gyration with respect to the y axis.

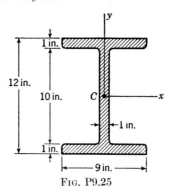

FIG. P9.25

9.25 and 9.26. Determine the centroidal moments of inertia $\bar{I}_x$ and $\bar{I}_y$ and the centroidal radii of gyration $\bar{k}_x$ and $\bar{k}_y$ for the structural shape shown. Neglect the effect of fillets.

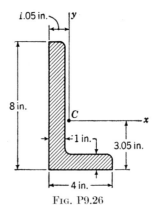

FIG. P9.26

9.27. Determine J_O and k_O with respect to the origin for the area of Prob. 9.21.

9.28. Determine J_O and k_O with respect to the origin for the area of Prob. 9.22.

9.29. A steel plate, 9 by $\frac{3}{4}$ in., is attached to the flange of an 18-in. 70-lb American Standard beam as shown. Determine the moments of inertia and the radii of gyration of the total section with respect to centroidal axes in the plane of the section and respectively parallel and perpendicular to the plate.

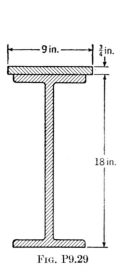

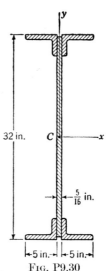

FIG. P9.29

FIG. P9.30

9.30. A plate-girder section consists of a $31\frac{1}{2}$- by $\frac{5}{16}$-in. plate and of four 5- by $3\frac{1}{2}$-in. angles each $\frac{1}{2}$ in. thick. Determine the centroidal moment of inertia of the total section with respect to the x axis.

9.31. Two 10-in. 25-lb American Standard channels and a 14- by $\frac{1}{2}$-in. plate are used to form the column section shown. Determine the moments of inertia and the radii of gyration of the total section with respect to the centroidal axes shown.

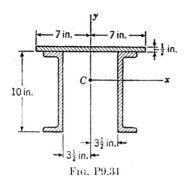

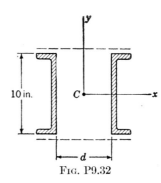

FIG. P9.31

FIG. P9.32

9.32. Two 10-in. 25-lb American Standard channels are laced together to form a single column section. Determine the distance d between the backs of the channels for which $\bar{I}_x = \bar{I}_y$.

9.33 and 9.34. For the plane area shown, determine the unknown dimension d for which $I_x = I_y$.

9.35. For the plane area shown, determine the unknown dimension d for which the polar moment of inertia J_O is equal to 200 in.[4]

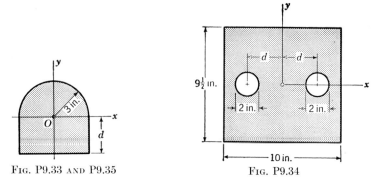

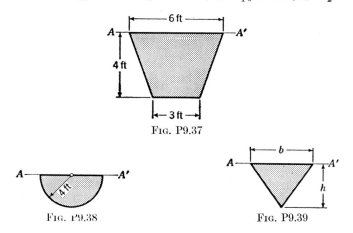

Fig. P9.33 and P9.35 Fig. P9.34

9.36. (a) Show that the moment of inertia of a thin annular area about its diameter is approximately $\pi r_m^3 t$, where r_m is the mean radius and t is the thickness. (*Hint.* Subtract the moments of inertia of the two concentric circles.) (b) Determine the per cent error of the approximate expression if $t/r_m = \frac{1}{10}$ and if $t/r_m = \frac{1}{2}$.

Fig. P9.37

Fig. P9.38 Fig. P9.39

9.37 through 9.39. The area shown forms the end of a trough which is filled with water to the line AA'. Referring to Sec. 9.1, determine the depth of the point of application of the resultant of the hydrostatic forces acting on the area (center of pressure).

9.40. A vertical circular gate of radius r is completely submerged in water. If the center of the gate is at a depth h, determine the depth of the center of pressure.

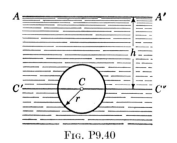

Fig. P9.40

9.41. Assuming that the circular gate of Prob. 9.40 is hinged about its diameter $C'C''$, and denoting the specific weight of water by γ, determine (a) the reaction at each hinge, (b) the moment of the couple required to keep the gate closed.

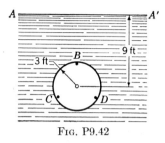

FIG. P9.42

9.42. The center of a vertical circular gate, 6 ft in diameter, is located 9 ft below the water surface. The gate is held by three bolts equally spaced as shown. Determine the force on each bolt.

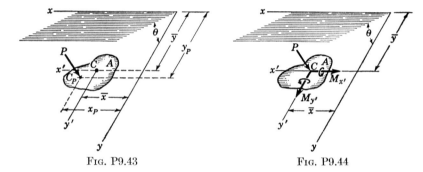

FIG. P9.43   FIG. P9.44

*9.43.** Show that the resultant of the hydrostatic forces acting on a submerged plane area A is a force P perpendicular to the area and of magnitude $P = \gamma A \bar{y} \sin \theta = \bar{p} A$ where γ is the specific weight of the liquid and $\bar{p}$ the pressure at the centroid C of the area. Show that P is applied at a point C_P, called the center of pressure, of coordinates $x_P = P_{xy}/A\bar{y}$ and $y_P = I_x/A\bar{y}$, where $P_{xy} = \int xy\, dA$ (see Sec. 9.7). Show also that the difference of ordinates $y_P - \bar{y}$ is equal to $\bar{k}_x^2/\bar{y}$ and thus depends upon the depth at which the area is submerged.

*9.44.** Show that the system of hydrostatic forces acting on a submerged plane area A may be reduced to a force P at the centroid C of the area and two couples. The force P is perpendicular to the area and of magnitude $P = \gamma A\bar{y} \sin \theta$, where γ is the specific weight of the liquid, and the couples are represented by vectors directed as shown and of magnitude $M_{x'} = \gamma \bar{I}_{x'} \sin \theta$ and $M_{y'} = \gamma \bar{P}_{x'y'} \sin \theta$, where, according to Sec. 9.7, $\bar{P}_{x'y'} = \int x'y'\, dA$. Note that the couples are independent of the depth at which the area is submerged.

*9.7. Product of Inertia.   The integral

$$P_{xy} = \int xy\, dA \qquad (9.12)$$

obtained by multiplying each element dA of an area A by its coordinates x and y and integrating over the area (Fig. 9.14) is known as the *product of inertia* of the area A with respect to the x and y axes. Unlike the moments of inertia I_x and I_y, the product of inertia P_{xy} may be either positive or negative.

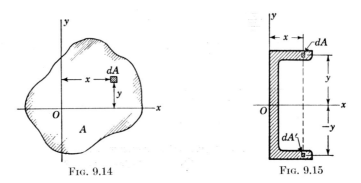

FIG. 9.14   FIG. 9.15

When one or both of the x and y axes are axes of symmetry for the area A, the product of inertia P_{xy} is zero. Consider, for example, the channel section shown in Fig. 9.15. Since this section is symmetrical with respect to the x axis, we can associate to each element dA of coordinates x and y an element dA' of coordinates x and $-y$. Clearly, the contributions of any pair of elements chosen in this way cancel out, and the integral (9.12) reduces to zero.

A parallel-axis theorem similar to the one established in Sec. 9.5 for moments of inertia may be derived for products of inertia. Consider an area A and a system of rectangular coordinates x and y (Fig. 9.16).

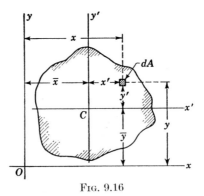

FIG. 9.16

Through the centroid C of the area, of coordinates $\bar{x}$ and $\bar{y}$, we draw two *centroidal axes* x' and y' parallel, respectively, to the x and y axes. Denoting by x and y the coordinates of an element of area dA with respect to the original axes, and by x' and y' the coordinates of the same element with respect to the centroidal axes, we write $x = x' + \bar{x}$ and $y = y' + \bar{y}$.

Substituting into (9.12), we obtain the following expression for the product of inertia P_{xy}:

$$P_{xy} = \int xy\, dA = \int (x' + \bar{x})(y' + \bar{y})\, dA$$
$$= \int x'y'\, dA + \bar{y}\int x'\, dA + \bar{x}\int y'\, dA + \bar{x}\bar{y}\int dA$$

The first integral represents the product of inertia $\bar{P}_{x'y'}$ of the area A with respect to the centroidal axes x' and y'. The next two integrals represent first moments of the area with respect to the centroidal axes; they reduce to zero, since the centroid C is located on these axes. Finally, we observe that the last integral is equal to the total area A. We write therefore

$$P_{xy} = \bar{P}_{x'y'} + \bar{x}\bar{y}A \tag{9.13}$$

*9.8. Principal Axes and Principal Moments of Inertia. Consider the area A and the coordinate axes x and y (Fig. 9.17). We assume that the moments and product of inertia

$$I_x = \int y^2\, dA \qquad I_y = \int x^2\, dA \qquad P_{xy} = \int xy\, dA \tag{9.14}$$

of the area A are known, and we propose to determine the moments and product of inertia I_u, I_v, and P_{uv} of A with respect to new axes u and v obtained by rotating the original axes about the origin through an angle θ.

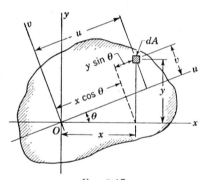

FIG. 9.17

We first note the following relations between the coordinates u, v and x, y of an element of area dA:

$$u = x \cos \theta + y \sin \theta \qquad v = y \cos \theta - x \sin \theta$$

Substituting for u and v into the expression for I_u, we write

$$I_u = \int v^2\, dA = \int (y \cos \theta - x \sin \theta)^2\, dA$$
$$= \cos^2 \theta \int y^2\, dA - 2 \sin \theta \cos \theta \int xy\, dA + \sin^2 \theta \int x^2\, dA$$

Taking the relations (9.14) into account, we write

$$I_u = I_x \cos^2 \theta - 2P_{xy} \sin \theta \cos \theta + I_y \sin^2 \theta \tag{9.15}$$

Similarly, we obtain for I_v and P_{uv} the expressions

$$I_v = I_x \sin^2 \theta + 2P_{xy} \sin \theta \cos \theta + I_y \cos^2 \theta \qquad (9.16)$$
$$P_{uv} = I_x \sin \theta \cos \theta + P_{xy} (\cos^2 \theta - \sin^2 \theta) - I_y \sin \theta \cos \theta \quad (9.17)$$

We observe, by adding (9.15) and (9.16) member by member, that

$$I_u + I_v = I_x + I_y \qquad (9.18)$$

This result could have been anticipated, since both members of (9.18) are equal to the polar moment of inertia J_O.

Making use of the trigonometric relations $\sin 2\theta = 2 \sin \theta \cos \theta$ and $\cos 2\theta = \cos^2 \theta - \sin^2 \theta$, we may write (9.15), (9.16), and (9.17) as follows:

$$I_u = \frac{I_x + I_y}{2} + \frac{I_x - I_y}{2} \cos 2\theta - P_{xy} \sin 2\theta \qquad (9.19)$$

$$I_v = \frac{I_x + I_y}{2} - \frac{I_x - I_y}{2} \cos 2\theta + P_{xy} \sin 2\theta \qquad (9.20)$$

$$P_{uv} = \frac{I_x - I_y}{2} \sin 2\theta + P_{xy} \cos 2\theta \qquad (9.21)$$

It appears from Eq. (9.21) that the product of inertia P_{uv} will vanish if θ has a value θ_m satisfying the relation

$$\tan 2\theta_m = - \frac{2P_{xy}}{I_x - I_y} \qquad (9.22)$$

Equation (9.22) defines two values $2\theta_m$ which are $180°$ apart and thus two values θ_m which are $90°$ apart. Given an area A and a point O, it is thus always possible to choose axes u and v through O, such that the product of inertia P_{uv} is zero. These axes are called the *principal axes of the area A about O*.[†] It may be checked that the derivatives $dI_u/d\theta$ and $dI_v/d\theta$ are equal to zero when $\theta = \theta_m$. The corresponding values of I_u and I_v thus represent the extreme values of the moment of inertia. They are called the *principal moments of inertia* of A about O and are equal to

$$I_{\text{max,min}} = \frac{I_x + I_y}{2} \pm \sqrt{\left(\frac{I_x - I_y}{2}\right)^2 + P_{xy}^2} \qquad (9.23)$$

*9.9. Mohr's Circle for Moments of Inertia. A useful graphical representation of formulas (9.19) to (9.23) is due to the German engineer Otto Mohr (1835–1918). Consider a given area A and coordinate axes x and y (Fig. 9.18a). We shall assume that the moments and product

† Referring to Sec. 9.7, we note that, if the area A possesses an axis of symmetry, this axis must be a principal axis.

of inertia I_x, I_y, and P_{xy} are known. We may then represent these moments and product of inertia on a diagram by plotting a point A of coordinates I_x and P_{xy} and a point B of coordinates I_y and $-P_{xy}$ (Fig. 9.18b). We now draw the circle of diameter AB. This circle, known as *Mohr's circle*, must be centered on the I axis at a point C of abscissa $\dfrac{I_x + I_y}{2}$ and must have a radius equal to $\left[\left(\dfrac{I_x - I_y}{2}\right)^2 + P_{xy}^2\right]^{\frac{1}{2}}$. It must therefore intersect the I axis at two points D and E located at distances from O respectively equal to the two expressions defined by the right-hand member of formula (9.23). Thus, the lengths OD and OE represent the principal moments of inertia of the area A. We also note

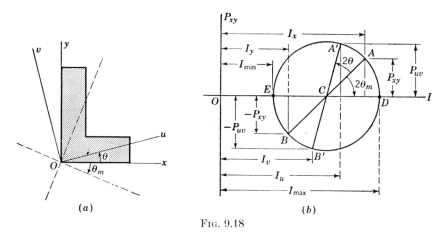

(a)   (b)

FIG. 9.18

that $\tan (ACD) = 2P_{xy}/(I_x - I_y)$; the angle ACD is thus equal in magnitude to one of the two angles defined by formula (9.22). Since in the case considered $I_x > I_y$, the angle $2\theta_m$ shown is negative. The angle θ_m defining the position of one of the two principal axes in Fig. 9.18a must therefore be drawn clockwise (counterclockwise is positive).

Since Mohr's circle is uniquely defined, the same circle would be obtained by considering the moments and product of inertia of the area A with respect to axes u and v (Fig. 9.18a). The point A' of coordinates I_u and P_{uv}, and the point B' of coordinates I_v and $-P_{uv}$, must therefore be located on Mohr's circle and the angle $A'CA$ must be equal to 2θ. This may also be verified from formulas (9.19) to (9.21).

If the moments and product of inertia of an area A are known with respect to two rectangular axes through a point O, Mohr's circle may thus be used to determine graphically the principal axes and principal moments of inertia of the area about O or to determine the moments and product of inertia of the area with respect to any other pair of rectangular axes through O.

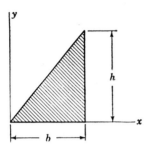

Determine the product of inertia of the right triangle shown (a) with respect to the x and y axes and (b) with respect to centroidal axes parallel to the x and y axes.

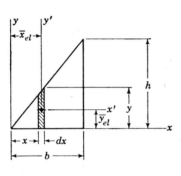

a. Product of Inertia P_{xy}. A vertical rectangular strip is chosen as the differential element of area. Using the parallel-axis theorem, we write

$$dP_{xy} = dP_{x'y'} + \bar{x}_{el}\bar{y}_{el}\, dA$$

Since the element is symmetrical with respect to the x' and y' axes, we note that $dP_{x'y'} = 0$. From the geometry of the triangle, we obtain

$$y = h\frac{x}{b} \qquad dA = y\, dx = h\frac{x}{b}\, dx$$

$$\bar{x}_{el} = x \qquad \bar{y}_{el} = \tfrac{1}{2}y = \tfrac{1}{2}h\frac{x}{b}$$

Integrating dP_{xy} from $x = 0$ to $x = b$, we obtain

$$P_{xy} = \int dP_{xy} = \int_0^b \bar{x}_{el}\bar{y}_{el}\, dA = \int_0^b x\left(\tfrac{1}{2}h\frac{x}{b}\right)h\frac{x}{b}\, dx$$

$$= \int_0^b \frac{h^2}{2b^2}x^3\, dx = \frac{h^2}{2b^2}\frac{b^4}{4} \qquad \boldsymbol{P_{xy} = \tfrac{1}{8}b^2h^2}$$

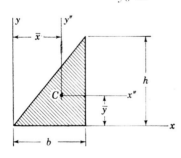

b. Product of Inertia $\bar{P}_{x''y''}$. The coordinates of the centroid of the triangle are

$$\bar{x} = \tfrac{2}{3}b \qquad \bar{y} = \frac{h}{3}$$

Using the expression for P_{xy} obtained in part a, we apply the parallel-axis theorem and write

$$P_{xy} = \bar{P}_{x''y''} + \bar{x}\bar{y}A$$

$$\tfrac{1}{8}b^2h^2 = \bar{P}_{x''y''} + \tfrac{2}{3}b\frac{h}{3}\tfrac{1}{2}bh$$

$$\bar{P}_{x''y''} = \tfrac{1}{8}b^2h^2 - \tfrac{1}{9}b^2h^2 \qquad \boldsymbol{\bar{P}_{x''y''} = \tfrac{1}{72}b^2h^2}$$

SAMPLE PROBLEM 9.7

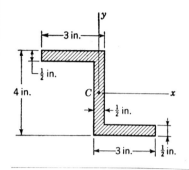

For the section shown, the moments of inertia with respect to the x and y axes have been computed and are known to be

$$I_x = 10.91 \text{ in.}^4 \qquad I_y = 6.94 \text{ in.}^4$$

Determine the principal axes through C and the values of the principal moments of inertia of the section with respect to axes through C.

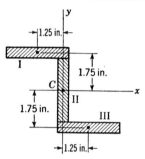

Solution. We first compute the product of inertia with respect to the x and y axes. The area is divided into three rectangles as shown. We note that the product of inertia $\bar{P}_{x'y'}$ with respect to centroidal axes parallel to the x and y axes is zero for each rectangle. Using the parallel-axis theorem $P_{xy} = \bar{P}_{x'y'} + \bar{x}\bar{y}A$, we thus find that for each rectangle P_{xy} reduces to $\bar{x}\bar{y}A$.

Rectangle	Area	$\bar{x}$	$\bar{y}$	$\bar{x}\bar{y}A$
I	1.5	-1.25	$+1.75$	-3.28
II	1.5	0	0	0
III	1.5	$+1.25$	-1.75	-3.28
				-6.56

$$P_{xy} = \Sigma \bar{x}\bar{y}A$$
$$= -6.56 \text{ in.}^4$$

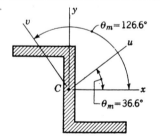

Principal Axes. Since the magnitudes of I_x, I_y, and P_{xy} are known, Eq. (9.22) is used to determine the values of θ_m,

$$\tan 2\theta_m = -\frac{2P_{xy}}{I_x - I_y} = -\frac{(2)(-6.56)}{10.91 - 6.94}$$
$$= +3.31$$
$$2\theta_m = 73.2° \text{ and } 253.2°$$
$$\theta_m = \mathbf{36.6°} \quad \text{and} \quad \theta_m = \mathbf{126.6°}$$

Principal Moments of Inertia. Using Eq. (9.23), we write

$$I_{\text{max,min}} = \frac{I_x + I_y}{2} \pm \sqrt{\left(\frac{I_x - I_y}{2}\right)^2 + P_{xy}^2}$$

$$= \frac{10.91 + 6.94}{2} \pm \sqrt{\left(\frac{10.91 - 6.94}{2}\right)^2 + (-6.56)^2}$$

$$I_{\text{max}} = \mathbf{15.78 \text{ in.}^4} \qquad I_{\text{min}} = \mathbf{2.07 \text{ in.}^4}$$

Noting that the area of the section is farther away from the u axis than from the v axis, we conclude that $I_u = I_{\text{max}} = 15.78 \text{ in.}^4$ and $I_v = I_{\text{min}} = 2.07 \text{ in.}^4$ This conclusion may be verified by substituting $\theta = 36.6°$ into Eqs. (9.19) and (9.20).

PROBLEMS

9.45 through 9.48. Determine by direct integration the product of inertia of the given area with respect to the x and y axes.

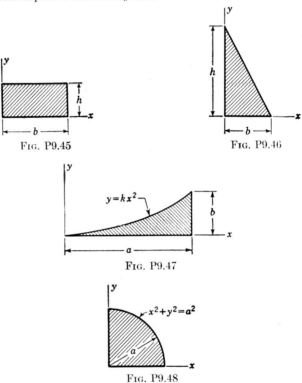

FIG. P9.45   FIG. P9.46

FIG. P9.47

FIG. P9.48

9.49 through 9.52. Using the parallel-axis theorem, determine the product of inertia of the structural shape shown with respect to horizontal and vertical axes through its centroid C. Neglect the effect of fillets, and choose positive senses to the right and up.

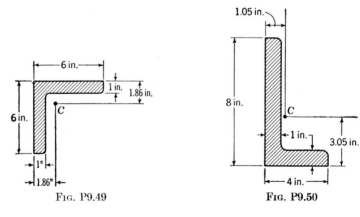

FIG. P9.49   FIG. P9.50

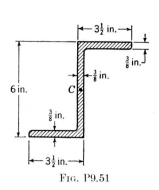

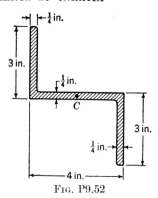

FIG. P9.51

FIG. P9.52

9.53 and 9.54. For the area shown, determine the moments of inertia and the product of inertia with respect to the centroidal u and v axes when $\theta = 30°$.

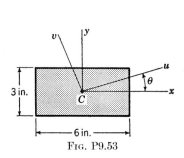

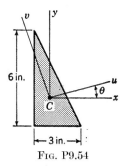

FIG. P9.53

FIG. P9.54

9.55. For the area shown, it is known that $\bar{I}_x = 30.8$ in.^{4}, $\bar{I}_y = 10.8$ in.^{4}, and $\bar{P}_{xy} = +6.5$ in.^{4}, where the x and y axes are centroidal axes. Determine the inclination θ_m of the principal axes through C and the corresponding values of the moment of inertia.

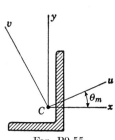

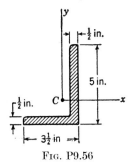

FIG. P9.55

FIG. P9.56

9.56. A 5- by $3\frac{1}{2}$- by $\frac{1}{2}$-in. angle is oriented as shown. Determine the principal axes through the centroid C and the corresponding values of the moment of inertia. Neglect the effect of fillets in computing $\bar{P}_{xy}$.

9.57. For the Z section of Prob. 9.51, determine the minimum centroidal moment of inertia and the orientation of the corresponding axis. Neglect the effect of fillets.

9.58. An 8- by 6- by 1-in. angle is oriented as indicated in Fig. 9.13. Determine the principal axes through the centroid C and the corresponding values of the moment of inertia. Neglect the effect of fillets in computing $\bar{P}_{xy}$.

9.59. Solve Prob. 9.53, using Mohr's circle.

9.60. Solve Prob. 9.54, using Mohr's circle.

9.61. Solve Prob. 9.55, using Mohr's circle.

9.62. Solve Prob. 9.56, using Mohr's circle.

9.63. Using Mohr's circle, show that for any area the axes corresponding to the principal moments of inertia are 45° from the axes corresponding to the maximum product of inertia.

9.64. Using Mohr's circle, show that for any regular polygon (such as a pentagon) the moment of inertia with respect to every axis through the centroid is the same.

***9.65.** The minimum moment of inertia of an 8- by 6- by 1-in. angle is known to be 21.3 in.⁴ Using Mohr's circle, determine the maximum moment of inertia and the principal axes through the centroid. [*Hint.* The point representing $\bar{I}_{\min}$ may be plotted directly and the abscissa $(\bar{I}_x + \bar{I}_y)/2$ of the center of the circle may be computed from Fig. 9.13. If the angle is oriented as shown in Fig. 9.13, $\bar{P}_{xy}$ is negative.]

MOMENTS OF INERTIA OF MASSES

9.10. Moment of Inertia of a Mass. Consider a small mass Δm mounted on a rod of negligible mass which may rotate freely about an

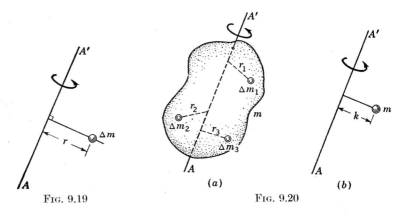

Fig. 9.19   Fig. 9.20

axis AA' (Fig. 9.19). If a couple is applied to the system, the rod and mass, assumed initially at rest, will start rotating about AA'. The details of this motion will be studied later in dynamics. At present, we wish only to indicate that the time required for the system to reach a given speed of rotation is proportional to the mass Δm and to the square of the distance r. The product $r^2 \Delta m$ provides, therefore, a measure of the *inertia* of the system, i.e., of the resistance the system offers when we try to set it in motion. For this reason, the product $r^2 \Delta m$ is called the *moment of inertia* of the mass Δm with respect to the axis AA'.

Consider now a body of mass m which is to be rotated about an axis AA' (Fig. 9.20a). Dividing the body into elements of mass Δm_1, Δm_2, etc., we find that the resistance offered by the body is measured by the sum $r_1^2 \Delta m_1 + r_2^2 \Delta m_2 + \cdots$. This sum defines therefore the moment of inertia of the body with respect to the axis AA'. Increasing the number of elements, we find that the moment of inertia is equal, at the limit, to the integral

$$I = \int r^2 \, dm \qquad (9.24)$$

The *radius of gyration* k of the body with respect to the axis AA' is defined by the relation

$$I = k^2 m \qquad \text{or} \qquad k = \sqrt{\frac{I}{m}} \qquad (9.25)$$

The radius of gyration k represents, therefore, the distance at which the entire mass of the body should be concentrated if its moment of inertia with respect to AA' is to remain unchanged (Fig. 9.20b). Whether it is kept in its original shape (Fig. 9.20a) or whether it is concentrated as shown in Fig. 9.20b, the mass m will react in the same way to a rotation, or *gyration*, about AA'.

The radius of gyration of a mass is usually expressed in feet. Since the moment of inertia of a mass is the product of a mass (expressed in lb-sec^2/ft) by a distance squared, it will generally be expressed in lb-ft-sec^2.

9.11. Parallel-axis Theorem. Consider a body of mass m; the moment of inertia of the body with respect to an axis AA' is $I = \int r^2 \, dm$, where r is the distance from the element of mass dm to AA' (Fig. 9.21). Sim-

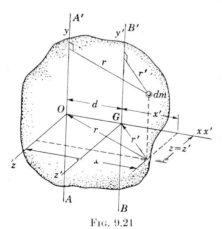

Fig. 9.21

ilarly, the moment of inertia of the body with respect to a centroidal† axis BB' parallel to AA' and passing through the center of gravity G of the body is $\bar{I} = \int r'^2 \, dm$, where r' is the distance from the element of mass

† Note that the term centroidal is used to define an axis passing through the center of gravity G of the body, whether or not G coincides with the centroid of the volume of the body.

to BB'.   Choosing two systems of axes as shown in Fig. 9.21, we write

$$r^2 = x^2 + z^2 \qquad r'^2 = x'^2 + z'^2$$

Observing that $x = x' + d$, where d is the distance between AA' and BB', and that $z = z'$, we write

$$r^2 = (x' + d)^2 + z'^2 = x'^2 + 2x'd + d^2 + z'^2$$
$$= r'^2 + 2x'd + d^2$$

Substituting for r^2 in the expression $I = \int r^2 \, dm$, we write the moment of inertia of the body with respect to AA' as follows:

$$I = \int r^2 \, dm = \int r'^2 \, dm + 2d\int x' \, dm + d^2\int dm$$

The first integral represents the moment of inertia $\bar{I}$ about the centroidal axis BB'; the second integral represents the first moment of the body with respect to the $y'z'$ plane and, since this plane contains G, is equal to zero; the last integral is equal to the total mass m of the body.   We write, therefore,

$$I = \bar{I} + md^2 \tag{9.26}$$

Expressing the moments of inertia in terms of the corresponding radii of gyration, we may also write

$$k^2 = \bar{k}^2 + d^2 \tag{9.27}$$

where k and $\bar{k}$ represent the radii of gyration about AA' and BB', respectively.

9.12. Moments of Inertia of Thin Plates.   Consider a thin plate of uniform thickness t, made of a homogeneous material of density ρ

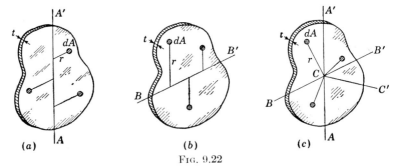

Fig. 9.22

(density = mass per unit volume).   The mass moment of inertia of the plate with respect to an axis AA' *contained in the plane* of the plate (Fig. 9.22a) is

$$I_{AA',\text{mass}} = \int r^2 \, dm \quad .$$

Since $dm = \rho t \, dA$, we write

$$I_{AA',\text{mass}} = \rho t \int r^2 \, dA$$

But r represents the distance of the element of area dA to the axis AA'; the integral is therefore equal to the moment of inertia of the area of the plate with respect to AA'. We have

$$I_{AA',\text{mass}} = \rho t I_{AA',\text{area}} \tag{9.28}$$

Similarly, we have with respect to an axis BB' perpendicular to AA' (Fig. 9.22b)

$$I_{BB',\text{mass}} = \rho t I_{BB',\text{area}} \tag{9.29}$$

Considering now the axis CC' *perpendicular* to the plate through the point of intersection C of AA' and BB' (Fig. 9.22c), we write

$$I_{CC',\text{mass}} = \rho t J_{C,\text{area}} \tag{9.30}$$

where J_C is the *polar* moment of inertia of the area of the plate with respect to point C.

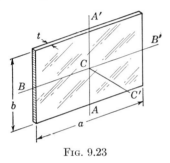

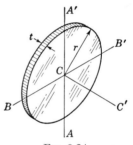

FIG. 9.23   FIG. 9.24

Recalling the relation $J_C = I_{AA'} + I_{BB'}$ existing between polar and rectangular moments of inertia of an area, we write the following relation between the mass moments of inertia of a thin plate:

$$I_{CC'} = I_{AA'} + I_{BB'} \tag{9.31}$$

Rectangular Plate. In the case of a rectangular plate of sides a and b (Fig. 9.23), we obtain the following mass moments of inertia with respect to axes through the center of gravity of the plate:

$$I_{AA',\text{mass}} = \rho t I_{AA',\text{area}} = \rho t (\tfrac{1}{12} a^3 b)$$
$$I_{BB',\text{mass}} = \rho t I_{BB',\text{area}} = \rho t (\tfrac{1}{12} a b^3)$$

Observing that the product $\rho a b t$ is equal to the mass m of the plate, we write the mass moments of inertia of a thin rectangular plate as follows:

$$I_{AA'} = \tfrac{1}{12} m a^2 \qquad I_{BB'} = \tfrac{1}{12} m b^2 \tag{9.32}$$
$$I_{CC'} = I_{AA'} + I_{BB'} = \tfrac{1}{12} m (a^2 + b^2) \tag{9.33}$$

Circular Plate. In the case of a circular plate, or disk, of radius r (Fig. 9.24), we write

$$I_{AA',\text{mass}} = \rho t I_{AA',\text{area}} = \rho t (\tfrac{1}{4} \pi r^4)$$

Observing that the product $\rho\pi r^2 t$ is equal to the mass m of the plate and that $I_{AA'} = I_{BB'}$, we write the mass moments of inertia of a circular plate as follows:

$$I_{AA'} = I_{BB'} = \tfrac{1}{4}mr^2 \tag{9.34}$$
$$I_{CC'} = I_{AA'} + I_{BB'} = \tfrac{1}{2}mr^2 \tag{9.35}$$

9.13. Determination of the Moment of Inertia of a Three-dimensional Body by Integration. The moment of inertia of a three-dimensional body is obtained by computing the integral $I = \int r^2 \, dm$. If the body is made of a homogeneous material of density ρ, we have $dm = \rho \, dV$ and write $I = \rho \int r^2 \, dV$. This integral depends only upon the shape of the body. In order to compute it, it will generally be necessary to perform a triple, or at least a double, integration.

However, if the body possesses two planes of symmetry, it is usually possible to determine its moment of inertia through a single integration by choosing as an element of mass dm the mass of a thin slab perpendicular

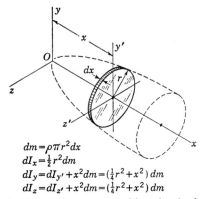

$$dm = \rho \pi r^2 dx$$
$$dI_x = \tfrac{1}{2} r^2 dm$$
$$dI_y = dI_{y'} + x^2 dm = (\tfrac{1}{4} r^2 + x^2) \, dm$$
$$dI_z = dI_{z'} + x^2 dm = (\tfrac{1}{4} r^2 + x^2) \, dm$$

Fɪɢ. 9.25. Determination of the moment of inertia of a body of revolution.

to the planes of symmetry. In the case of bodies of revolution, for example, the element of mass should be a thin disk (Fig. 9.25). Using formula (9.35), the moment of inertia of the disk with respect to the axis of revolution may be readily expressed as indicated in Fig. 9.25. Its moment of inertia with respect to each of the other two axes of coordinates will be obtained by using formula (9.34) and the parallel-axis theorem. Integration of the expressions obtained will yield the desired moments of inertia of the body of revolution.

9.14. Moments of Inertia of Composite Bodies. The moments of inertia of a few common shapes are shown in Fig. 9.26. The moment of inertia with respect to a given axis of a body made of several of these simple shapes may be obtained by computing the moments of inertia of its component parts about the desired axis and adding them together. We should note, as we already have noted in the case of areas, that the radius of gyration of a composite body *cannot* be obtained by adding the radii of gyration of its component parts.

Slender rod	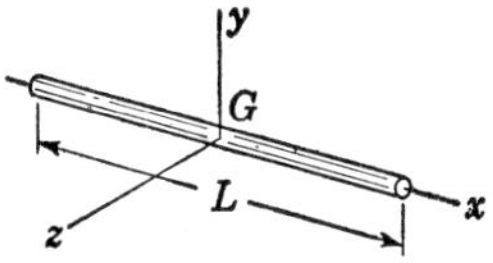	$I_y = I_z = \frac{1}{12}mL^2$
Thin rectangular plate	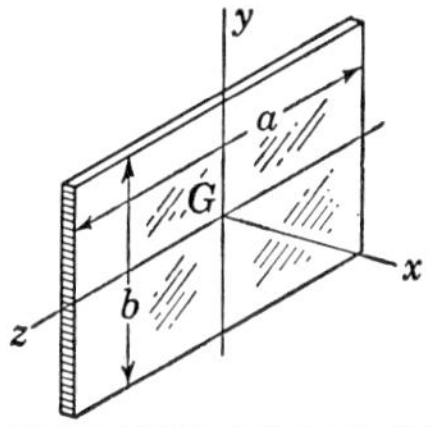	$I_x = \frac{1}{12}m(a^2 + b^2)$ $I_y = \frac{1}{12}ma^2$ $I_z = \frac{1}{12}mb^2$
Rectangular prism	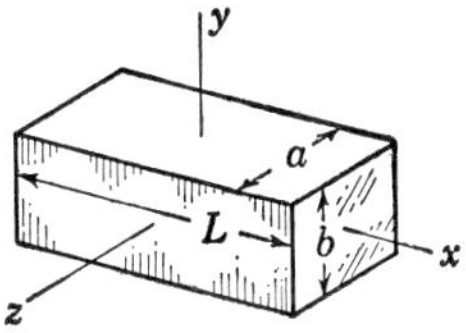	$I_x = \frac{1}{12}m(a^2 + b^2)$ $I_y = \frac{1}{12}m(a^2 + L^2)$ $I_z = \frac{1}{12}m(b^2 + L^2)$
Thin disk	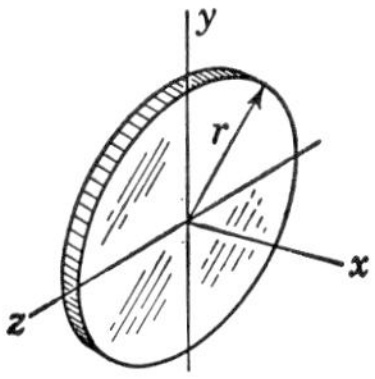	$I_x = \frac{1}{2}mr^2$ $I_y = I_z = \frac{1}{4}mr^2$
Circular cylinder	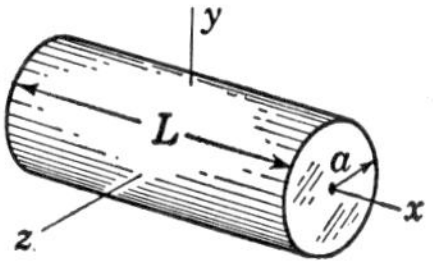	$I_x = \frac{1}{2}ma^2$ $I_y = I_z = \frac{1}{12}m(3a^2 + L^2)$
Circular cone	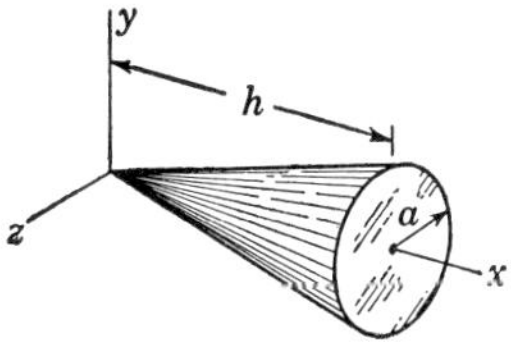	$I_x = \frac{3}{10}ma^2$ $I_y = I_z = \frac{3}{5}m\left(\frac{a^2}{4} + h^2\right)$
Sphere	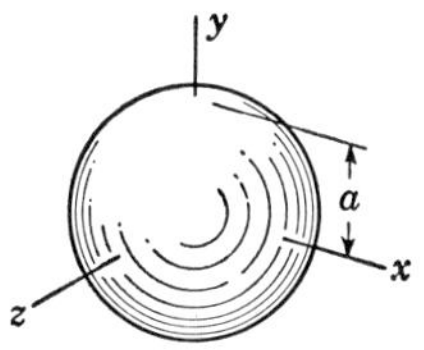	$I_x = I_y = I_z = \frac{2}{5}ma^2$

Fig. 9.26. Mass moments of inertia of common geometric shapes.

SAMPLE PROBLEM 9.8

Determine the mass moment of inertia of a slender rod of length L and mass m with respect to an axis perpendicular to the rod and passing through one end of the rod.

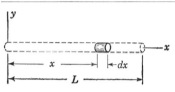

Solution. Choosing the differential element of mass shown, we write

$$dm = \frac{m}{L}\, dx$$

$$I_y = \int x^2\, dm = \int_0^L x^2 \frac{m}{L}\, dx = \left[\frac{m}{L}\frac{x^3}{3}\right]_0^L$$

$$I_y = \frac{mL^2}{3}$$

SAMPLE PROBLEM 9.9

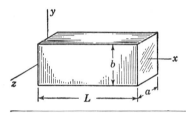

Determine the mass moment of inertia of the homogeneous rectangular prism shown with respect to the z axis.

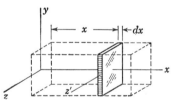

Solution. We choose as a differential element of mass the thin slab shown for which

$$dm = \rho ab\, dx$$

Referring to Sec. 9.12, we find that the moment of inertia of the element with respect to the z' axis is

$$dI_{z'} = \frac{b^2}{12}\, dm$$

Applying the parallel-axis theorem, we obtain the mass moment of inertia of the slab with respect to the z axis.

$$dI_z = dI_{z'} + x^2\, dm = \frac{b^2}{12}\, dm + x^2\, dm = \left(\frac{b^2}{12} + x^2\right)\rho ab\, dx$$

Integrating from $x = 0$ to $x = L$, we obtain

$$I_z = \int dI_z = \int_0^L \left(\frac{b^2}{12} + x^2\right)\rho ab\, dx = \rho abL\left(\frac{b^2}{12} + \frac{L^2}{3}\right)$$

Since the total mass of the prism is $m = \rho abL$, we may write

$$I_z = m\left(\frac{b^2}{12} + \frac{L^2}{3}\right) \qquad I_z = \tfrac{1}{12}m(b^2 + 4L^2)$$

We note that if the prism is slender, b is small compared to L and the expression for I_z reduces to $mL^2/3$ (see Sample Prob. 9.8).

SAMPLE PROBLEM 9.10

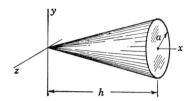

Determine the mass moment of inertia of a right circular cone with respect to (*a*) its longitudinal axis and (*b*) an axis through the apex and perpendicular to the longitudinal axis of the cone.

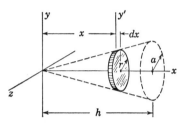

Solution. We choose the differential element of mass shown for which

$$r = a\frac{x}{h} \qquad dm = \rho \pi r^2\, dx = \rho \pi \frac{a^2}{h^2} x^2\, dx$$

a. Moment of Inertia I_x. Using the expression derived in Sec. 9.12 for a thin disk, we compute the mass moment of inertia of the differential element with respect to the *x* axis.

$$dI_x = \tfrac{1}{2} r^2\, dm = \frac{1}{2}\left(a\frac{x}{h}\right)^2 \left(\rho \pi \frac{a^2}{h^2} x^2\, dx\right) = \tfrac{1}{2}\rho\pi \frac{a^4}{h^4} x^4\, dx$$

Integrating from $x = 0$ to $x = h$, we obtain

$$I_x = \int dI_x = \int_0^h \tfrac{1}{2}\rho\pi \frac{a^4}{h^4} x^4\, dx = \tfrac{1}{2}\rho\pi \frac{a^4}{h^4}\frac{h^5}{5} = \tfrac{1}{10}\rho\pi a^4 h$$

Since the total mass of the cone is $m = \tfrac{1}{3}\rho\pi a^2 h$, we may express I_x as follows:

$$I_x = \tfrac{1}{10}\rho\pi a^4 h = \tfrac{3}{10}a^2(\tfrac{1}{3}\rho\pi a^2 h) = \tfrac{3}{10}ma^2 \qquad I_x = \tfrac{3}{10}ma^2$$

b. Moment of Inertia I_y. The same differential element will be used. Applying the parallel-axis theorem and using the expression derived in Sec. 9.12 for a thin disk, we write

$$dI_y = dI_{y'} + x^2\, dm = \tfrac{1}{4}r^2\, dm + x^2\, dm = (\tfrac{1}{4}r^2 + x^2)\, dm$$

Substituting the expressions for r and dm, we obtain

$$dI_y = \left(\frac{1}{4}\frac{a^2}{h^2}x^2 + x^2\right)\left(\rho\pi \frac{a^2}{h^2}x^2\, dx\right) = \rho\pi \frac{a^2}{h^2}\left(\frac{a^2}{4h^2} + 1\right)x^4\, dx$$

$$I_y = \int dI_y = \int_0^h \rho\pi \frac{a^2}{h^2}\left(\frac{a^2}{4h^2} + 1\right)x^4\, dx = \rho\pi \frac{a^2}{h^2}\left(\frac{a^2}{4h^2} + 1\right)\frac{h^5}{5}$$

Introducing the total mass of the cone *m*, we rewrite I_y as follows:

$$I_y = \frac{3}{5}\left(\frac{a^2}{4} + h^2\right)\tfrac{1}{3}\rho\pi a^2 h \qquad I_y = \tfrac{3}{5}m\left(\frac{a^2}{4} + h^2\right)$$

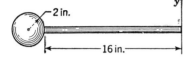

A portion of a governor consists of a 20-lb sphere welded to a 5-lb rod as shown. Determine the mass moment of inertia and the radius of gyration of the body with respect to the y axis.

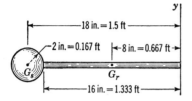

Moment of Inertia I_y. The mass moment of inertia of each component with respect to the y axis is computed in the following table. The expression for $\bar{I}_y$ of each component is obtained from Fig. 9.26, and the parallel-axis theorem is used to obtain the corresponding value of I_y. Note that all lengths should be expressed in feet.

	Weight	Mass, lb-sec²/ft	$\bar{I}_y + md^2$, lb-ft-sec²
Sphere	20 lb	$\dfrac{20}{32.2} = 0.621$	$\dfrac{2}{5}(0.621)(0.167)^2 + (0.621)(1.5)^2 \quad = 1.404$
Rod	5 lb	$\dfrac{5}{32.2} = 0.155$	$\dfrac{1}{12}(0.155)(1.333)^2 + (0.155)(0.667)^2 = 0.092$
		$m = 0.776$	$I_y = 1.496$

The moment of inertia of the composite body is

$$I_y = 1.496 \text{ lb-ft-sec}^2$$

Radius of Gyration k_y

$$k_y^2 = \frac{I_y}{m} = \frac{1.496 \text{ lb-ft-sec}^2}{0.776 \text{ lb-sec}^2/\text{ft}} \qquad k_y = 1.388 \text{ ft}$$

PROBLEMS

9.66. A thin semicircular plate has a radius a and a mass m. Determine the mass moment of inertia of the plate with respect to (a) the centroidal axis BB', (b) the centroidal axis CC'.

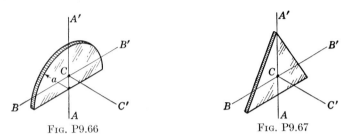

FIG. P9.66   FIG. P9.67

9.67. A thin plate is cut in the shape of an equilateral triangle of side a. If the total mass of the plate is m, determine the mass moment of inertia of the plate with respect to one of its edges.

9.68. Determine the mass moment of inertia of the plate of Prob. 9.67 (a) with respect to axis AA', (b) with respect to axis BB' through the center of gravity C of the plate.

9.69. Show that the moment of inertia of the plate of Prob. 9.67 is the same with respect to any axis contained in the plane of the plate and passing through the center of gravity C. Further show that $I_{CC'} = 2I_{AA'} = 2I_{BB'}$.

9.70. Determine by direct integration the mass moment of inertia of a sphere of radius a and mass m with respect to a diameter.

9.71 and 9.72. Determine by direct integration the mass moment of inertia with respect to the x axis for the homogeneous body shown. Express the result in terms of the total mass of the body.

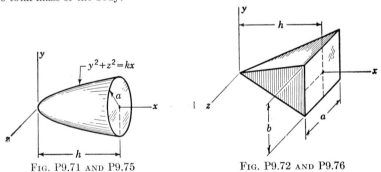

FIG. P9.71 AND P9.75   FIG. P9.72 AND P9.76

9.73. The parabolic area shown (on the next page) is revolved about the x axis to form a homogeneous solid of revolution. If the mass density of the solid is ρ, determine the mass moment of inertia of the solid with respect to the x axis.

9.74. Determine the mass moment of inertia of the solid of Prob. 9.73 with respect to the y axis.

9.75 through 9.77. Determine by direct integration the mass moment of inertia with respect to the y axis for the homogeneous body shown. Express the result in terms of the total mass of the body.

9.78. A slender rod of mass m and length L forms an angle θ with the vertical axis AA'. Determine the mass moment of inertia and the radius of gyration of the rod

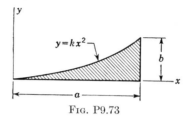

FIG. P9.73

with respect to the axis AA'.   Check the result obtained when $\theta = 90°$ with Sample Prob. 9.8.

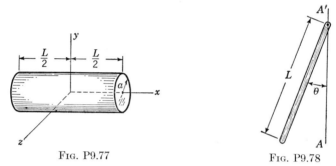

FIG. P9.77   FIG. P9.78

*9.79. Determine by direct integration the mass moment of inertia of the circular ring shown with respect to the y axis.   Express the result in terms of the total mass m of the ring.   (Hint.   As a differential element of mass, use the thin cylindrical element shown.)

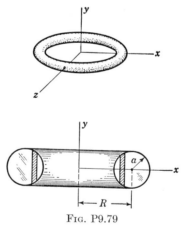

FIG. P9.79

9.80. Determine the mass moment of inertia of a sphere of radius a and mass m with respect to a line tangent to the surface of the sphere.

9.81. Determine the mass moments of inertia of the hemispherical steel shell shown with respect to both the x and y axes.   (Specific weight of steel $= 490\ \mathrm{lb/ft^3}$.)

9.82. Determine the radii of gyration of the hemispherical shell shown with respect to both the x and y axes.

9.83. Determine the mass moment of inertia of the steel ring shown with respect to the axis AA'.   Determine the per cent error in the result if the moment of inertia is approximated by the expression $I \approx ma_m^2$, where $a_m = (a_1 + a_2)/2$.

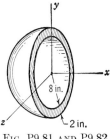

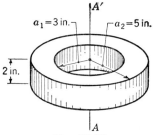

FIG. P9.81 AND P9.82   FIG. P9.83

9.84. In using the parallel-axis theorem, the error introduced by neglecting the centroidal moment of inertia is sometimes small. For a homogeneous sphere of radius a, determine the ratio R/a for which the error in the mass moment of inertia with respect to the axis AA' is 0.2 per cent when the centroidal moment of inertia is neglected.

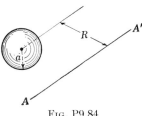

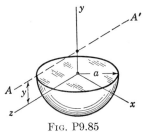

FIG. P9.84   FIG. P9.85

9.85. A homogeneous hemisphere of radius a and mass m is oriented as shown. Determine the distance y for which the radius of gyration with respect to the axis AA' is twice the radius of gyration with respect to the z axis.

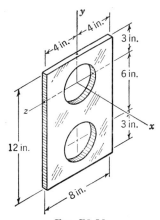

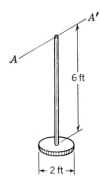

FIG. P9.86   FIG. P9.87

9.86. In order to shape a machine part, two holes, each of 3 in. diameter, are drilled in a steel plate 1 in. thick. Determine the mass moment of inertia with respect to the x axis for the resulting machine part. (Specific weight of steel = 490 lb/ft³.)

9.87. A thin steel plate weighing 64.4 lb is welded to the end of a slender rod weighing 32.2 lb. Determine the moment of inertia and the radius of gyration of the composite body with respect to the axis AA' perpendicular to the rod.

9.88. Two holes, each of diameter 2 in., are drilled through the steel block shown. Determine the mass moment of inertia of the body with respect to the axis of either of the holes. (Specific weight of steel = 490 lb/ft³.)

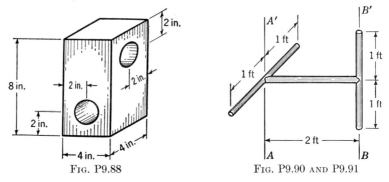

FIG. P9.88   FIG. P9.90 AND P9.91

9.89. Determine the radius of gyration with respect to a vertical axis through the center of gravity of the body of Prob. 9.88.

9.90. Three slender homogeneous rods, each 2 ft long and weighing 5 lb/ft, are welded together as shown. Determine the mass moment of inertia and the radius of gyration of the assembly with respect to the axis AA'.

9.91. Show that $I_{AA'} = I_{BB'}$ for the assembly of three rods shown.

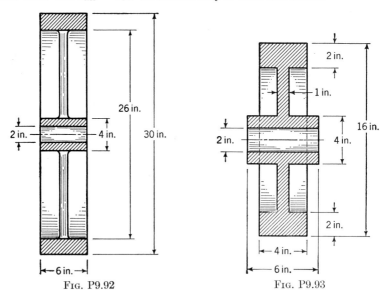

FIG. P9.92   FIG. P9.93

9.92. The cross section of a small steel flywheel is shown. The rim and hub are connected by eight spokes (two of which are shown in the cross section). Each spoke has a cross-sectional area of 0.75 in.² Determine the mass moment of inertia and radius of gyration of the flywheel with respect to the axis of rotation. (Specific weight of steel = 490 lb/ft³.)

9.93. Determine the mass moment of inertia and the radius of gyration of the steel flywheel shown with respect to the axis of rotation. The web of the flywheel consists of a solid plate 1 in. thick. (Specific weight of steel = 490 lb/ft³.)

10. Method of Virtual Work

10.1. Work of a Force. In the preceding chapters, problems involving the equilibrium of rigid bodies were solved by expressing that the external forces acting on the bodies were balanced. The equations of equilibrium $\Sigma F_x = 0$, $\Sigma F_y = 0$, $\Sigma M_A = 0$ were written and solved for the desired unknowns. We shall now consider a different method, which will prove more effective for solving certain types of equilibrium problems. This method is based on the concept of the *work of a force* and was first formally used by the Swiss mathematician Jean Bernoulli in the eighteenth century.

We shall first define the term *work* as it is used in mechanics. Consider a force F acting on a particle located at A (Fig. 10.1a). If the particle moves from A to A' through a small distance ds, *the work of the force F during the displacement ds is*

$$dU = F\,ds\,\cos\alpha \qquad (10.1)$$

where α is the angle between F and ds. The work dU is a *scalar quantity;* it has a magnitude and a sign, but no direction. We note that work should be expressed in units such as ft-lb or in.-lb, obtained by multiplying units of length by units of force.

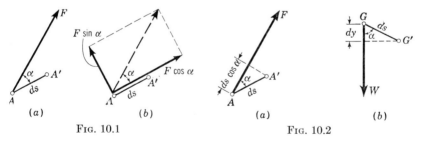

Fig. 10.1   Fig. 10.2

It appears from (10.1) that the work dU may be considered as the product of the displacement ds and of the component $F\cos\alpha$ of the force F along ds (Fig. 10.1b). If this component and the displacement ds have same sense, the work is positive; if they have opposite sense, the work is negative. Three particular cases are of special interest. If the force F has the same direction as ds, the work dU reduces to $F\,ds$. If F has a direction opposite to that of ds, the work is $dU = -F\,ds$. Finally, if F is perpendicular to ds, the work dU is zero.

329

The work dU of a force F during a displacement ds may also be considered as the product of F and of the component $ds \cos \alpha$ of the displacement ds along F (Fig. 10.2a). This view is particularly useful in the computation of the work done by the weight W of a body (Fig. 10.2b). The work of W is equal to the product of W and of the vertical displacement dy of the center of gravity G of the body. If the displacement is downward, the work is positive; if it is upward, the work is negative.

A number of forces frequently encountered in statics *do no work*. They are forces applied to fixed points ($ds = 0$) or acting in a direction perpendicular to the displacement ($\cos \alpha = 0$). Among the forces which do no work are the following: the reaction at a smooth pin when the body supported rotates about the pin, the reaction at a smooth frictionless surface when the body in contact moves along the surface, the reaction at a roller moving along its track, the weight of a body when its center of gravity moves horizontally, the friction force acting on a wheel rolling without slipping (since at any instant the point of contact does not move). Examples of forces which *do work* are the weight of a body (except in the case considered above), the friction force acting on a body sliding on a rough surface, and most forces applied on a moving body.

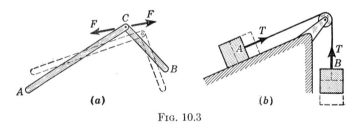

FIG. 10.3

In certain cases, the sum of the work done by several forces is zero. Consider, for example, two rigid bodies AC and BC connected at C by a *smooth pin* (Fig. 10.3a). Among the forces acting on AC is the force F exerted at C by BC. In general, the work of this force will not be zero, but it will be equal in magnitude and opposite in sign to the work of the force F exerted at C by AC on BC. Thus, when the total work done by all the forces acting on AB and BC is considered, the work of the two internal forces at C cancels out. A similar result is obtained if we consider a system consisting of two blocks connected by an *inextensible cord* AB (Fig. 10.3b). The work of the tension T at A and at B is of same magnitude, since A and B move through the same distance, but in one case the work is positive, and in the other it is negative. Thus, the work of the internal forces again cancels out.

It may be shown that the total work of the internal forces holding together the particles of a rigid body is zero. Consider two particles A and B of a rigid body and the two equal and opposite forces they exert on each other (Fig. 10.4). While, in general, the displacements AA' and BB' of the two particles are different, the components of these displacements along AB must be equal; otherwise, the particles would not remain at the same distance from each other, and the body would not be rigid. Therefore, the work of the force at A is equal in magnitude and opposite in sign to the work of the force at B, and their sum is zero.

In computing the work of the external forces acting on a rigid body, it is often convenient to determine the work of a couple without considering separately the work of each of the two forces forming the couple. Consider the two forces F forming a couple of moment $M = Fr$ acting on a rigid body (Fig. 10.5). Any small displacement of the rigid body bringing A and B, respectively, into A' and B'' may be divided into two displacements, one in which the line AB moves into a parallel line $A'B'$, the other in which A' remains fixed and B' moves into B'' through an

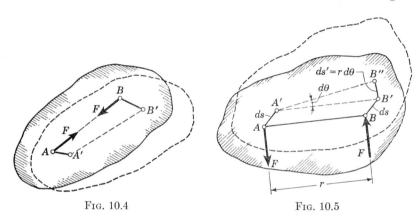

FIG. 10.4   FIG. 10.5

arc of circle $ds' = r\,d\theta$. In the first part of the motion, the work of the force at A is equal and opposite to the work of the force at B, and their sum is zero. In the second part of the motion, only the force at B' works, and its work is $dU = F\,ds' = Fr\,d\theta = M\,d\theta$. Thus, the work of a couple of moment M acting on a rigid body is

$$dU = M\,d\theta \qquad (10.2)$$

where $d\theta$ is the small angle expressed in radians through which the body rotates. We again note that work should be expressed in units obtained by multiplying units of force by units of length.

*10.2. Principle of Virtual Work. Consider a particle acted upon by several forces F_1, F_2, ... , F_n (Fig. 10.6). We shall assume that the particle undergoes a small displacement from A to A'. This displacement is possible, but it will not necessarily take place. The forces may be balanced and the particle at rest, or the particle may move under the action of the given forces in a direction different from that of AA'.

The displacement AA' is therefore an imaginary displacement; it is called a *virtual displacement* and is denoted by δs. The symbol δs represents a differential of the first order; it is used to distinguish the virtual displacement from the displacement ds which would take place under actual motion. As we shall see, virtual displacements may be used to determine whether the conditions of equilibrium of a particle are satisfied.

The work of each of the forces F_1, F_2, . . . , F_n during the virtual displacement δs is called *virtual work*. The virtual work of all the forces acting on the particle of Fig. 10.6 is

$$\delta U = F_1 \cos \alpha_1 \, \delta s + F_2 \cos \alpha_2 \, \delta s + \cdot \cdot \cdot + F_n \cos \alpha_n \, \delta s$$
$$= (F_1 \cos \alpha_1 + F_2 \cos \alpha_2 + \cdot \cdot \cdot + F_n \cos \alpha_n) \, \delta s \qquad (10.3)$$

Since the expression in parentheses represents the component of the resultant of the forces F_1, F_2, . . . , F_n along AA', it is seen that the total virtual work of the forces F_1, F_2, . . . , F_n is equal to the virtual work of their resultant.

The principle of virtual work for a particle states that, *if a particle is in equilibrium, the total virtual work of the forces acting on the particle is zero for any virtual displacement of the particle.* This condition is necessary: if the particle is in equilibrium, the resultant of the forces is zero, the expression in parentheses in (10.3) is zero, and the total virtual work is zero. The condition is also sufficient: choosing AA' successively along the x axis and the y axis, and making $\delta U = 0$ in (10.3), we find that the equilibrium equations $\Sigma F_x = 0$ and $\Sigma F_y = 0$ are satisfied.

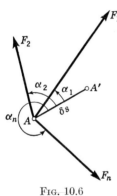

FIG. 10.6

In the case of a rigid body, the principle of virtual work states that, *if a rigid body is in equilibrium, the total virtual work of the external forces acting on the rigid body is zero for any virtual displacement of the body.* The condition is necessary: if the body is in equilibrium, all the particles forming the body are in equilibrium and the total virtual work of the forces acting on all the particles must be zero; but we have seen in the preceding section that the total work of the internal forces is zero; the total work of the external forces must therefore also be zero. The condition may also be proved to be sufficient.

The principle of virtual work may be extended to the case of a *system of connected rigid bodies.* If the system remains connected during the virtual displacement, *only the work of the forces external to the system need be considered,* since the total work of the internal forces at the various connections is zero.

10.3. Applications of the Principle of Virtual Work. The principle of virtual work is particularly effective when applied to the solution of

problems involving machines or mechanisms consisting of several connected rigid bodies. Consider for instance the toggle vise ACB of Fig.
10.7a; we wish to determine the force Q exerted on the block when a
given force P is applied at C. We shall assume that there is no friction.
If the linkage is given the virtual displacement shown in the free-body
diagram of Fig. 10.7b, the reactions A_x, A_y, and N will do no work and
we need consider only the work of P and Q in applying the principle of
virtual work. Choosing a system of coordinate axes with origin at A,
we find that the virtual work of Q is $\delta U_Q = -Q\ \delta x_B$, where the minus
sign indicates that, for a positive value of δx_B, δU_Q is negative. The
virtual work of P is $\delta U_P = -P\ \delta y_C$, the minus sign indicating that,
for a positive value of δy_C (point C moving *upward*), δU_P is negative.

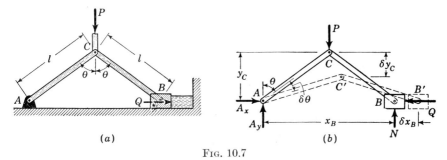

(a)   (b)

FIG. 10.7

Expressing the coordinates x_B and y_C in terms of the angle θ and differentiating, we obtain

$$x_B = 2l \sin \theta \qquad y_C = l \cos \theta$$
$$\delta x_B = 2l \cos \theta\ \delta\theta \qquad \delta y_C = -l \sin \theta\ \delta\theta \tag{10.4}$$

The total virtual work of the forces Q and P is thus

$$\delta U = \delta U_Q + \delta U_P = -Q\ \delta x_B - P\ \delta y_C$$
$$= -2Ql \cos \theta\ \delta\theta + Pl \sin \theta\ \delta\theta$$

Making $\delta U = \mathbf{0}$, we obtain

$$2Ql \cos \theta\ \delta\theta = Pl \sin \theta\ \delta\theta \tag{10.5}$$
$$Q = \tfrac{1}{2}P \tan \theta \tag{10.6}$$

The superiority of the method of virtual work over the conventional
equilibrium equations in the problem considered here is clear: by using
the method of virtual work, we were able to eliminate all unknown reactions, while the equation $\Sigma M_A = 0$ would have eliminated only two of
the unknown reactions. We may take advantage of this characteristic
of the method of virtual work to solve many problems involving machines
and mechanisms. *If the virtual displacement considered is consistent with
the constraints imposed by the supports and connections, all reactions and*

internal forces are eliminated and only the work of the loads, applied forces, and friction forces need be considered.

We shall observe that the method of virtual work may also be used to solve problems involving stable structures, although the virtual displacements are then completely imaginary and will never actually take place. Consider, for example, the frame ACB shown in Fig. 10.8a. If point A is kept fixed, while B is given a horizontal virtual displacement (Fig. 10.8b), we need consider only the work of P and B_x. We may thus determine the reaction component B_x in the same way as the force Q of the preceding example (Fig. 10.7b); we have

$$B_x = \tfrac{1}{2}P \tan \theta$$

Keeping B fixed and giving to A a horizontal virtual displacement, we may similarly determine the reaction component A_x. The components

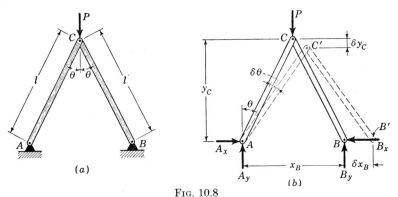

Fig. 10.8

A_y and B_y may be determined by rotating the frame ACB as a rigid body about B and A, respectively.

The method of virtual work may also be used to determine the configuration of a system in equilibrium under given forces. For example, the value of the angle θ for which the linkage of Fig. 10.7b is in equilibrium under two given forces P and Q may be obtained by solving Eq. (10.6) for $\tan \theta$.

10.4. Real Machines. Mechanical Efficiency. In analyzing the toggle vise in the preceding section, we assumed that no friction forces were involved. Thus, the virtual work consisted only of the work of the input force P and of the output force Q. Equation (10.5) expressed, then, that the *output work* $2Ql \cos \theta\, \delta\theta$ was equal to the *input work* $Pl \sin \theta\, \delta\theta$. A machine in which input and output work are equal is said to be an "ideal" machine. In a "real" machine, friction forces will always do some work, and the output work will be smaller than the input work.

Consider, for example, the toggle vise of Fig. 10.7b, and assume now that a friction force F develops between the sliding block B and the horizontal plane (Fig. 10.9). Using the conventional methods of statics and summing moments about A, we find $N = P/2$. Denoting by μ the coefficient of friction between block B and the horizontal plane, we have $F = \mu N = \mu P/2$. Recalling formulas (10.4), we find that the total virtual work of the forces Q, P, and F during the virtual displacement shown in Fig. 10.9 is

$$\delta U = -Q\,\delta x_B - P\,\delta y_C - F\,\delta x_B$$
$$= -2Ql \cos\theta\,\delta\theta + Pl \sin\theta\,\delta\theta - \mu Pl \cos\theta\,\delta\theta$$

Making $\delta U = 0$, we obtain

$$2Ql \cos\theta\,\delta\theta = Pl \sin\theta\,\delta\theta - \mu Pl \cos\theta\,\delta\theta \qquad (10.7)$$

which expresses that the output work is equal to the input work minus the work of the friction force. Solving for Q, we have

$$Q = \tfrac{1}{2}P(\tan\theta - \mu) \qquad (10.8)$$

We note that $Q = 0$ when $\tan\theta = \mu$, that is, when θ is equal to the angle of friction ϕ, and that $Q < 0$ when $\theta < \phi$. The toggle vise may thus be used only for values θ larger than the angle of friction.

The *mechanical efficiency* of a machine is defined by the ratio

$$\eta = \frac{output\ work}{input\ work} \qquad (10.9)$$

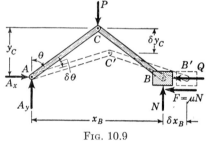

FIG. 10.9

Clearly, the mechanical efficiency of an ideal machine is $\eta = 1$, since input and output work are then equal, while the mechanical efficiency of a real machine will always be less than 1.

In the case of the toggle vise we have just analyzed, we write

$$\eta = \frac{output\ work}{input\ work} = \frac{2Ql \cos\theta\,\delta\theta}{Pl \sin\theta\,\delta\theta}$$

Substituting from (10.8) for Q, we obtain

$$\eta = \frac{P(\tan\theta - \mu)l \cos\theta\,\delta\theta}{Pl \sin\theta\,\delta\theta} = 1 - \mu \cot\theta \qquad (10.10)$$

We check that, in the absence of friction forces, we would have $\mu = 0$ and $\eta = 1$. In the general case, when μ is different from zero, the efficiency η becomes zero for $\mu \cot\theta = 1$, that is, for $\tan\theta = \mu$, or $\theta = \tan^{-1}\mu = \phi$. We check again that the toggle vise may be used only for values of θ larger than the angle of friction ϕ.

SAMPLE PROBLEM 10.1

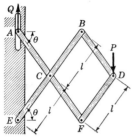

Using the method of virtual work, determine the force Q required to maintain the equilibrium of the mechanism shown.

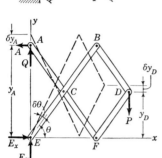

Solution. Choosing a coordinate system with origin at E, we write

$$y_A = 2l \sin \theta \qquad y_D = l \sin \theta$$

$$\delta y_A = 2l \cos \theta \; \delta\theta \qquad \delta y_D = l \cos \theta \; \delta\theta$$

Principle of Virtual Work. Since the reactions A, E_x, and E_y will do no work during the virtual displacement, the total virtual work done by P and Q must be zero.

$$\delta U = 0: \qquad +Q \, \delta y_A - P \, \delta y_D = 0$$
$$+Q(2l \cos \theta \; \delta\theta) - P(l \cos \theta \; \delta\theta) = 0$$

$$Q = \tfrac{1}{2}P$$

SAMPLE PROBLEM 10.2

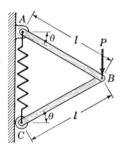

Determine the expressions for θ and for the tension in the spring which correspond to the equilibrium position of the mechanism. The unstretched length of the spring is h, and the constant of the spring is k. Neglect the weight of the mechanism.

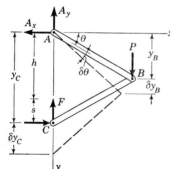

Solution. With the coordinate system shown

$$y_B = l \sin \theta \qquad y_C = 2l \sin \theta$$

$$\delta y_B = l \cos \theta \; \delta\theta \qquad \delta y_C = 2l \cos \theta \; \delta\theta$$

Elongation of spring

$$s = y_C - h = 2l \sin \theta - h$$

The tension exerted at C by the spring is

$$F = ks = k(2l \sin \theta - h)$$

Principle of Virtual Work

$$\delta U = 0: \qquad P \, \delta y_B - F \, \delta y_C = 0$$

$$P(l \cos \theta \; \delta\theta) - k(2l \sin \theta - h)(2l \cos \theta \; \delta\theta) = 0$$

$$\sin \theta = \frac{P + 2kh}{4kl} \qquad F = \tfrac{1}{2}P$$

SAMPLE PROBLEM 10.3

Determine the magnitude of the couple M which must be applied to the crank CD to hold the mechanism in equilibrium. The block at D is pinned to the crank CD and is free to slide in a slot cut in member AB. This mechanism has been previously considered in Sample Prob. 6.8.

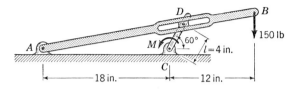

Solution. Referring to Sample Prob. 6.8, we obtain the following dimensions:

$$b = 2 \text{ in.} \qquad \alpha = 9.8°$$

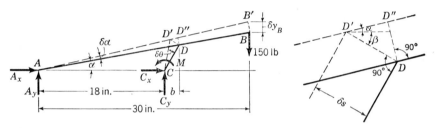

Virtual Displacement $\delta\theta$. After a virtual rotation $\delta\theta$ of the crank CD, the mechanism assumes the position indicated by the dashed lines. Member AB rotates through $\delta\alpha$ into AB', and the block D moves through δs into D'. Since the virtual rotation $\delta\theta$ represents a differential of the first order, DD' is perpendicular to CD.

$$\beta = 30° \qquad \delta s = l\,\delta\theta$$

The component of the displacement of the block perpendicular to member AB is

$$DD'' = \delta s \sin(\alpha + \beta) = (l\,\delta\theta) \sin(9.8° + 30°) = l \sin 39.8°\,\delta\theta \qquad (1)$$

By similar triangles, we obtain

$$\frac{AB}{AD} = \frac{30 \text{ in.}}{18 \text{ in.} + b} \qquad \frac{AB}{AD} = \frac{30 \text{ in.}}{20 \text{ in.}} \qquad (2)$$

Using the similar triangles ABB' and ADD'' together with (1) and (2), we find

$$\frac{BB'}{DD''} = \frac{AB}{AD} = \tfrac{30}{20} \qquad BB' = \tfrac{30}{20}\,DD'' = \tfrac{30}{20}\,l \sin 39.8°\,\delta\theta$$

Finally, since BB' is perpendicular to AB and $l = 4$ in., we obtain

$$\delta y_B = BB' \cos \alpha = [(\tfrac{30}{20})(4 \text{ in.}) \sin 39.8°\,\delta\theta] \cos 9.8° = (3.78 \text{ in.})\,\delta\theta$$

Principle of Virtual Work

$$\delta U = 0: \qquad +M\,\delta\theta - (150 \text{ lb})\,\delta y_B = 0$$

$$+M\,\delta\theta - (150 \text{ lb})(3.78 \text{ in.})\,\delta\theta = 0 \qquad M = \textbf{567 lb-in.}\ \rangle$$

PROBLEMS

10.1. For the lever system shown, determine the force P required to maintain equilibrium.

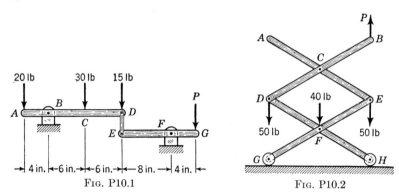

Fig. P10.1   Fig. P10.2

10.2. Determine the force P required to maintain the equilibrium of the linkage shown. All members are of the same length.

10.3. Determine the weight W which balances the 45-lb load.

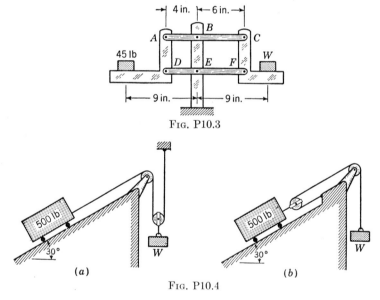

Fig. P10.3

Fig. P10.4

10.4. Determine the counterweight W required to hold the 500-lb car on the 30° incline.

10.5. If gripping forces $Q = 450$ lb are desired, determine the forces P which must be applied to the pliers of Prob. 6.93. Assume that pins B and E slide freely in the slots shown. Also show that the required forces P are independent of the position of the object gripped by the jaws.

10.6 through 10.8. The mechanism shown is acted upon by the force P; determine an expression for the force Q required to maintain equilibrium.

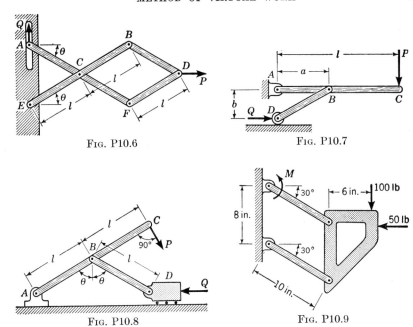

FIG. P10.6   FIG. P10.7

FIG. P10.8   FIG. P10.9

10.9. Determine the moment of the couple M required to maintain the equilibrium of the mechanism. Neglect the weight of the mechanism.

10.10. Using the method of virtual work, solve Prob. 6.88.

10.11. Using the method of virtual work, solve Prob. 6.89.

10.12. Using the method of virtual work, solve Prob. 6.91.

10.13. Determine the value of θ corresponding to the equilibrium position of the mechanism of Prob. 10.6 when $P = 75$ lb and $Q = 4,000$ lb.

10.14. Determine the value of θ corresponding to the equilibrium position of the mechanism of Prob. 10.6 when $P = 75$ lb and $Q = 400$ lb.

10.15. Determine the value of the distance b corresponding to the equilibrium position of the mechanism of Prob. 10.7 when $P = 30$ lb, $Q = 150$ lb, $l = 15$ in., and $a = 6$ in.

10.16. Determine the value of θ corresponding to the equilibrium position of the mechanism of Prob. 10.8 when $P = 75$ lb and $Q = 200$ lb.

10.17. Two uniform bars AB and BC are connected by a pin at B and by a spring DE. When unstretched, the spring is 5 in. long, and the constant of the spring is

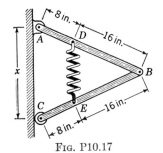

FIG. P10.17

5 lb/in., that is, a force of 5 lb elongates the spring 1 in. If the weight of each bar is 10 lb, determine the value of x for equilibrium.

10.18. A vertical load $W = 100$ lb is applied to the linkage at B. Neglecting the weight of the linkage and knowing that $l = 10$ in., determine the value of θ corresponding to equilibrium. The constant of the spring is $k = 30$ lb/in., and the spring is unstretched when AB and BC are horizontal. (*Hint.* Obtain the approximate value of θ by solving by trial and error the equation obtained.)

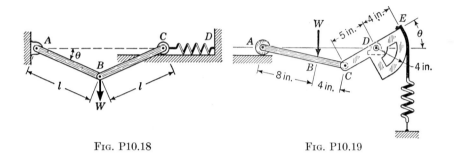

Fɪɢ. P10.18   Fɪɢ. P10.19

10.19. A vertical load $W = 200$ lb is applied to the mechanism at B. Neglecting the weight of the mechanism, determine the value of θ corresponding to equilibrium. The constant of the spring is $k = 40$ lb/in., and the spring is unstretched when bar AC is horizontal.

10.20. Solve Prob. 10.19 when the constant of the spring is $k = 400$ lb/in.

10.21. A block of weight W is pulled up a plane forming an angle α with the horizontal by a force P directed along the plane. If μ is the coefficient of friction between the block and the plane, derive an expression for the mechanical efficiency of the system. Show that the mechanical efficiency cannot exceed $\frac{1}{2}$ if the block is to remain in place when the force P is removed.

10.22. Derive an expression for the mechanical efficiency of the jack discussed in Sec. 8.6. Show that if the jack is to be self-locking the mechanical efficiency cannot exceed $\frac{1}{2}$.

10.23. In Prob. 10.6, assume that friction exists between the pin and the slot at A. Denoting by μ the coefficient of friction, determine the smallest and the largest values of Q for which equilibrium is maintained.

10.24. In Prob. 10.6, assume that the coefficient of friction between the pin and the slot at A is $\mu = 0.15$, and determine the smallest and the largest values of Q required to maintain equilibrium when $\theta = 30°$ and $P = 40$ lb.

10.25. Using the method of virtual work, determine the reaction at D.

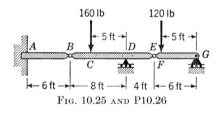

Fɪɢ. 10.25 ᴀɴᴅ P10.26

10.26. Using the method of virtual work, determine separately the force and couple representing the reaction at A.

10.27. Using the method of virtual work, solve Prob. 6.76b.

10.28. Determine the vertical movement of joint G if member BD is shortened 1.5 in. (*Hint*. Apply a vertical load at joint G, and, using the methods of Chap. 6, compute the force exerted by member BD on joints B and D. Then apply the method of virtual work for a virtual displacement making member BD shorter. This method should be used only for small changes in the length of members.)

10.29. Determine the vertical movement of joint B if the length of member DG is changed to 50 ft $1\frac{1}{2}$ in. (See hint of Prob. 10.28.)

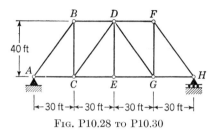

Fig. P10.28 to P10.30

10.30. Determine the horizontal movement of joint B if the length of member DG is changed to 50 ft $1\frac{1}{2}$ in. (See hint of Prob. 10.28.)

*10.5. Work of a Force during a Finite Displacement. Consider a force F acting on a particle. The work of F during an infinitesimal dis-

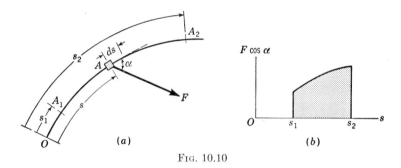

Fig. 10.10

placement ds of the particle was defined in Sec. 10.1 as

$$dU = F \, ds \cos \alpha \tag{10.1}$$

The work of F during a *finite* displacement of the particle from A_1 to A_2 (Fig. 10.10a) is obtained by integrating Eq. (10.1) from s_1 to s_2. This work, denoted by $U_{1\to2}$, is

$$U_{1\to2} = \int_{s_1}^{s_2} (F \cos \alpha) \, ds \tag{10.11}$$

The work $U_{1\to2}$ is represented by the area under the curve obtained by plotting $F \cos \alpha$ against s (Fig. 10.10b). In the case of a force F of con-

stant magnitude acting in the direction of motion, formula (10.11) yields
$U_{1\to2} = F(s_2 - s_1)$.

Recalling from Sec. 10.1 that the work of a couple of moment M during an infinitesimal rotation $d\theta$ of a rigid body is

$$dU = M\,d\theta \qquad (10.2)$$

we express as follows the work of the couple during a finite rotation of the body

$$U_{1\to2} = \int_{\theta_1}^{\theta_2} M\,d\theta \qquad (10.12)$$

In the case of a constant couple, formula (10.12) yields

$$U_{1\to2} = M(\theta_2 - \theta_1)$$

Work of a Weight. It was stated in Sec. 10.1 that the work of the weight W of a body during an infinitesimal displacement of the body is

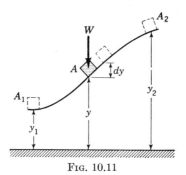

FIG. 10.11

equal to the product of W and of the vertical displacement of the center of gravity of the body. With the y axis pointing upward, the work of W during a finite displacement of the body (Fig. 10.11) is obtained by writing

$$dU = -W\,dy \qquad U_{1\to2} = -\int_{y_1}^{y_2} W\,dy = Wy_1 - Wy_2 \qquad (10.13)$$

or $\qquad U_{1\to2} = -W(y_2 - y_1) = -W\,\Delta y \qquad (10.13')$

where Δy is the vertical displacement from A_1 to A_2. The work of the weight W is thus equal to *the product of W and of the vertical displacement of the center of gravity of the body.* The work is *positive* when $\Delta y < 0$, that is, *when the body moves down.*

Work of the Force Exerted by a Spring. Consider a body A attached to a fixed point B by a spring; it is assumed that the spring is undeformed when the body is at A_0 (Fig. 10.12a). Experimental evidence shows that the force F exerted by the spring on a body A is proportional to the deflection x of the spring measured from the position A_0. We have

$$F = kx \qquad (10.14)$$

where k is the *spring constant*, expressed in lb/ft or lb/in. The work of the force F exerted by the spring during a finite displacement of the body from $A_1(x = x_1)$ to $A_2(x = x_2)$ is obtained by writing

$$dU = -F\,dx = -kx\,dx$$
$$U_{1\to 2} = -\int_{x_1}^{x_2} kx\,dx = \tfrac{1}{2}kx_1^2 - \tfrac{1}{2}kx_2^2 \qquad (10.15)$$

Care should be taken to express k and x in consistent units, that is, k in lb/ft and x in feet, or k in lb/in. and x in inches; in the first case, the

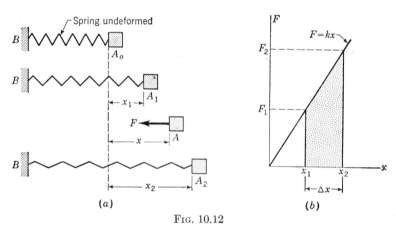

(a)   (b)

FIG. 10.12

work is obtained in ft-lb; in the second case, in in.-lb. We note that the work of the force F exerted by the spring on the body is *positive* when $x_2 < x_1$, that is, *when the spring is returning to its undeformed position*.

Since Eq. (10.14) is the equation of a straight line of slope k passing through the origin, the work $U_{1\to 2}$ of F during the displacement from A_1 to A_2 may be obtained by evaluating the area of the trapezoid shown in Fig. 10.12b. This is done by computing F_1 and F_2 and multiplying the base Δx of the trapezoid by its mean height $\tfrac{1}{2}(F_1 + F_2)$. Since the work of the force F exerted by the spring is positive for a negative value of Δx, we write

$$U_{1\to 2} = -\tfrac{1}{2}(F_1 + F_2)\,\Delta x \qquad (10.16)$$

Formula (10.16) is usually more convenient to use than (10.15) and affords fewer chances of confusing the units involved.

10.6. Potential Energy. Considering again the body of Fig. 10.11, we note from (10.13) that the work of the weight W during a finite displacement is obtained by subtracting the value of the function Wy

corresponding to the second position of the body from its value corresponding to the first position. The work of W is thus independent of the actual path followed; it depends only upon the initial and final values of the function Wy. This function is called the *potential energy* of the body with respect to the *force of gravity* W and is denoted by V_g. We write

$$U_{1 \to 2} = (V_g)_1 - (V_g)_2 \qquad \text{with } V_g = Wy \qquad (10.17)$$

We note that if $(V_g)_2 > (V_g)_1$, that is, *if the potential energy increases* during the displacement (as in the case considered here), *the work $U_{1 \to 2}$ is negative.* If, on the other hand, the work of W is positive, the potential energy decreases. Therefore, the potential energy V_g of the body provides a measure of *the work which may be done* by its weight W. Since only the *change* in potential energy, and not the actual value of V_g, is involved in formula (10.17), an arbitrary constant may be added to the expression obtained for V_g. In other words, the level from which the elevation y is measured may be chosen arbitrarily. Note that potential energy is expressed in the same units as work, i.e., in ft-lb or in in.-lb.

Considering now the body of Fig. 10.12a, we note from formula (10.15) that the work of the elastic force F is obtained by subtracting the value of the function $\frac{1}{2}kx^2$ corresponding to the second position of the body from its value corresponding to the first position. This function is denoted by V_e and is called the *potential energy* of the body with respect to the *elastic force F*. We write

$$U_{1 \to 2} = (V_e)_1 - (V_e)_2 \qquad \text{with } V_e = \tfrac{1}{2}kx^2 \qquad (10.18)$$

and observe that, during the displacement considered, the work of the force F exerted by the spring on the body is negative and the potential energy V_e increases. We should note that the expression obtained for V_e is valid only if the deflection of the spring is measured from its undeformed position.

The concept of potential energy may be used when forces other than gravity forces and elastic forces are involved. It remains valid as long as the elementary work dU of the force considered is an *exact differential.* It is then possible to find a function V, called potential energy, such that

$$dU = -dV \qquad \textbf{(10.19)}$$

Integrating (10.19) over a finite displacement, we obtain the general formula

$$U_{1 \to 2} = V_1 - V_2 \qquad \textbf{(10.20)}$$

which expresses that *the work of the force is independent of the path followed and is equal to minus the change in potential energy.* A force which satisfies Eq. (10.20) is said to be a *conservative force.*

*10.7. Potential Energy and Equilibrium. The application of the principle of virtual work is considerably simplified when the potential energy of a system is known. In the case of a virtual displacement, formula (10.19) becomes $\delta U = -\delta V$. Besides, if the position of the system is defined by a single independent variable θ we may write $\delta V = (dV/d\theta)\, \delta\theta$. Since $\delta\theta$ must be different from zero, the condition $\delta U = 0$ for the equilibrium of the system becomes

$$\frac{dV}{d\theta} = 0 \qquad (10.21)$$

In terms of potential energy, the principle of virtual work states therefore that, *if a system is in equilibrium, the derivative of its total potential*

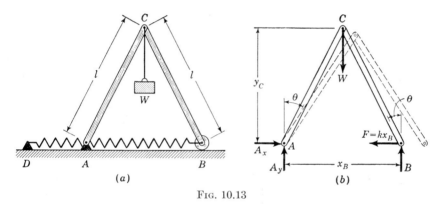

(a)

(b)

Fig. 10.13

energy is zero. If the position of the system depends upon several independent variables (the system is then said to possess *several degrees of freedom*), the partial derivatives of V with respect to each of the independent variables should be zero.

Consider, for example, a structure made of two members AC and CB and carrying a load W at C. The structure is supported by a pin at A and a roller at B, and a spring BD connects B to a fixed point D (Fig. 10.13a). The constant of the spring is k, and it is assumed that the natural length of the spring is equal to AD, and thus that the spring is undeformed when B coincides with A. Neglecting the friction forces and the weight of the members, we find that the only forces which work during a displacement of the structure are the weight W and the force F exerted by the spring at point B. The total potential energy of the system will thus be obtained by adding the potential energy V_g corresponding to the gravity force W and the potential energy V_e corresponding to the elastic force F.

Choosing a coordinate system with origin at A and noting that the deflection of the spring, measured from its undeformed position, is $AB = x_B$, we write

$$V_e = \tfrac{1}{2}kx_B^2 \qquad V_g = Wy_C$$

Expressing the coordinates x_B and y_C in terms of the angle θ, we have

$$x_B = 2l \sin \theta \qquad y_C = l \cos \theta$$
$$V_e = \tfrac{1}{2}k(2l \sin \theta)^2 \qquad V_g = W(l \cos \theta)$$
$$V = V_e + V_g = 2kl^2 \sin^2 \theta + Wl \cos \theta \qquad (10.22)$$

The positions of equilibrium of the system are obtained by equating to zero the derivative of the potential energy V,

$$\frac{dV}{d\theta} = 4kl^2 \sin \theta \cos \theta - Wl \sin \theta = 0$$

$$\sin \theta = 0 \qquad 4kl \cos \theta - W = 0$$

There are therefore two positions of equilibrium, corresponding to the values $\theta = 0$ and $\theta = \cos^{-1} (W/4kl)$.†

10.8. Stability of Equilibrium. Consider the three uniform rods of length $2a$ and weight W shown in Fig. 10.14. All are in equilibrium, yet all are unstable, according to the definition of the stability of a rigid body given in Sec. 3.15; each rod will move if a horizontal force is applied to point B.

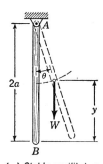
(a) Stable equilibrium

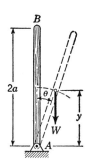
(b) Unstable equilibrium

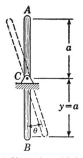
(c) Neutral equilibrium

Fig. 10.14

There is, however, an important difference between the three cases considered. Suppose that each rod is slightly disturbed from its position of equilibrium and then released: rod a will move back toward its original position, rod b will keep moving away from its original position, and rod c will remain in its new position. In case a, the equilibrium of the rod

† The second position does not exist if $W > 4kl$ (see Prob. 10.33 for a further discussion of the equilibrium of this system).

is said to be *stable;* in case *b*, the equilibrium is said to be *unstable;* and, in case *c*, to be *neutral.* Note that these definitions apply to the *equilibrium* of the rods; as pointed out above, each of the rods is itself an *unstable rigid body.*

Recalling from Sec. 10.6 that the potential energy V_g with respect to gravity is equal to Wy, where y is the elevation of the point of application of W measured from an arbitrary level, we observe that the potential energy of rod *a* is minimum in the position of equilibrium considered, that the potential energy of rod *b* is maximum, and that the potential energy of rod *c* is constant. Equilibrium is thus *stable, unstable,* or *neutral* according to whether the potential energy is *minimum, maximum,* or *constant.*

That the result obtained is quite general may be seen as follows: We first observe that a force always tends to do positive work and thus to

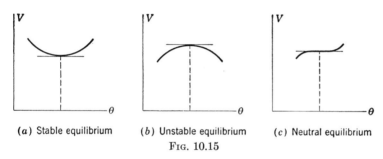

(*a*) Stable equilibrium   (*b*) Unstable equilibrium   (*c*) Neutral equilibrium

Fig. 10.15

decrease the potential energy of the system on which it is applied. Therefore, when a system is disturbed from its position of equilibrium, the forces acting on the system will tend to bring it back to its original position if V is minimum (Fig. 10.15*a*) and to move it farther away if V is maximum (Fig. 10.15*b*). If V is constant or, more generally, if the change in potential energy and the corresponding work are infinitesimals of the third order (Fig. 10.15*c*) or of a higher order, the forces will not tend to move the system either way as long as the disturbance is small.

Recalling from calculus that a function is minimum or maximum, according to whether its second derivative is positive or negative, we may summarize as follows the conditions for the equilibrium of a system with one degree of freedom (i.e., a system the position of which is defined by a single independent variable θ):

Stable equilibrium: $\dfrac{dV}{d\theta} = 0$ $\dfrac{d^2V}{d\theta^2} > 0$

Unstable equilibrium: $\dfrac{dV}{d\theta} = 0$ $\dfrac{d^2V}{d\theta^2} < 0$

Neutral equilibrium: $\dfrac{dV}{d\theta} = 0$ $\dfrac{d^2V}{d\theta^2} = 0$

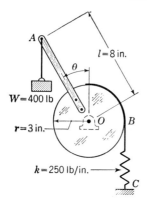

A 400-lb weight is attached to the lever AO as shown. The constant of the spring BC is $k = 250$ lb/in., and the spring is unstretched when $\theta = 0$. Determine the position or positions of equilibrium, and state in each case whether the equilibrium is stable, unstable, or neutral.

Potential Energy. Denoting by s the deflection of the spring from its undeformed position and placing the origin of coordinates at O, the potential energy of the system is

$$V_e = \tfrac{1}{2}ks^2 \qquad V_g = Wy$$

Measuring θ in radians, we have

$$s = r\theta \qquad\qquad y = l \cos \theta$$
$$V_e = \tfrac{1}{2}kr^2\theta^2 \qquad V_g = Wl \cos \theta$$
$$V = V_e + V_g = \tfrac{1}{2}kr^2\theta^2 + Wl \cos \theta$$

Positions of Equilibrium. Writing

$$\frac{dV}{d\theta} = 0$$

we obtain

$$\frac{dV}{d\theta} = kr^2\theta - Wl \sin \theta = 0$$

$$\sin \theta = \frac{kr^2}{Wl}\theta$$

Substituting the given data, we obtain

$$\sin \theta = \frac{(250 \text{ lb/in.})(3 \text{ in.})^2}{(400 \text{ lb})(8 \text{ in.})}\theta \qquad \sin \theta = 0.703\theta$$

Solving by trial and error, we find

$$\theta = 0 \qquad \text{and} \qquad \theta = 80.4°$$

Stability of Equilibrium. The second derivative of the potential energy V with respect to θ is

$$\frac{d^2V}{d\theta^2} = kr^2 - Wl \cos \theta = (250 \text{ lb/in.})(3 \text{ in.})^2 - (400 \text{ lb})(8 \text{ in.}) \cos \theta$$

$$= 2{,}250 - 3{,}200 \cos \theta$$

For $\theta = 0$: $\quad \dfrac{d^2V}{d\theta^2} = 2{,}250 - 3{,}200 \cos 0° = -950 \qquad$ **unstable equilibrium**

For $\theta = 80.4°$: $\quad \dfrac{d^2V}{d\theta^2} = 2{,}250 - 3{,}200 \cos 80.4° = +1{,}716 \qquad$ **stable equilibrium**

PROBLEMS

10.31. In Probs. 10.1 and 10.2, show that the position of equilibrium is neutral for the required value of P.

10.32. In Probs. 10.3 and 10.4, show that the position of equilibrium is neutral for the required value of W.

10.33. In Sec. 10.7, two positions of equilibrium were obtained for the system shown in Fig. 10.13, namely, $\theta = 0$ and $\theta = \cos^{-1} (W/4kl)$. Show that (a) if $W < 4kl$ the equilibrium is stable in the first position ($\theta = 0$) and unstable in the second, (b) if $W = 4kl$, the two positions coincide and the equilibrium is neutral, (c) if $W > 4kl$, the equilibrium is unstable in the first position ($\theta = 0$) and the second position does not exist. (*Note.* It is assumed that the system must deform as shown and that the system cannot rotate as a single rigid body about A when A and B coincide.)

10.34. Using the method of Sec. 10.7, solve Prob. 10.18. Determine whether the position of equilibrium is stable, unstable, or neutral.

10.35. Using the method of Sec. 10.7, solve Prob. 10.19. Determine whether the position of equilibrium is stable, unstable, or neutral.

10.36. For the mechanism considered in Prob. 10.18, show that for any finite values of W and k there is only one equilibrium position. Further show that the equilibrium position is stable.

10.37. A spring AB of constant $k = 100$ lb/in. is attached to two identical gears as shown. A uniform bar CD of weight $W = 250$ lb is supported by cords wrapped around drums of radius $b = 3$ in. which are attached to the gears. If the spring is undeformed when $\theta = 0$ and if $a = 4$ in., determine the positions of equilibrium of the system, and state in each case whether the equilibrium is stable, unstable, or neutral.

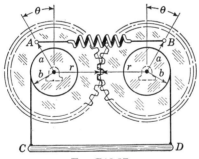

FIG. P10.37

10.38. In Prob. 10.37, determine the largest value of the weight W for which an equilibrium position exists. Also find the corresponding value of θ, and state whether the equilibrium is stable, unstable, or neutral.

10.39. For the mechanism of Sample Prob. 10.4, determine the largest value of the vertical load W for which stable equilibrium exists when lever AO is vertical. Express the result in terms of l, r, and k.

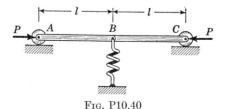

FIG. P10.40

10.40 and 10.41. Two bars AB and BC of negligible weight are attached to a spring of constant k. The spring is undeformed, and the system is in equilibrium in the position shown. Determine the largest value of the forces P for which the equilibrium of the system is stable.

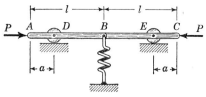

Fig. P10.41

10.42. In the system shown, bars BC and EF are connected at G by a pin which is attached to BC and slides freely in a slot cut in EF. If a weight W_2 is placed on bar BC, determine the smallest value of the weight W_1 for which the equilibrium of the system is stable in the position shown.

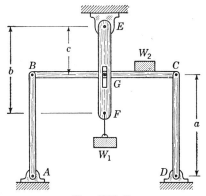

Fig. P10.42

Index

Answers to Even-numbered Problems in Statics

2.2. 330 lb ∠ 66.7°.   **2.4.** (a) 14,200 lb ⊤ 5.1°.   (b) 14,850 lb.
2.6. 3,030 lb ⊽ 7.6°.   **2.8.** 607 lb ⊤ 89.1°.
2.10. 691 lb ∠ 84.3°.   **2.12.** aa = 8,640 lb ∠ ; bb = 8,510 lb ↗.
2.14. 187.9 lb ↗; 68.4 lb ↖.   **2.16.** 42.6 lb; 14.56 lb.
2.18. P_x = 150 lb ←; P_y = 200 lb ↑; Q_x = 570 lb →; Q_y = 407 lb ↑.
2.20. 196.5 kips ⊽ 83.3°.   **2.22.** 14,210 lb ⊤ 5.1°.
2.24. 86.2° ↙ or 86.2° ⊽.   **2.26.** 24.0 kips.
2.28. 738 lb ∠ 55.3°.   **2.30.** T_{AC} = 152.7 lb; T_{BC} = 196 lb.
2.32. (a) 35°. (b) T_A = 410 lb. T_B = 287 lb.   **2.34.** 6.09 lb ↙ 7.5°.
2.36. T_{AC} = 133.5 lb; T_{BC} = 145.6 lb.   **2.38.** 123.0 lb ↙ 6.6°.
2.40. (a) 300 lb. (b) 300 lb. (c) 200 lb. (d) 200 lb.   **2.42.** 13.0 lb.
2.44. $W = 5[1 + (12/h)^2]^{\frac{1}{2}}$.   **2.46.** −13.19 lb; +36.2 lb; +46.0 lb.
2.48. −38.3 lb; −23.0 lb; +66.4 lb. 118.6°; 106.7°; 33.9°.
2.50. 45.7°. +349 lb; +347 lb; +86.8 lb.   **2.52.** +300 lb; −150 lb; +300 lb.
2.54. 718 lb. 51.2°; 134.2°; 69.6°.   **2.56.** 48.2°; 109.5°; 48.2°.
2.58. +300 lb.
2.60. (a) +1,200 lb; −1,200 lb; +600 lb. (b) +400 lb; −1,200 lb; +1,400 lb.
(c) +400 lb; −1,200 lb; +600 lb.
2.62. T_{AD} = 359 lb; T_{BD} = 274 lb; T_{CD} = 252 lb.
2.64. T_{AD} = 32.8 lb; T_{BD} = 25.5 lb; T_{CD} = 16.7 lb.
2.66. 781 lb. θ_x = 140.2°; θ_y = 90°; θ_z = 50.2°.
2.68. P = 60 lb; T_{AC} = 358 lb; T_{BC} = 316 lb.
2.70. T_{AD} = 0; T_{CD} = T_{ED} = 42.8 lb.
2.72. F_{wall} = 533 lb; F_{AC} = 622 lb; F_{BC} = 223 lb.

3.2. 320 lb-ft ⟩ ; α = 30°.   **3.4.** At upper right-hand corner, ↙ 45°.
3.6. 493 lb-ft ⟩.   **3.8.** 1,018 lb-ft ⟩.
3.12. $x = aQ/(Q − P)$.   **3.14.** (a) 25 lb. (b) 60 lb.
3.16. 67 lb-in. ⟩.   **3.18.** 500 lb ↓ and 250 lb-ft ⟩.
3.20. (a) 50 lb ⊽ 60°; 367 lb-in. ⟩. (b) 50 lb ⊽ 60°; 571 lb-in. ⟩.
3.22. (a) 100 lb →; 400 lb-in. ⟩. (b) A = 300 lb →; B = 200 lb ←.
3.24. (a) 1 kip ↓; 4 kip-ft ⟩. (b) A = 667 lb ↓; B = 333 lb ↓.
3.26. a and d.   **3.28.** 8.06 kips ⊤ 60.3°; 46.6 ft to right of A.
3.30. 391 lb ⊽ 50.2°; couple = 0.
3.32. (a) 1,300 lb ↓; 8,400 lb-ft ⟩ ; (b) 1,300 lb ↓; 3.46 ft to right of **A.**
3.34. (a) 400 lb ↑. (b) 120 lb ↑.

3.36. 68.0 lb ⦨ 54.0°. (a) 0.500 in. above B. (b) 0.364 in. to right of B.
3.38. (a) 1,073 lb →; 24,200 lb-ft ⟩. (b) R = 1,073 lb →; 22.5 ft below AB.
3.40. 25 lb; 43.3 lb ⦨ 60°.
3.42. (a) $T = \frac{1}{2}W(1 - r_1/r_2)$. (b) 200 lb. **3.44.** 467 lb.
3.46. 135.9 lb; 341 lb ⦨ 67.4°. **3.48.** A = 180 lb ↓; B = 180 lb ↑.
3.50. A = 7.12 kips ⦨ 42.0°; B = 2.58 kips ⦨ 60°.
3.52. A = 4.29 kips ⦨ 21.5°; B = 5.43 kips ↑.
3.54. A = 5 lb ↑; B = 6.25 lb ⦨ 30°; C = 6.25 lb ⦨ 30°.
3.56. (a) A = 625 lb ⦨ 53.1°; B = 375 lb ←. (b) A = 1,210 lb ⦨ 71.9°;
B = 750 lb ⦨ 60°. (c) A = 500 lb ↑ and 3,000 lb-ft ⟩.
3.58. (a) B = 67.2 lb ⦨ 53.4°; C = 1.053 lb ↓. (b) B = 53.9 lb ↓;
C = 40.0 lb ⦨ 1.5°. (c) B = 68.0 lb ⦨ 54.0° and couple M = 20 lb-in. ⟩.
3.60. A = 3.31 kips ⦨ 84.0°; B = 4.69 kips ↑. **3.62.** 400 lb ↑ and 1,200 lb-ft ⟩.
3.64. A = 403 lb ↑; B = 1,150 lb ⦨ 20.5°.
3.66. 335 lb ⦨ 77.0° and 1,202 lb-ft ⟩.
3.68. T = 74.8 lb; C = 168 lb ⦨ 39.8°. **3.70.** θ = 43.0°.
3.72. C = 1,250 lb ↓; F = 1,126 lb ⦨ 60°; G = 650 lb ⦨ 30°.
3.74. (1) Det.; stable; A = 12.02 kips ⦨ 56.3°; B = 6.67 kips ←. (2) Indet.;
geom. unst.; no equil. (3) Det.; stable; A = C = 5 kips ↑. (4) Indet.;
stable; A_x = 6.67 kips →; B_x = 6.67 kips ← (A_y + B_y = 10 kips ↑).
(5) Indet.; geom. unst.; no equil. (6) Det.; unst.; equil.; A = C = 5 kips ↑.
(7) Det.; stable; A = 5 kips ↑; B = 8.33 kips ⦨ 36.9°; C = 6.67 kips →.
(8) Indet.; stable; A_y = 5 kips ↑.
3.80. B = 126.7 lb ↓; C = 169.3 lb ⦨ 79.8°.
3.82. 33.7°; 3.61 lb.   7.48 in.; 2.00 lb.
3.84. A = 81.2 lb ⦨ 80.0°; B = 14.14 lb.   **3.86.** 5.29 ft.
3.96. 18 in.   **3.98.** R = 0; M = 436 lb-in. ⟩.
3.100. A = 4.29 kips ⦨ 21.5°; B = 5.43 kips ↑.
3.102. A = 738 lb ↑; B = 562 lb ↑.

CHAPTER 4

4.2. 200 lb force: M_{AD} = +400 lb-ft; M_{GF} = +1,200 lb-ft; M_{BC} = 0;
M_{AC} = +379 lb-ft.   300 lb force: M_{AD} = 0; M_{GF} = +900 lb-ft;
M_{BC} = M_{AC} = 0.   500 lb force: M_{AD} = M_{GF} = M_{BC} = M_{AC} = 0.
4.4. M_x = +3,600 lb-ft; M_y = 0; M_z = −3,600 lb-ft.
4.6. M_x = −600 sin θ; M_y = 0; M_z = −600 lb-in.   **4.8.** 500 lb-in.
4.10. M_x = +40 lb-in.; M_y = 0; M_z = −24 lb-in.
4.12. M_x = −693 lb-ft; M_y = +300 lb-ft; M_z = 0.
4.14. F_x = 0; F_y = −15 kips; F_z = 0. M_x = −30 kip-in.; M_y = 0;
M_z = −60 kip-in.
4.16. F = 50 lb downward; M = 794 lb-in. ϕ_x = 130.9°; ϕ_y = 90°; ϕ_z = 139.1°.
4.18. F_x = −30 lb; F_y = −34.6 lb; F_z = +20 lb. M_x = +20 lb-in.;
M_y = −60 lb-in.; M_z = −163.9 lb-in.
4.20. (a) C_y = +15 lb; C_z = 0. (b) F_x = −10 lb; F_y = −15 lb; F_z = 0.
M_x = −180 lb-in.; M_y = M_z = 0.
4.22. x = 28.4 in.; z = 12.0 in.   **4.24.** R = 200 lb ↓; x = 2.30 ft; z = 2.25 ft.
4.26. (a) F = 42.4 lb (F_x = −30; F_y = 0; F_z = −30);
M = 56.6 lb-ft (M_x = +40; M_y = 0; M_z = −40). (b) Horizontal,
1.33 ft below C, forming 45° angle with xy plane.
4.28. T_{AB} = 206 lb; T_{AC} = 116.8 lb; T_{AD} = 249 lb.
4.30. (a) 5 lb ↑. (b) 5.32 lb along leg.
4.32. T_{BC} = 963 lb; T_{BD} = 1,151 lb; R = 2,880 lb.

4.34. $T_{BD} = 245$ lb. $T_{CE} = 78.75$ lb. $A_x = +262.5$ lb; $A_y = +18.75$ lb; $A_z = -17.50$ lb.

4.36. $A = 22.5$ lb; $B = 7.5$ lb; $C = 30$ lb.   **4.38.** 1.40 ft.

4.40. $A_x = -9,600$ lb; $A_y =$ indet.; $A_z = -2,400$ lb. $B_x = +9,600$ lb; $B_y =$ indet.; $B_z = +2,400$ lb. $(A_y + B_y = 12,000$ lb.)

4.42. (a) 125 lb. (b) $A_y = -190.5$ lb; $A_z = +225$ lb. $B_x = 0$; $B_y = -271$ lb; $B_z = +66.4$ lb.

4.44. $F_{CD} = 3.00$ lb. $A_x = -2.94$ lb; $A_y = +6.90$ lb; $A_z = 0$. $B_x = 0$; $B_y = 7.50$ lb; $B_z = 0$.

4.46. $F_{CE} = 303$ lb. $A_x = -84.4$ lb; $A_y = -200$ lb; $A_z =$ indet. $B_x = -84.4$ lb; $B_y = +225$ lb; $B_z =$ indet. $(A_z + B_z = -112.3$ lb.)

4.48. $A_x = 1.18$ lb; $A_y =$ indet.; $A_z = +14.96$ lb; $M_{Ay} =$ indet. $B_x = -1.18$ lb; $B_y =$ indet.; $B_z = +20.4$ lb; $M_{By} =$ indet. $(M_{Ay} + M_{By} = -141.4$ lb-in.; $A_y + B_y = 35.4$ lb.)

4.50. (a) Force: 160 lb ↑. Couple: $M_x = -320$ lb-ft; $M_y = 0$; $M_z = +480$ lb-ft. (b) 3,460 lb in vertical plane through y axis and seat.

4.52. $P = 9$ lb; $\alpha = 36.9°$.

CHAPTER 5

5.2. $\bar{x} = 4.72$ in.; $\bar{y} = 2.62$ in.   **5.4.** $\bar{x} = 1.654$ in.; $\bar{y} = 2.65$ in.

5.6. $\bar{x} = 3.55$ in.; $\bar{y} = 4.00$ in.   **5.8.** $\bar{x} = 0$; $\bar{y} = -6.81$ in.

5.10. $\bar{x} = 10.6$ in.; $\bar{y} = 0$.   **5.12.** $\bar{x} = 8.43$ in.; $\bar{y} = 3.28$ in.

5.14. $\bar{x} = 6.00$ in.; $\bar{y} = 2.85$ in.   **5.16.** $\bar{x} = 0$; $\bar{y} = -0.837$ in.

5.18. $x = 2.78$ in.   **5.20.** $a = 2.88$ in.; $b = 6.75$ in.

5.22. $\bar{x} = 8$ in.; $\bar{y} = 6$ in.   **5.24.** $\bar{x} = 5.09$ in.; $\bar{y} = 0$.

5.26. $\bar{x} = 5.69$ in.; $\bar{y} = 3.06$ in.   **5.34.** $V = \frac{1}{3}\pi r^2 h$; $A = \pi r^2 + \pi r(h^2 + r^2)^{\frac{1}{2}}$.

5.36. $V = \frac{1}{2}\pi a^2 h$.   **5.38.** 50.3 ft².

5.40. 3,180 lb.   **5.42.** 5.96 in.

5.44. $R = 750$ lb ↓, 8.50 ft to right of A. $A = 325$ lb ↑; $B = 425$ lb ↑.

5.46. $A = 18.3$ kips ↑; $B = 15.7$ kips ↑.   **5.48.** $A = 19.0$ kips ↑; $B = 42.5$ kips ↑.

5.50. (a) $A = 4,990$ lb ←, 2.27 ft below A. (b) $B = 2,830$ lb →.

5.52. 9 in.   **5.54.** $A = 1,191$ lb→; $B = 1,200$ lb →.

5.56. 2.23 ft.   **5.58.** 3.87 ft.

5.60. 5,230 lb ∡ 57.5°, through center of drum.

5.62. 0.707.   **5.64.** 6.90 in. above base.

5.66. 6.74 in.; -2.14 in.; 1.193 in.   **5.68.** $h^2/(2h + r)$ above base.

5.70. $\frac{1}{2}r$ above base.   **5.76.** $(\pi + 2)h/16$.

5.78. $\bar{x} = 0$; $\bar{y} = 5h/16$; $\bar{z} = -a/4$.

CHAPTER 6

6.2 and 6.18. 1-$2 = 2$-$4 = 17$ kips C; 1-$3 = 3$-$4 = 15$ kips T; 2-$3 = 16$ kips T.

6.4 and 6.20. 1-$2 = 250$ lb C; 1-$4 = 354$ lb T; 1-$6 = 750$ lb C; 2-$4 = 250$ lb C; 2-$5 = 354$ lb C; 3-$5 = 500$ lb C; 4-$5 = 250$ lb T; 5-$7 = 750$ lb C; 2-$3 = 4$-$7 = 6$-$7 = 0$.

6.6 and 6.22. 1-$2 = 1$-$4 = 4$-$5 = 1$ kip T; 1-$3 = 2$-$3 = 3$-$4 = 3$-$5 = 1.414$ kips C.

6.8 and 6.24. 1-$2 = 1$-$3 = 0$; 2-$3 = 4.01$ kips C; 2-$4 = 7.02$ kips C; 3-$4 = 2.22$ kips T; 3-$5 = 3.33$ kips C; 4-$5 = 2.36$ kips C; 4-$6 = 5.27$ kips C; 5-$6 = 1.667$ kips T.

6.10 and 6.26. 1-$2 = 2$-$4 = 1,000$ lb T; 1-$3 = 3$-$6 = 1,000$ lb C; 4-$5 = 5$-$6 = 500$ lb T; 2-$3 = 2$-$5 = 3$-$5 = 0$.

6.12 and 6.28. 1-$2 = 375$ lb C; 2-$3 = 607$ lb C; 1-$5 = 5$-$3 = 181$ lb T; 2-$5 = 5$-$4 = 577$ lb T; 3-$4 = 1,200$ lb C.

6.14. 2-3; 3-4; 4-5; 5-6; 9-10.

6.16. All simple except 6.13.

6.30. $1\text{-}2 = 300$ lb T; $2\text{-}3 = 200$ lb T; $3\text{-}5 = 0$; $2\text{-}5 = 141.4$ lb T;
$2\text{-}4 = 100$ lb C; $4\text{-}5 = 5\text{-}6 = 100$ lb T; $1\text{-}4 = 70.7$ lb T; $4\text{-}6 = 70.7$ lb C.

6.32. $1\text{-}2 = 900$ lb C; $1\text{-}3 = 3\text{-}5 = 0$; $2\text{-}3 = 3\text{-}4 = 1{,}000$ lb T; $2\text{-}5 = 800$ lb C;
$4\text{-}5 = 1{,}200$ lb C; $4\text{-}6 = 5\text{-}6 = 1{,}000$ lb T; $5\text{-}8 = 1{,}600$ lb C.

6.34. $F_{CE} = 40$ kips T; $F_{BC} = 25$ kips T.

6.36. $F_{DF} = 40$ kips C; $F_{DE} = 6.01$ kips T.

6.38. $F_{DF} = 18.29$ kips T; $F_{DE} = 7.71$ kips C; $F_{CE} = 18.43$ kips C.

6.40. $F_{CD} = 9.38$ kips T.

6.42. $F_{DF} = 8.25$ kips T; $F_{EF} = 5$ kips T; $F_{EG} = 12$ kips C.   **6.44.** 6.67 kips C.

6.46. $F_{CE} = 10$ kips C; $F_{DF} = 5$ kips T; $F_{CF} = 7.07$ kips T.

6.48. (a) Stable; det.   (b) Unst.   (c) Stable; indet.   (d) Stable; det.
(e) Stable; indet.   (f) Unstable.

6.50. $B_x = 20$ lb $\leftarrow$; $B_y = 20$ lb $\uparrow$; $F_{DE} = 20$ lb.

6.52. $B_x = 225$ lb $\rightarrow$; $B_y = 300$ lb $\uparrow$; $C_x = 225$ lb $\leftarrow$; $C_y = 200$ lb $\downarrow$.

6.54. $A_x = 125$ lb $\leftarrow$; $A_y = 300$ lb $\uparrow$; $B_x = 395$ lb $\leftarrow$; $B_y = 0$.

6.56. $A = 162.4$ lb $\rightarrow$; $B = 33.2$ lb $\leftarrow$; $C_x = 129.2$ lb $\leftarrow$; $C_y = 120$ lb $\uparrow$.

6.58. $A = 460$ lb $\measuredangle\ 42.5°$; $B = 378$ lb; $E = 833$ lb.

6.60. $A = 30.6$ lb $\measuredangle\ 45°$; $B = 15.85$ lb $\uparrow$.

6.62. (a) $A = B = 55.9$ lb $\measuredangle\ 63.4°$; $C = 103.1$ lb $\measuredangle\ 76.0°$.   (b) $A = 50$ lb $\uparrow$;
$C = 100$ lb $\uparrow$; $B = 70.7$ lb $\measuredangle\ 45°$.

6.64. $E = 132.0$ lb $\measuredangle\ 16.5°$; $F = 169.3$ lb $\measuredangle\ 41.6°$; $C = 339$ lb $\measuredangle\ 41.6°$.

6.66. $A = 11.27$ kips $\measuredangle\ 33.7°$; $C = B = 10.10$ kips $\measuredangle\ 21.8°$.

6.68. (a) Stable; $A = 2.24$ kips $\measuredangle\ 26.6°$; $B = 3.61$ kips $\measuredangle\ 56.3°$.   (b) Unstable.

6.70. $A = 100$ lb $\uparrow$; $M_A = 400$ lb-ft $\rangle$; $D = 400$ lb $\uparrow$.

6.72. $A_x = 500$ lb $\leftarrow$; $A_y = 227$ lb $\uparrow$; $E_x = 500$ lb $\rightarrow$; $E_y = 273$ lb $\uparrow$.

6.74. (a) $1{,}600$ lb $\uparrow$; $9{,}600$ lb-ft $\rangle$; $D = 4{,}520$ lb $\measuredangle\ 45°$.   (b) 800 lb $\uparrow$;
$5{,}200$ lb-ft $\rangle$; $D = 2{,}260$ lb $\measuredangle\ 45°$.   (c) $1{,}131$ lb $\measuredangle\ 45°$; $1{,}600$ lb-ft $\rangle$;
$D = 2{,}260$ lb $\measuredangle\ 45°$.

6.76. (a) $A = 37.5$ lb $\uparrow$; $C = 75.0$ lb $\downarrow$; $E = 37.5$ lb $\uparrow$.   (b) 100 lb compression.

6.78. $B = 17.07$ lb $\leftarrow$; $E_x = 36.3$ lb $\rightarrow$; $E_y = 32.0$ lb $\downarrow$; $H_x = 19.20$ lb $\leftarrow$;
$H_y = 32.0$ lb $\uparrow$.

6.80. 150 lb.   **6.82.** 640 lb.

6.84. 18.75 lb.   **6.86.** $D = 515$ lb $\measuredangle\ 29.1°$; $C = 950$ lb $\rightarrow$.

6.88. 800 lb.   **6.90.** 28.4 lb.

6.92. 14,625 lb.   **6.96.** 290 lb.

6.98. 190.1 lb.

CHAPTER 7

7.2. (On AJ) $F = 198.5$ lb $\nearrow$; $V = 257$ lb $\searrow$; $M = 1{,}186$ lb-ft $\rangle$.

7.4. (On BJ) $F = 17.68$ lb $\searrow$; $V = 53.0$ lb $\nearrow$; $M = 600$ lb-in. $\rangle$.

7.6. (On BJ) $F = 0$; $V = 70.7$ lb $\nearrow$; $M = 800$ lb-in. $\rangle$.

7.8. At J (on JC): $F = 100$ lb $\uparrow$; $V = 0$; $M = 300$ lb-ft $\rangle$.
At K (on KC): $F = 180$ lb $\uparrow$; $V = 60$ lb $\rightarrow$; $M = 420$ lb-ft $\rangle$.

7.10. (On BC) 95.5 lb-in. $\rangle$.

7.12. (On left section) $F = 206$ lb $\nearrow$; $V = 15.81$ lb $\nwarrow$; $M = 300$ lb-in. $\rangle$.

7.14. $M_B = +Pa$.   **7.16.** $M_A = -\frac{1}{2}wL^2$.

7.18. $M_C = +180$ kip-ft.   **7.20.** $M_C = +20$ kip-ft.

7.22. $M_C = +46.4$ kip-ft.   **7.24.** $M_B = -27.4$ kip-ft.

7.26. $M_A = -640$ lb-ft; $M_D = +960$ lb-ft.   **7.28.** $M_B = +200$ kip-ft.

7.30. $M = -20$ kip-ft at center.   **7.32.** $M_C = +85$ kip-ft.

7.34. $M = +28.0$ kip-ft just to right of C.   **7.36.** $a = 0.207L$.

7.38. $M_A = -\frac{1}{2}wL^2$.   **7.40.** $M_C = +180$ kip-ft.

7.42. $M_C = +46.4$ kip-ft.   **7.44.** $M_B = -27.4$ kip-ft.

7.46. $M_B = -252$ kip-ft.

7.48. $M = +40$ kip-ft at center.

7.50. $M_B = -168$ kip-ft.

7.52. $+55.0$ lb-in. at C.

7.54. $V = +(2L/\pi)w_0[\cos (\pi x/2L) - 1]$.
$M = +(2L/\pi)^2 w_0 \sin (\pi x/2L) - (2L/\pi)w_0 x$.

7.56. $M_{\max} = 0.0394 w_0 L^2$, at $x = 0.630L$.

7.58. $M = +1{,}035$ lb-in.; 11.75 in. from A.

7.60. $M_C = +105$ lb-in.

7.62. 200 lb $\leftarrow$; 120 lb $\uparrow$; 233 lb.

7.64. $A_x = 75$ lb $\leftarrow$; $A_y = 90$ lb$\uparrow$; $E_x = 75$ lb $\rightarrow$; $E_y = 30$ lb $\uparrow$.

7.66. 583 kips; 500 kips.

7.68. 0.192 lb/ft; 80.6 lb.

7.70. 0.751 ft.

7.72. 54.8 ft.

7.74. 43.1 ft to right of A; 58.8 kips.

7.76. $\frac{2}{3}h$, $A_x = \frac{3}{32}(wL^2/h) \leftarrow$; $A_y = \frac{1}{4}wL \uparrow$.

7.78. $y = h[1 - \cos (\pi x/L)]$; $T_{\max} = (w_0 L/\pi) \sqrt{1 + L^2/h^2\pi^2}$; $T_0 = w_0 L^2/h\pi^2$.

7.80. 177.9 ft; 690 lb.

7.82. 309 ft; 765 lb.

7.84. 363 ft; 2,390 lb.

7.86. 73.1 ft; 788 lb.

7.88. 38.0 ft to the right of A; 628 lb.

7.90. 33.7 ft.

7.92. 0.65 in.

CHAPTER 8

8.2. $P = 29$ lb; $\alpha = -16.7°$.

8.4. (a) 75 lb. (b) 150 lb.

8.6. (a) Moves down; 38.6 lb $\nearrow$. (b) Does not move; 48.0 lb $\nearrow$.

8.8. (a) Moves down; 5.2 lb $\nearrow$. (b) Does not move; 5.0 lb $\nearrow$.

8.10. Cabinet tips.

8.12. 5 in.

8.14. 140 lb $\rightarrow$.

8.16. 319 lb.

8.18. 12 in.

8.20. 8.92 ft above ground.

8.22. 0.58.

8.24. 0.27.

8.26. 38.8 lb-in.

8.28. $38.9° < \phi < 54.4.°$

8.30. 473 lb.

8.32. 23.8 lb.

8.34. 11.9 in.

8.36. 57.4°.

8.38. 57.8 lb; does not move.

8.42. 3,840 lb.

8.44. 0.044.

8.46. (a) 72.8 lb. (b) 62.8 lb.

8.48. 5.0 in.

8.50. 0.005 radian.

8.52. (a) 348 lb-ft. (b) 232 lb-ft.

8.54. 100 lb-ft.

8.56. 807 lb.

8.58. 138 lb.

8.62. 6.4 lb.

8.64. 46.7 lb.

8.66. 4.14 ft.

8.68. 0.29.

8.70. 36.7 lb-ft.

8.72. 131 lb.

8.74. 93.3 lb-ft.

8.76. 3.17 ft.

8.78. 0.11.

CHAPTER 9

9.2. $\frac{1}{4}\pi r^4$.

9.4. $\frac{4}{15}a^3 b$.

9.6. $0.935a$.

9.8. $\frac{5}{9}a^3$.

9.10. $r/\sqrt{2}$.

9.12. $ab(a^2/5 + b^2/21)$; $(\frac{3}{5}a^2 + b^2/7)^{\frac{1}{2}}$.

9.14. (a) 855 in.^{4} (b) 427 in.^{4}

9.16. $xy^2 = c$.

9.18. (a) $\frac{1}{2}r$. (b) $r/\sqrt{2}$.

9.20. 342 in.^{4}

9.22. 5,570 in.^{4}; 7.50 in.

9.24. 3,035 in.^{4}; 4.83 in.

9.26. 69.6 in.^{4}; 11.64 in.^{4}; 2.52 in.; 1.029 in.

9.28. 11,130 in.^{4}; 10.60 in.

9.30. 4,470 in.^{4}

9.32. 5.66 in.

9.34. 3.51 in.

9.36. (b) 0.249%; 5.88%.

9.38. 2.36 ft.

9.40. $h + (r^2/4h)$.

9.42. $B = 4{,}410$ lb; $C = D = 5{,}730$ lb.

9.46. $b^2h^2/24$.

9.48. $a^4/8$.

9.50. -15.27 in.^{4}

9.52. -3.87 in.^{4}

9.54. 18.52 in.^{4}; 3.98 in.^{4}; $+3.60$ in.^{4}

9.56. $-25.7°$; 11.78 in.^{4}; 2.33 in.^{4}

9.58. $+28.5°$; 98.3 in.^{4}; 21.3 in.^{4}

9.66. (a) $0.0699ma^2$. (b) $0.320ma^2$.

9.68. (a) $ma^2/24$. (b) $ma^2/24$.

9.70. $\frac{2}{5}ma^2$.

9.72. $\frac{1}{20}m(a^2 + b^2)$.

9.74. $5m(a^2/7 + b^2/36)$.

9.76. $(m/20)(a^2 + 12h^2)$.

9.78. $\frac{1}{3}mL^2 \sin^2 \theta$.

9.80. $\frac{7}{5}ma^2$.

9.82. $k_x = k_y = 7.42$ in.

9.84. 14.13.

9.86. 0.1386 lb-ft-sec^2.

9.88. 0.0696 lb-ft-sec^2.

9.90. 1.760 lb-ft-sec^2; 1.374 ft.

9.92. 12.99 lb-ft-sec^2; 13.43 in.

CHAPTER 10

10.2. 60 lb.

10.4. (a) 500 lb. (b) 125 lb.

10.6. $\frac{3}{2}P \tan \theta$.

10.8. $P/\cos \theta$.

10.10. 800 lb.

10.12. 100 lb-in.

10.14. 74.3°.

10.16. 68.0°.

10.18. 30.7°.

10.20. 5.9°.

10.22. $\tan \theta/\tan (\theta + \phi_s)$, where $\tan \phi_s = \mu$.

10.24. 31.6 lb; 37.6 lb.

10.26. 50 lb ↑; 300 lb-ft ↻.

10.28. 0.281 in. ↓.

10.30. 0.625 in. ←.

10.34. 30.7°; stable.

10.38. 1,067 lb; 45.0°; neutral.

10.40. $kl/2$.

10.42. $(c^2/ab)W_2$.